Edwin Ramer

Nappanee

Ind

9-1920.

8

8

ELSON

GRAMMAR SCHOOL READER

BOOK TWO

BY

WILLIAM H. ELSON
AUTHOR ELSON PRIMARY SCHOOL READERS

AND

CHRISTINE KECK
PRINCIPAL OF UNION HIGH SCHOOL, GRAND RAPIDS, MICH.

SCOTT, FORESMAN AND COMPANY
CHICAGO   NEW YORK

ROBERT O. LAW COMPANY
EDITION BOOK MANUFACTURERS
CHICAGO, U. S. A.

TABLE OF CONTENTS

5

COURSE OF READING

In the ELSON READERS selections are grouped according to theme or authorship. This arrangement, however, is not intended to fix an order for reading in class; its purpose is to emphasize classification, facilitate comparison, and enable pupils to appreciate similarities and contrasts in the treatment of like themes by different authors.

To give variety, to meet the interests at different seasons and festivals, and to go from prose to poetry and from long to short selections, a carefully planned order of reading should be followed. Such an order of reading calls for a full consideration of all the factors mentioned above. The Course here offered meets these ends but may easily be varied to fit local conditions.

FIRST HALF-YEAR

7

SECOND HALF-YEAR

THE STORY OF ULYSSES (138)
THE FLAG (15)
HAIL, COLUMBIA (17)
OUR COUNTRY (19) ....LINCOLN'S BIRTHDAY, FEB. 12
ONE COUNTRY (36) ....WASHINGTON'S BIRTHDAY, FEB. 22
AMERICA (38)
BIOGRAPHY OF LOWELL (281)
THE FOUNTAIN (330) ....LOWELL'S BIRTHDAY, FEB. 22
LONGING (332)
THE VILLAGE BLACKSMITH (300)
THE OLD CLOCK ON THE STAIRS (303) .....LONGFELLOW'S BIRTHDAY, FEB. 27
THE BIRDS OF KILLINGWORTH (307)
THE STORY OF AENEAS (225)
MARCH (94)
MARCH (293) ....SPRING
THE VOICE OF SPRING (95)
BIOGRAPHY OF IRVING (278)
THE BOBOLINK (289) ....IRVING'S BIRTHDAY, APRIL 3
THE PLANTING OF THE APPLE TREE (296)
APPLE BLOSSOMS (100) ....ARBOR DAY
AN APRIL DAY (97)
BIOGRAPHY OF HOLMES (282)
LEXINGTON (336) ....APRIL 17
CONTENTMENT (339)
THE STORY OF HORATIUS (254)
HORATIUS AT THE BRIDGE (259)
BIOGRAPHY OF EMERSON (279)
THE RHODORA (318) ....EMERSON'S BIRTHDAY, MAY 25
THE HUMBLEBEE (319)
MY HEART LEAPS UP (89)
THE SPACIOUS FIRMAMENT (90)

INTRODUCTION

This book is designed to furnish a rich and varied supply of reading matter suited to the interests and needs of children in the early part of the grammar school work. The selections have been made with great care from among the masterpieces of British and American literature. Many familiar old pieces that have stood the test of time are included in the list. They are the songs that will always be sung and the stories that will always be told. The grouping into separate parts will aid both teachers and pupils in classifying the material, indicating at a glance the range and variety of literature offered.

Part One includes both poetry and prose. The stirring notes of patriotism with which the book opens find fitting supplement in the charming stories which follow, "The Barefoot Boy" being typical of the entire group. The series of nature poems, the group relating to character and that relating to the music of the bells, complete a collection of literary creations notable for their charm of expression and conspicuous for their beauty of thought and imagery.

Part Two contains some of the heroic tales of Greece and Rome. These fine old legends of adventure and heroism, handed down from the dawn of history, have delighted old and young for countless generations. They typify the noblest and best ideals of heroic conduct in ancient times and offer exceptional material for character-building at this impressionable period in the child's life. These stories are adapted from the stories from Homer and Virgil by Prof. Alfred J. Church.

Part Three presents a few of the great American authors, and no apology is needed for the names included in the list offered. They represent the makers of American literature and the

9

selections chosen are those best suited to children of this age.
From Franklin to Holmes, the spirit and thoughts of our developing nation are set forth in a literature distinctively American,
and some of the choicest treasures of that creative period are
here brought together. Through these, the children may become
familiar with the life of the past and may be made conscious of
some of its lessons for the present and the future. They may
thus come to know and love American authors and their works.

The biographies are intended to portray in brief form the
personal characteristics and lives of the authors, making them
more interesting and real to the children, giving them the
human touch and incidentally furnishing helpful data for interpreting their writings. The biographical introduction to Part
Three gives a related story of the lives of American authors
from whose writings selections have been made in this book.
"Helps to Study" include questions and notes designed to
stimulate inquiry on the part of pupils and to suggest fruitful
lines for discussion. Only a few points are suggested, to indicate
the way, and no attempt is made to cover the ground in all
directions; that remains for the teacher to do.

While placing emphasis primarily on interpreting the selection
for the reader himself, the formalities necessary to give the full
force of the selection to the hearer must not be overlooked.
The technique of reading, though always subordinate and sec-
ondary to the mastery of the thought, nevertheless claims constant and careful attention. Good reading requires clear enunci-
ation and correct pronunciation, and these can be secured only
when the teacher steadily insists upon them. The increase in
our school population of children in whose homes a foreign language is spoken, and the influence this has upon clearness and
accuracy of speech furnish added reason for attention to these
details. Special drill exercises should be given and the habit
of using the dictionary freely should be firmly established in
pupils. The ready use of the dictionary and other reference
books for pronunciation and meaning of words, for historical

and mythical allusions should be steadily cultivated. Without doubt much of the reading accepted in the public schools is seriously deficient in these particulars. The art of good reading can be cultivated by judicious training and the school should spare no pains to realize this result.

To discriminating teachers it will be apparent that this book is not the usual school reader. On the contrary it differs widely from this in the cultural value of the selections, in the classification and arrangement of material, in the variety of interest to which it appeals, and in the abundance of classic literature from British and American authors which it contains. It aims to furnish the best in poetry and prose to be found in the literature of the English-speaking race and to furnish it in abundance. If these familiar old selections, long accepted as among the best in literature, shall be the means of cultivating in pupils a taste for good reading, and at the same time shall have that refining influence on character which good literature always has, then the book will have fulfilled its purpose.

Grateful acknowledgment is made to those teachers who have given valuable suggestions and help in the compilation of this book.

THE AUTHORS.

September, 1910.

PART I

PATRIOTISM, STORIES,
POEMS OF NATURE AND DUTY

"It is better to inspire the heart with a noble sentiment than to teach the mind a truth of science."

EDWARD BROOKS.

PART I

THE FLAG

ARTHUR MACY

Arthur Macy (1842-1904) was born at Nantucket, Mass. He served in the Civil War, was wounded at Gettysburg three times, and was there taken prisoner. As a soldier he learned what it means to march with the flag in front of him. It is not surprising, therefore, that his poem, "The Flag," is full of stirring patriotism.

> Here comes The Flag!
> Hail it!
> Who dares to drag
> Or trail it?
> Give it hurrahs,—
> Three for the stars,
> Three for the bars.
> Uncover your head to it!
> The soldiers who tread to it
> Shout at the sight of it,
> The justice and right of it,
> The unsullied white of it,
> The blue and red of it,
> And tyranny's dread of it!

15

Here comes The Flag!
Cheer it!
Valley and crag
Shall hear it.
Fathers shall bless it,
Children caress it,
All shall maintain it,
No one shall stain it,
Cheers for the sailors that fought on the
wave for it,
Cheers for the soldiers that always were brave
for it!
Tears for the men that went down to the
grave for it!
Here comes The Flag.

HELPS TO STUDY

Notes and Questions

What feeling does this poem express?

Why should men and boys uncover their heads to the flag?

Give another phrase for "tread to it."

Why do tyrants dread our flag?

What picture does the whole poem suggest?

What does the poem say "valley and crag" will hear?

What do we call all the men who fight "on the wave" for the flag?

When did men go "down to the grave" for the flag?

How do we honor these men?

Why is this poem easy to read?

Words and Phrases for Discussion

"unsullied white"   "Valley and crag"
"All shall maintain it"

HAIL, COLUMBIA

Joseph Hopkinson

Joseph Hopkinson (1770-1842) was born at Philadelphia, where he lived and died. He was a noted jurist. His father, Francis H. Hopkinson, was one of the signers of the Declaration of Independence in 1776. Judge Hopkinson wrote the song, "Hail, Columbia," which is one of the most beautiful of our American patriotic poems.

1

Hail, Columbia! happy land,
Hail, ye heroes, heav'n born band;
   Who fought and bled in Freedom's cause,
And when the storm of war was gone
Enjoyed the peace your valor won.
Let independence be our boast,
Ever mindful what it cost!
Ever grateful for the prize,
Let its altar reach the skies.

    Firm, united, let us be,
    Rallying round our Liberty!
    As a band of brothers joined,
    Peace and safety we shall find.

2

Immortal patriots, rise once more!
Defend your rights, defend your shore!
   Let no rude foe, with impious hand,
Invade the shrine where sacred lies,
Of toil and blood, the well-earned prize.
While offering peace, sincere and just,
In heav'n we place a manly trust,
That truth and justice shall prevail
And ev'ry scheme of bondage fail.

3

Sound, sound the trump of fame!
Let Washington's great name
    Ring through the world with loud applause,
Let ev'ry clime to Freedom dear,
Listen with a joyful ear.
With equal skill and Godlike pow'r,
He governed in the fearful hour
Of horrid war; or guides with ease
The happier times of honest peace.

4

Behold the chief who now commands,
Once more to serve his country stands—
    The rock on which the storm will beat;
But armed in virtue firm and true,
His hopes are fixed on heaven and you.
When hope was sinking in dismay,
And glooms obscur'd Columbia's day,
His steady mind from changes free,
Resolved on death or liberty.

HELPS TO STUDY

Historical: This song was written in 1798, when there was danger of a war with France. An army had been raised and Washington, though in his sixty-seventh year, was appointed to command it. Many people in the United States were eager for war, but both President Adams and Washington knew that it was extremely undesirable for the country at the time. The author of the song said that he wished to rouse an "American spirit," which should hold the country's honor above political parties or private interests.

Notes and Questions

Who is addressed in the first line of the poem?

Who were the heroes to whom the second line is addressed?

When had they fought in "Freedom's cause"?

How does the author say they had won peace?

Read the lines in the refrain or chorus which tell how Liberty must be protected.

Whom does the author address as "Immortal patriots"?

What does he call upon them to do?

What "rude foe" might he have had in mind when writing the song?

What does he mean by the "well-earned prize" of "toil and blood"?

Who had toiled for this prize?

When had blood been shed for it?

To whom was Columbia offering peace at this time?

Read lines which show that the author believed the United States would conquer if forced into war.

In whose praise was the third stanza written?

Show how the second and third lines of this stanza have come true.

Find lines in this stanza which explain the words: "First in war, first in peace."

Who was the chief described in the fourth stanza?

To what is he compared?

What was the storm that the author expected?

How is a rock affected by the storms which beat upon it?

What words in this stanza show that Washington had served his country before?

How had he served it?

When had Washington resolved on "death or liberty"?

Words and Phrases for Discussion

"impious hand"

"scheme of bondage"

"trump of fame"

"Godlike pow'r"

"clime to Freedom dear"

"armed in virtue"

OUR COUNTRY

(AUTHOR UNKNOWN)

1

Our country! 'tis a glorious land!
  With broad arms stretched from shore to shore,
The proud Pacific chafes her strand,
  She hears the dark Atlantic roar;
And, nurtured on her ample breast,
  How many a goodly prospect lies
In Nature's wildest grandeur dressed,
  Enameled with her loveliest dyes.

2

Rich prairies, decked with flowers of gold
    Like sunlit oceans roll afar;
Broad lakes her azure heavens behold,
    Reflecting clear each trembling star;
And mighty rivers, mountain born,
    Go sweeping onward, dark and deep,
Through forests where the bounding fawn
    Beneath their sheltering branches leap.

3

Great God! we thank thee for this home,
    This bounteous birth-land of the free;
Where wanderers from afar may come,
    And breathe the air of liberty!
Still may her flowers untrampled spring,
    Her harvests wave, her cities rise;
And yet, till Time shall fold his wing,
    Remain earth's loveliest paradise!

HELPS TO STUDY

Notes and Questions

To what does the author wish to call our attention when he speaks of the two oceans?

What things are mentioned in the second stanza as lying on the breast of our country?

To what are the prairies compared?

What gives them this appearance?

What broad lakes lie on the breast of our country?

What is meant by rivers which are "mountain born"?

Name some such river.

Why do "wanderers from afar" come to America?

From what places do they come?

What do they find here?

Words and Phrases for Discussion

"proud Pacific"   "loveliest dyes"   "trembling star"
"chafes her strand"   "flowers of gold"   "cities rise"
"goodly prospect"   "azure heavens"   "loveliest paradise"

HOHENLINDEN

Thomas Campbell

Thomas Campbell (1777-1844) was a Scotch poet. He was born at Glasgow. At the time this battle was fought he was on a visit to Germany for the purpose of studying the literature of that country. He was then only twenty-three years old.

1

On Linden, when the sun was low,
All bloodless lay th' untrodden snow;
And dark as winter was the flow
    Of Iser, rolling rapidly:

2

But Linden saw another sight,
When the drum beat at dead of night,
Commanding fires of death to light
    The darkness of her scenery.

3

By torch and trumpet fast arrayed,
Each horseman drew his battle blade,
And furious every charger neighed
    To join the dreadful revelry.

4

Then shook the hills with thunder riven;
Then rushed the steed to battle driven;
And, louder than the bolts of heaven
    Far flashed the red artillery.

5

But redder yet that light shall glow
On Linden's hill of stainèd snow
And darker yet shall be the flow
    Of Iser, rolling rapidly.

6

'Tis morn; but scarce yon level sun
Can pierce the war clouds, rolling dun,
Where furious Frank and fiery Hun
    Shout in their sulphurous canopy.

7

The combat deepens. On, ye brave,
Who rush to glory or the grave!
Wave, Munich! all thy banners wave,
    And charge with all thy chivalry!

8

Few, few shall part where many meet!
The snow shall be their winding sheet,
And every turf beneath their feet
    Shall be a soldier's sepulcher.

HELPS TO STUDY

Historical: December 3, 1800, a battle between the Austrians and the French occurred at Hohenlinden, a village in Upper Bavaria. The French were victorious. The Franks were a powerful German tribe who mastered the Romans in Gaul and gave their name to France. The Huns were a warlike race living between the Ural and the Volga; in the fifth century they overran Europe and laid waste much territory. The poet uses the word "Hun" in referring to the Austrians. In this poem the author tries to make the reader see the battle as it really occurred.

Notes and Questions

What time of day is described in the first stanza?

What is meant by the "dead of night"?

What did the beating of the drums mean to the soldiers?

What did the beating of the drums tell the people?

For what were the torches used?

Read the lines which tell you that the horses were eager for the battle.

Read the following description of a warhorse from a much older poem; "He saith among the trumpets, Ha, ha! and he smelleth the battle afar off, the thunder of the captains and the shouting.''—Job XXXIX, 25.

In what are the two descriptions alike?

What was the thunder which ''shook the hills''?

What does the first stanza tell you about the snow?

How is the snow described in the fifth stanza?

What tells you that the battle lasted several hours?

What caused the ''war clouds''?

What words in the seventh stanza might have been addressed to soldiers on either side?

What words in the same stanza make you think that the poet wished the Austrians to be victorious?

Find on a map: Bavaria, the Iser, Munich.

Words and Phrases for Discussion

''battle blade''	''bolts of heaven''	''fires of death''
''dreadful revelry''	''chivalry''	''rolling dun''
''furious Frank''	''fiery Hun''	''sulphurous canopy''
''winding sheet''	Hohenlinden = linden heights.	

THE EMIGRATION OF THE PILGRIM FATHERS

Edward Everett

Edward Everett (1794-1865) was a noted American orator and statesman. He lived in Boston and was a graduate of Harvard College. He began life as a clergyman, but was soon made a professor in Harvard College. He filled many important places, among which are the following: Member of Congress, Governor of Massachusetts, Minister to England, President of Harvard College, and United States Senator. He was an industrious worker, and whatever he undertook was well done.

Methinks I see one solitary, adventurous vessel, the "Mayflower," of a forlorn hope, freighted with the prospects of a future State, and bound across the unknown sea. I behold it pursuing, with a thousand misgivings, the uncertain, the tedious
5 voyage. Suns rise and set, and weeks and months pass, and winter surprises them on the deep, but brings them not the sight of the wished-for shore. I see them now, scantily supplied

with provisions, crowded almost to suffocation, in their ill-
stored prison, delayed by calms, pursuing a circuitous route,—
and now, driven in fury before the raging tempest, on the high
and giddy waves. The awful voice of the storm brawls through
5 the rigging.

The laboring masts seem straining from their base; the dismal
sound of the pumps is heard; the ship leaps, as it were, madly,
from billow to billow; the ocean breaks, and settles with engulfing floods over the floating deck, and beats with deadening,
10 shivering weight, against the staggering vessel.

I see them escape from these perils, pursuing their all but
desperate undertaking, and landed at last, after a five months'
passage, on the ice-clad rocks of Plymouth,—weak and weary
from the voyage, poorly armed, scantily provisioned, without
15 shelter, without means, surrounded by hostile tribes.

Shut now the volume of history, and tell me, on any principle
of human probability, what shall be the fate of this handful of
adventurers? Tell me, man of military science, in how many
months were they all swept off by the thirty savage tribes,
20 enumerated within the early limits of New England?

Tell me, politician, how long did a shadow of a colony on
which your conventions and treaties had not smiled, languish
on the distant coast? Student of history, compare for me the
baffled projects, the deserted settlements, the abandoned adven-
25 tures of other times, and find the parallel of this.

Was it the winter's storm, beating upon the houseless heads
of women and children; was it hard labor and spare meals; was
it disease; was it the tomahawk; was it the deep malady of a
blighted hope, a ruined enterprise, and a broken heart, aching
30 in its last moments at the recollection of the loved and left,
beyond the sea; was it some, or all of these united, that hurried
this forsaken company to their melancholy fate?

And is it possible, that neither of these causes, that not all
combined, were able to blast this bud of hope? Is it possible,
35 that from a beginning so feeble, so frail, so worthy not so much

of admiration as of pity, there has gone forth a progress so steady, a growth so wonderful, an expansion so ample, a reality so important, a promise, yet to be fulfilled, so glorious?

HELPS TO STUDY
Notes and Questions

What does the author say was the freight which the Mayflower carried?

What meaning has the word "State" in the first paragraph?

What was the "unknown sea" which the Pilgrims crossed?

How long were they on the ocean?

Read the lines which tell why the voyage was such a long one.

Read the sentence which describes a storm at sea.

In what month did the Pilgrims land?

What trials awaited them in their new home?

What "hostile tribes" surrounded them?

To whom is the author speaking when he says, "Shut now, the volume of history"?

What questions does he then ask?

Why does he not wish you to refer to history for the answers?

Why did it seem almost impossible that this colony should succeed?

Words and Phrases for Discussion

"forlorn hope"

"circuitous route"

"engulfing floods"

"ice-clad rocks"

"scantily provisioned"

"military science"

"baffled projects"

"abandoned adventures"

ARNOLD WINKELRIED

James Montgomery

James Montgomery (1771-1854) was born in Scotland. He was the son of a clergyman. He established a newspaper, which he edited for more than thirty years. When a mere boy he wrote poetry. "Arnold Winkelried" is one of his best patriotic poems.

1

"Make way for liberty!" he cried—
Made way for liberty, and died.

In arms the Austrian phalanx stood,
A living wall, a human wood;
All-horrent with projected spears.
Opposed to these, a hovering band
Impregnable their front appears,
Contended for their fatherland;
Peasants, whose new-found strength had broke
From manly necks the ignoble yoke;
Marshalled once more at freedom's call,
They came to conquer or to fall.

2

And now the work of life and death
Hung on the passing of a breath;
The fire of conflict burned within;
The battle trembled to begin:
Yet, while the Austrians held their ground,
Point for assault was nowhere found;
Where'er the impatient Switzers gazed,
The unbroken line of lances blazed;
That line 'twere suicide to meet,
And perish at their tyrants' feet.
How could they rest within their graves,
To leave their homes the haunts of slaves?
Would they not feel their children tread,
With clanking chains, above their head?

3

It must not be: this day, this hour,
Annihilates the invader's power!
All Switzerland is in the field—
She will not fly, she cannot yield,
She must not fall; her better fate
Here gives her an immortal date.

The 13 Colonies.

1607 - Vir. by the English — 1
1613 - N.Y. " " Dutch 2
1620 - Mass " " English. 3
1623 - New H " " " 4
1628 - Boston " " English 5
1633 - Conn. " " " 6
1634 - Maryland by the English 7
1636 - R. Island " " E. 8
1638 - Deleware " " Swedes 9
1651 - N. Carolina by the, " 10
1664 - N. Jersey " " E. 11
1683 - Penn.
1670 - South C by the Engl. 12
1733 - Georgia " " 13

1687-97 — 8
Queen Anne's war King G's war
1702-13 — 11 g'n.
French & Indian war
1754-63 — 1763

1607 Virg[?]

1618

1620 Mass. at Plymouth — (Sep. from English)

1623 New Hampshire English

1626 Mass. at Boston

1623 Connecticut English

1634 Maryland

1635 [?] English

1638 [?] at — English

[?] Wilmington Swedes

1664 Jersey English

1680 Pennsylvania English

1733 Georgia English

1650 North Carolina 11.

Few were the numbers she could boast,
Yet every freeman was a host,
And felt as 'twere a secret known
That one should turn the scale alone,
While each unto himself was he
On whose sole arm hung victory.

4

It did depend on one, indeed;
Behold him—Arnold Winkelried!
There sounds not to the trump of Fame
The echo of a nobler name.
Unmarked, he stood amid the throng,
In rumination deep and long,
Till you might see, with sudden grace,
The very thought come o'er his face,
And, by the motion of his form,
Anticipate the bursting storm,
And, by the uplifting of his brow,
Tell where the bolt would strike, and how.

5

But 'twas no sooner thought than done—
The field was in a moment won!
"Make way for liberty!" he cried,
Then ran, with arms extended wide,
As if his dearest friend to clasp;
Ten spears he swept within his grasp;
"Make way for liberty!" he cried;
Their keen points crossed from side to side;
He bowed amidst them like a tree,
And thus made way for liberty.
Swift to the breach his comrades fly—
"Make way for liberty!" they cry,
And through the Austrian phalanx dart,

As rushed the spears through Arnold's heart.
While, instantaneous as his fall,
Rout, ruin, panic, seized them all;
An earthquake could not overthrow
A city with a surer blow.

6

Thus Switzerland again was free;
Thus death made way for liberty.

HELPS TO STUDY

Historical: July 9, 1386, a battle between the Swiss and Austrians took place at Sempach, a small town of Switzerland. The Austrian troops were well trained and well armed. As the cavalry were unable to manage their horses in the mountain pass, they dismounted and stood shoulder to shoulder, forming a solid mass and using their spears as weapons. The Swiss mountaineers were not able to break through the Austrian lines until Arnold von Winkelried rushed forward, grasped as many spears as he could reach with his outstretched arms, pressed them into his body and, falling, bore them down with him to the ground. His companions rushed over his body into the opening thus made in the Austrian lines and won a victory which secured the independence of Switzerland.

Notes and Questions

Who cried, "Make way for liberty"?

In what way did the Austrians resemble a wall?

What does the poet mean by comparing them to a wood?

Who were the "hovering band?"

For what were they fighting?

Why does the poet describe them as hovering instead of attacking?

What line tells you that the Swiss were not accustomed to war?

What lines tell you that the Austrians were well disciplined soldiers?

What gave the Swiss courage to face so strong a foe?

Read the lines in the third stanza which tell you that each of the Swiss felt that the victory depended on him alone.

What effect did this thought have upon their efforts?

Words and Phrases for Discussion

"projected spears"   "ignoble yoke"
"new-found strength"   "All Switzerland is in the field"
"unbroken line of lances"   "every freeman was a host"

A LEGEND OF BREGENZ

ADELAIDE PROCTER

Adelaide A. Procter (1825-1864) was an English poet. She was born in London, where she also lived and died. She was the daughter of Bryan Waller Procter, who wrote under the name of Barry Cornwall. Her poems are full of sympathy and sweetness.

1

GIRT round with rugged mountains
    The fair Lake Constance lies;
In her blue heart reflected
    Shine back the starry skies;
And, watching each white cloudlet
    Float silently and slow,
You think a piece of Heaven
    Lies on our earth below!

2

Midnight is there: and Silence,
    Enthroned in Heaven, looks down
Upon her own calm mirror,
    Upon a sleeping town:
For Bregenz, that quaint city
    Upon the Tyrol shore,
Has stood above Lake Constance
    A thousand years and more.

3

Her battlements and towers,
 From off their rocky steep,
Have cast their trembling shadow
 For ages on the deep:
Mountain, and lake, and valley,
 A sacred legend know,
Of how the town was saved, one night,
 Three hundred years ago.

4

Far from her home and kindred,
 A Tyrol maid had fled,
To serve in the Swiss valleys,
 And toil for daily bread;
And every year that fleeted
 So silently and fast,
Seemed to bear farther from her
 The memory of the Past.

5

She served kind, gentle masters,
 Nor asked for rest or change;
Her friends seemed no more new ones,
 Their speech seemed no more strange;
And when she led her cattle
 To pasture every day,
She ceased to look and wonder
 On which side Bregenz lay.

6

She spoke no more of Bregenz,
 With longing and with tears;
Her Tyrol home seemed faded
 In a deep mist of years;

She heeded not the rumors
  Of Austrian war and strife;
Each day she rose, contented,
  To the calm toils of life.

7

Yet, when her master's children
  Would clustering round her stand,
She sang them ancient ballads
  Of her own native land;
And when at morn and evening
  She knelt before God's throne,
The accents of her childhood
  Rose to her lips alone.

8

And so she dwelt: the valley
  More peaceful year by year;
When suddenly strange portents
  Of some great deed seemed near.
The golden corn was bending
  Upon its fragile stock,
While farmers, heedless of their fields,
  Paced up and down in talk.

9

The men seemed stern and altered,
  With looks cast on the ground;
With anxious faces, one by one,
  The women gathered round;
All talk of flax, or spinning,
  Or work, was put away;
The very children seemed afraid
  To go alone to play.

10

One day, out in the meadow
  With strangers from the town,
Some secret plan discussing,
  The men walked up and down.
Yet now and then seemed watching
  A strange uncertain gleam,
That looked like lances 'mid the trees,
  That stood below the stream.

11

At eve they all assembled,
  Then care and doubt were fled;
With jovial laugh they feasted;
  The board was nobly spread.
The elder of the village
  Rose up, his glass in hand,
And cried, "We drink the downfall
  Of an accurséd land!

12

"The night is growing darker,
  Ere one more day is flown,
Bregenz, our foeman's stronghold,
  Bregenz shall be our own!"
The women shrank in terror,
  (Yet Pride, too, had her part.)
But one poor Tyrol maiden
Felt death within her heart.

13

Before her stood fair Bregenz;
  Once more her towers arose;
What were the friends beside her?
  Only her country's foes!

The faces of her kinsfolk,
　The days of childhood flown,
The echoes of her mountains,
　Reclaimed her as their own!

14

Nothing she heard around her,
　(Though shouts rang forth again,)
Gone were the green Swiss valleys,
　The pasture, and the plain;
Before her eyes one vision,
　And in her heart one cry,
That said, "Go forth, save Bregenz,
　And then, if need be, die!"

15

With trembling haste and breathless,
　With noiseless step, she sped;
Horses and weary cattle
　Were standing in the shed;
She loosed the strong, white charger,
　That fed from out her hand,
She mounted, and she turned his head
　Towards her native land.

16

Out—out into the darkness—
　Faster, and still more fast;
The smooth grass flies behind her,
　The chestnut wood is past;
She looks up; clouds are heavy:
　Why is her steed so slow?—
Scarcely the wind beside them
　Can pass them as they go.

17

"Faster!" she cries, "O faster!"
  Eleven the church-bells chime:
"O God," she cries, "help Bregenz,
  And bring me there in time!"
But louder than bells' ringing,
  Or lowing of the kine,
Grows nearer in the midnight
  The rushing of the Rhine.

18

Shall not the roaring waters
  Their headlong gallop check?
The steed draws back in terror,
  She leans upon his neck
To watch the flowing darkness;
  The bank is high and steep;
One pause—he staggers forward,
  And plunges in the deep.

19

She strives to pierce the blackness,
  And looser throws the rein;
Her steed must breast the waters
  That dash above his mane.
How gallantly, how nobly,
  He struggles through the foam,
And see—in the far distance
Shine out the lights of home!

20

Up the steep banks he bears her,
  And now, they rush again
Towards the heights of Bregenz
  That tower above the plain.

They reach the gate of Bregenz,
   Just as the midnight rings,
And out come serf and soldier
   To meet the news she brings.

21

Bregenz is saved! Ere daylight
   Her battlements are manned;
Defiance greets the army
   That marches on the land.
And if to deeds heroic
   Should endless fame be paid,
Bregenz does well to honor
   The noble Tyrol maid.

22

Three hundred years are vanished,
   And yet upon the hill
An old stone gateway rises,
   To do her honor still.
And there, when Bregenz women
   Sit spinning in the shade,
They see in quaint old carving
   The Charger and the Maid.

23

And when, to guard old Bregenz,
   By gateway, street, and tower,
The warder paces all night long
   And calls each passing hour;
"Nine," "ten," "eleven," he cries aloud,
   And then (O crown of Fame!)
When midnight pauses in the skies,
   He calls the maiden's name!

HELPS TO STUDY

Notes and Questions

Find the Tyrol on your map of Europe.

What mountains surround Lake Constance?

Where is the town of Bregenz?

Read the lines which tell you that the town is very old.

Why did the Tyrol maid leave her home?

How was she treated in her new home?

Read the lines which tell you that she became contented in the Swiss valley.

Read the lines which tell that she did not forget her native land.

What were the "accents of her childhood"?

Why would the "accents of her childhood" rise to her lips when she knelt to pray?

How did she learn that an attack on Bregenz was planned?

What did she resolve to do?

Why was there need of haste?

What river flowed between the Swiss valley and Bregenz?

How did the maid cross it?

What did the people of Bregenz do when they heard the news which she brought?

What happened when the army came to attack the town?

What did the people of Bregenz build to honor the maiden?

How is she remembered when the watchman makes his rounds at night?

How long ago does the poet say the events of this story occurred?

Words and Phrases for Discussion

"sacred legend"

"ancient ballads"

"strange portents"

"lowing of the kine"

"deeds heroic"

"endless fame"

"heedless of their fields"

"battlements are manned"

ONE COUNTRY

Frank L. Stanton

Frank L. Stanton's home is in South Carolina. He writes for the "Atlanta Constitution," one of the great dailies of the South. His writings are full of his love of country.

1

After all,
One country, brethren! We must rise or fall
With the Supreme Republic. We must be
The makers of her immortality,—
Her freedom, fame,
Her glory or her shame:
Liegemen to God and fathers of the free!

2

After all—
Hark! from the heights the clear, strong, clarion call
And the command imperious: "Stand forth,
Sons of the South and brothers of the North!
Stand forth and be
As one on soil and sea—
Your country's honor more than empire's worth!"

3

After all,
'Tis Freedom wears the loveliest coronal;
Her brow is to the morning; in the sod
She breathes the breath of patriots; every clod
Answers her call
And rises like a wall
Against the foes of liberty and God!

HELPS TO STUDY

Notes and Questions

To whom is this poem addressed?

What is the "Supreme Republic"?

What kind of deeds makes the glory of a country?

What deeds bring shame upon a country?

Of what does the poet say we must be the makers?

Why should boys and girls think of these things?

From whom do you think the command given in the second stanza comes?

Read the lines which give the "command imperious."

How may many people be as one in the performance of an act?

Where are the North and South to be as one?

What is worth more than empire?

What does Freedom breathe into the sod?

Read the lines which tell how Freedom may raise up patriots to defend her.

Words and Phrases for Discussion

"liegemen to God"

"clarion call"

"soil and sea"

"coronal"

AMERICA*

SIDNEY LANIER

Sidney Lanier (1842-1881) was an American poet. He was born in Georgia and was the poet of the South. He was very musical and could play on the guitar, banjo, violin, and flute. His books for boys have been widely read, especially his "Boys' King Arthur."

Long as thine art shall love true love,
Long as thy science truth shall know,
Long as thine eagle harms no dove,
Long as thy law by law shall grow,
Long as thy God is God above,
Thy brother every man below,
So long, dear land of all my love,
Thy name shall shine, thy fame shall glow.

HELPS TO STUDY

Notes and Questions

How does the poet address his country in this stanza?

How long does he say her "name shall shine" and her "fame shall glow"?

Read the lines which tell you this.

How do the eagle and the dove compare in size? In strength?

If the eagle represents the United States, what does the dove represent?

If we look upon all men as

---

* From "The Centennial Cantata." Copyright, 1885, by Charles Scribner's Sons, Publishers.

brothers, how shall we feel toward the people of other countries?

How are the laws of our country made?

Words and Phrases for Discussion

"name shall shine"
"fame shall glow"

"law by law shall grow" = laws shall be made in accordance with justice.

ABOU BEN ADHEM

LEIGH HUNT

Leigh Hunt (1784-1859) was an English poet. He was born near London and went to school at Christ's Hospital, the famous Blue Coat School, in London. He wrote both prose and poetry. A monument was erected to his memory in the Kensal Green Cemetery on which is the inscription: "Write me as one that loves his fellow-men."

Abou Ben Adhem (may his tribe increase!)
Awoke one night from a deep dream of peace,
And saw, within the moonlight in his room,
Making it rich, and like a lily in bloom,
5 An angel writing in a book of gold:
Exceeding peace had made Ben Adhem bold,
And to the presence in the room he said,
"What writest thou?"—The vision raised its head,
And, with a look made of all sweet accord,
10 Answered, "The names of those who love the Lord."
"And is mine one?" said Abou. "Nay, not so,"
Replied the angel. Abou spoke more low,
But cheerly still; and said, "I pray thee, then,
Write me as one that loves his fellow men."

15 The angel wrote and vanished. The next night
It came again, with a great wakening light,
And showed the names whom love of God had blessed,
And, lo! Ben Adhem's name led all the rest!

HELPS TO STUDY
Notes and Questions

Read the line that tells what Abou saw when he awoke the first time.

By what other names does the poet speak of the angel?

Why does he change the name?

Read the line that answers Abou's question.

Read the line that tells how he wished to have himself recorded.

How do you account for the fact that "Ben Adhem's name led all the rest"?

This kind of story is called a parable. What is its theme?

What was the poet's purpose in writing this parable?

Why did he choose an oriental name for the hero?

What does this story teach us?

What prose story in this book has a similar theme to this?

What things are compared in lines four and five?

Do you like this story? Why?

Read the line or lines that you like best.

Words and Phrases for Discussion

"may his tribe increase"

"a look made of all sweet accord"

"book of gold"

"deep dream of peace"

"making it rich"

"wakening light"

"led all the rest"

THE BAREFOOT BOY

JOHN GREENLEAF WHITTIER*

Blessings on thee, little man,
Barefoot boy, with cheek of tan!
With thy turned-up pantaloons,
And thy merry whistled tunes;
With thy red lip, redder still
5   Kissed by strawberries on the hill;
With the sunshine on thy face,
Through thy torn brim's jaunty grace;
From my heart I give thee joy, —
I was once a barefoot boy!
10   Prince thou art, — the grown-up man

* For Biography, see p. 281.

Only is republican.
Let the million-dollared ride!
Barefoot, trudging at his side,
Thou hast more than he can buy
In the reach of ear and eye, —
Outward sunshine, inward joy:
Blessings on thee, barefoot boy!

O for boyhood's painless play,
Sleep that wakes in laughing day,
Health that mocks the doctor's rules,
Knowledge never learned of schools,
Of the wild bee's morning chase,
Of the wild-flower's time and place,
Flight of fowl and habitude
Of the tenants of the wood;
How the tortoise bears his shell,
How the woodchuck digs his cell,
And the ground-mole sinks his well;
How the robin feeds her young,
How the oriole's nest is hung;
Where the whitest lilies blow,
Where the freshest berries grow,
Where the groundnut trails its vine,
Where the wood-grape's clusters shine;
Of the black wasp's cunning way,
Mason of his walls of clay,
And the architectural plans
Of gray hornet artisans! —
For, eschewing books and tasks,
Nature answers all he asks;
Hand in hand with her he walks,
Face to face with her he talks,
Part and parcel of her joy, —
Blessings on the barefoot boy!

O for boyhood's time of June,
Crowding years in one brief moon,
When all things I heard or saw,
Me, their master, waited for.
50　I was rich in flowers and trees,
Humming-birds and honey-bees;
For my sport the squirrel played,
Plied the snouted mole his spade;
For my taste the blackberry cone
55　Purpled over hedge and stone;
Laughed the brook for my delight
Through the day and through the night,
Whispering at the garden wall,
Talked with me from fall to fall;
60　Mine the sand-rimmed pickerel pond,
Mine the walnut slopes beyond,
Mine, on bending orchard trees,
Apples of Hesperides!
Still as my horizon grew,
65　Larger grew my riches too;
All the world I saw or knew
Seemed a complex Chinese toy,
Fashioned for a barefoot boy!

O for festal dainties spread,
70　Like my bowl of milk and bread, —
Pewter spoon and bowl of wood,
On the door-stone, gray and rude!
O'er me, like a regal tent,
Cloudy-ribbed, the sunset bent,
75　Purple-curtained, fringed with gold,
Looped in many a wind-swung fold;
While for music came the play
Of the pied frogs' orchestra;
And, to light the noisy choir,

80 Lit the fly his lamp of fire.
I was monarch: pomp and joy
Waited on the barefoot boy!

Cheerily, then, my little man,
Live and laugh, as boyhood can!
85 Though the flinty slopes be hard,
Stubble-speared the new-mown sward,
Every morn shall lead thee through
Fresh baptisms of the dew;
Every evening from thy feet
90 Shall the cool wind kiss the heat;
All too soon these feet must hide
In the prison cells of pride,
Lose the freedom of the sod,
Like a colt's for work be shod,
95 Made to tread the mills of toil,
Up and down in ceaseless moil:
Happy if their track be found
Never on forbidden ground;
Happy if they sink not in
100 Quick and treacherous sands of sin.
Ah! that thou couldst know thy joy,
Ere it passes, barefoot boy!

HELPS TO STUDY
Notes and Questions

Why was the poet able to make so good a picture of the barefoot boy?

What picture of the barefoot boy does the first stanza give you?

Why does the poet call him a "Prince"?

What does the boy have that the "million-dollared" can not buy?

What does the barefoot boy know that he "never learned" from books?

Who taught him these things?

What things has Nature taught you?

Why is June "boyhood's time"?

What is meant by "all things"

waiting for him, "their master"?

What fly lights "his lamp of
fire"?

Why did the poet say "I was
monarch"?

What is the mole's spade?

What does Whittier think are the
boy's greatest troubles?

What does the poet call "prison
cells of pride"?

Why does he call them "prison
cells of pride"?

What wish does the poet express
for the barefoot boy in the last
stanza?

Read the lines that tell you this.

Which stanza do you like best?

Words and Phrases for Discussion

"mocks"   "Chinese toy"   "purple-curtained"

"eschewing"   "snouted"   "ceaseless moil"

"cheek of tan"   "cunning"   "Apples of Hesperides"

"jaunty grace"   "treacherous"   "sand-rimmed pickerel pond"

"republican"   "cloudy-ribbed"   "from fall to fall"

"hornet artisans" "fresh baptisms of the dew"

THE PIED PIPER OF HAMELIN
Robert Browning

Robert Browning (1812-1889) was, along with Tennyson, one of the
great poets of the Victorian age. He was born at Camberwell, a sub-
urb of London. He began early to read Shelley and Keats and all his
life was a lover and student of music. In 1846 he married Elizabeth
Barrett and went to Italy, where for fifteen years he lived and wrote,
and where Mrs. Browning died in 1861. After the death of his wife he
returned to England and spent most of his time in London, where he
continued his literary work. He died at the home of his son in Venice
and was buried in the Poets' Corner of Westminster Abbey.

Hamelin Town's in Brunswick,
　　By famous Hanover city;
　　　The river Weser deep and wide
　　　Washes its wall on the southern side;
　　　A pleasanter spot you never spied;
　　But, when begins my ditty,
　　　Almost five hundred years ago,
　　　To see the townsfolk suffer so
　　From vermin, was a pity.

5

Rats!
They fought the dogs and killed the cats,
    And bit the babies in the cradles,
And ate the cheeses out of the vats,
    And licked the soup from the cooks' own ladles.
Split open the kegs of salted sprats,
Made nests inside men's Sunday hats,
And even spoiled the women's chats,
        By drowning their speaking
        With shrieking and squeaking
In fifty different sharps and flats.

At last the people in a body
    To the Town-hall came flocking:
"'Tis clear," cried they, "our Mayor's a noddy:
    And as for our Corporation—shocking
    To think we buy gowns lined with ermine
    For dolts that can't or won't determine
    What's best to rid us of our vermin!
    You hope, because you're old and obese,
    To find in the furry civic robe ease!
Rouse up, sirs! Give your brains a racking
To find the remedy we're lacking,
Or, sure as fate, we'll send you packing!"
At this the Mayor and Corporation
Quaked with a mighty consternation.

An hour they sat in council;
    At length the Mayor broke silence:
"For a guilder I'd my ermine gown sell;
    I wish I were a mile hence!
It's easy to bid one rack one's brain—
I'm sure my poor head aches again,
I've scratched it so, and all in vain.
Oh, for a trap, a trap, a trap!"

Just as he said this what should hap
At the chamber door but a gentle tap?
45   " Bless us," cried the Mayor, "what's that?
Anything like the sound of a rat
Makes my heart go pit-a-pat!

"Come in," the Mayor cried, looking bigger;
And in did come the strangest figure!
50   His queer long coat from heel to head
Was half of yellow, and half of red;
And he himself was tall and thin,
With sharp blue eyes each like a pin,
And light loose hair, yet swarthy skin,
55   No tuft on cheek, nor beard on chin,
But lips where smiles went out and in.
There was no guessing his kith or kin!
And nobody could enough admire
The tall man and his quaint attire:
60   Quoth one, "It's as if my great-grandsire,
Starting up at the trump of doom's tone,
Had walked this way from his painted tombstone!"

He advanced to the council table:
And, "Please your honors," said he, "I'm able,
65   By means of a secret charm, to draw
All creatures living beneath the sun,
That creep, or swim, or fly, or run,
After me so as you never saw!
And I chiefly use my charm
70   On creatures that do people harm,
The mole, and toad, and newt, and viper;
And people call me the Pied Piper.
(And here they noticed round his neck
A scarf of red and yellow stripe,
75   To match with his coat of the self-same cheque;

And at the scarf's end hung a pipe;
And his fingers, they noticed, were ever straying
As if impatient to be playing
Upon this pipe, as low it dangled
80   Over his vesture so old-fangled.)
"Yet," said he, "poor piper as I am,
In Tartary I freed the Cham
Last June from his huge swarms of gnats;
I eased in Asia the Nizam
85   Of a monstrous brood of vampire-bats;
And as for what your brain bewilders,
If I can rid your town of rats
Will you give me a thousand guilders?"
"One? fifty thousand!" was the exclamation
90   Of the astonished Mayor and Corporation.

Into the street the Piper stept,
    Smiling first a little smile,
As if he knew what magic slept
    In his quiet pipe the while;
95   Then like a musical adept,
To blow the pipe his lips he wrinkled,
And green and blue his sharp eyes twinkled,
Like a candle flame where salt is sprinkled;
And ere three shrill notes the pipe uttered,
100   You heard as if an army muttered;
And the muttering grew to a grumbling;
And the grumbling grew to a mighty rumbling;
And out of the houses the rats came tumbling—
Great rats, small rats, lean rats, brawny rats,
105   Brown rats, black rats, gray rats, tawny rats,
Grave old plodders, gay young friskers,
    Fathers, mothers, uncles, cousins,
Cocking tails, and pricking whiskers,
    Families by tens and dozens,

110 Brothers, sisters, husbands, wives—
  Followed the Piper for their lives.
  From street to street he piped, advancing,
  And step for step they followed dancing,
  Until they came to the river Weser
115 Wherein all plunged and perished,
  Save one, who stout as Julius Cæsar,
  Swam across, and lived to carry
  (As he the manuscript he cherished)
  To Rat-land home his commentary,
120 Which was, "At the first shrill notes of the pipe,
  I heard a sound as of scraping tripe,
  And putting apples wondrous ripe
  Into a cider press's gripe;
  And a moving away of pickle-tub boards,
125 And a leaving ajar of conserve cupboards,
  And a drawing the corks of train-oil flasks,
  And a breaking the hoops of butter casks;
  And it seemed as if a voice
  (Sweeter far than by harp, or by psaltery
130 Is breathed) called out, 'O rats, rejoice!
  The world is grown to one vast drysaltery!
  So munch on, crunch on, take your nuncheon,
  Breakfast, dinner, supper, luncheon!'
  And just as a bulky sugar puncheon,
135 All ready staved, like a great sun shone
  Glorious, scarce an inch before me,
  Just as methought it said, 'Come, bore me!'
  I found the Weser rolling o'er me."

  You should have heard the Hamelin people
140 Ringing the bells till they rocked the steeple;
  " Go," cried the Mayor, "and get long poles!
  Poke out the nests, and block up the holes!
  Consult with carpenters and builders,

And leave in our town not even a trace
145　Of the rats!" When suddenly, up the face
Of the Piper perched in the market-place,
With a "First, if you please, my thousand guilders!"

A thousand guilders! The Mayor looked blue,
So did the Corporation too.
150　For council dinners made rare havoc
With Claret, Moselle, Vin-de-Grave, Hock;
And half the money would replenish
Their cellar's biggest butt with Rhenish.
To pay this sum to a wandering fellow
155　With a gypsy coat of red and yellow!
"Beside," quoth the Mayor, with a knowing wink,
"Our business was done at the river's brink;
We saw with our eyes the vermin sink,
And what's dead can't come to life, I think.
160　So, friend, we're not the folks to shrink
From the duty of giving you something for drink,
And a matter of money to put in your poke;
But, as for the guilders, what we spoke
Of them, as you very well know, was in joke.
165　Beside, our losses have made us thrifty:
A thousand guilders! come, take fifty!"

The Piper's face fell, and he cried,
"No trifling! I can't wait! beside
I've promised to visit by dinner-time
170　Bagdat, and accept the prime
Of the head cook's pottage, all he's rich in,
For having left in the caliph's kitchen,
Of a nest of scorpions no survivor.
With him I proved no bargain-driver,
175　With you, don't think I'll bate a stiver!
And folks who put me in a passion
May find me pipe after another fashion."

" How?" cried the mayor, "d'ye think I brook
Being worse treated than a cook?
180   Insulted by a lazy ribald
With idle pipe and vesture piebald?
You threaten us, fellow? Do your worst,
Blow your pipe there till you burst."

Once more he stept into the street,
185   And to his lips again
Laid his long pipe of smooth, straight cane;
          And ere he blew three notes (such sweet
Soft notes as yet musician's cunning
          Never gave the enraptured air,)
190   There was a rustling that seemed like a bustling,
Of merry crowds justling at pitching and hustling,
Small feet were pattering, wooden shoes clattering,
Little hands clapping and little tongues chattering,
And, like fowls in a farmyard when barley is scattering,
195   Out came the children running:
All the little boys and girls,
With rosy cheeks and flaxen curls,
And sparkling eyes and teeth like pearls,
Tripping and skipping ran merrily after
200   The wonderful music with shouting and laughter.

The Mayor was dumb, and the Council stood
As if they were changed into blocks of wood,
Unable to move a step, or cry
To the children merrily skipping by—
205   And could only follow with the eye
That joyous crowd at the Piper's back.
But how the Mayor was on the rack,
And the wretched Council's bosoms beat,
As the Piper turned from the High Street
210   To where the Weser rolled its waters

Right in the way of their sons and daughters!
However he turned from south to west,
And to Koppelberg Hill his steps addressed,
And after him the children pressed;
215   Great was the joy in every breast.
" He never can cross that mighty top;
He's forced to let the piping drop,
And we shall see our children stop!"
When, lo! as they reached the mountain's side,
220   A wondrous portal opened wide,
As if a cavern was suddenly hollowed;
And the Piper advanced, and the children followed,
And when all were in to the very last,
The door in the mountain side shut fast.
225   Did I say, all? No! One was lame,
And could not dance the whole of the way;
And in after years, if you would blame
His sadness, he was used to say,—
" It's dull in our town since my playmates left!
230   I can't forget that I am bereft
Of all the pleasant sights they see,
Which the Piper also promised me:
For he led us, he said, to a joyous land,
Joining the town and just at hand,
235   Where waters gushed and fruit-trees grew,
And flowers put forth a fairer hue,
And everything was strange and new;
The sparrows were brighter than peacocks **here,**
And their dogs outran our fallow-deer,
240   And honey-bees had lost their stings,
And horses were born with eagles' wings;
And just as I became assured
My lame foot would be speedily cured,
The music stopped and I stood still,

245   And found myself outside the hill,
Left alone against my will,
To go now limping as before,
And never hear of that country more!"

Alas! alas for Hamelin!
250   There came into many a burgher's pate
    A text which says, that Heaven's Gate
Opes to the rich at as easy rate
As the needle's eye takes a camel in!
The Mayor sent east, west, north, and south
255   To offer the Piper by word of mouth,
    Wherever it was men's lot to find him,
Silver and gold to his heart's content,
If he'd only return the way he went,
    And bring the children behind him.
260 But when they saw 'twas a lost endeavor,
And Piper and dancers were gone forever,
They made a decree that lawyers never
    Should think their records dated duly,
If, after the day of the month and year
265 These words did not as well appear,
"And so long after what happened here
    On the twenty-second day of July,
Thirteen hundred and seventy-six:"
And the better in memory to fix
270 The place of the children's last retreat,
They called it the Pied Piper's Street—
Where any one playing on pipe or tabor,
Was sure for the future to lose his labor.
Nor suffered they hostelry or tavern
275   To shock with mirth a street so solemn;
But opposite the place of the cavern
    They wrote the story on a column,
And on the great church window painted

The same, to make the world acquainted
280 How their children were stolen away;—
And there it stands to this very day.

And I must not omit to say
That in Transylvania there's a tribe
Of alien people, who ascribe
285 The outlandish ways and dress
On which their neighbors lay such stress,
To their fathers and mothers having risen
Out of some subterraneous prison
Into which they were trepanned
290 Long time ago in a mighty band,
Out of Hamelin town in Brunswick land,
But how or why, they don't understand.

So Willy, let me and you be wipers
Of scores out with all men,—especially pipers;
295 And whether they pipe us free from rats or from mice
If we've promised them aught, let us keep our promise.

HELPS TO STUDY
Notes and Questions

Find Hanover and the Weser River on your map.

Whom did the people blame for the condition of their city?

What threat did they make?

What effect did this have upon the Mayor?

Describe the appearance of the Mayor's strange visitor.

What did the Pied Piper offer to do?

How did the Mayor and Corporation receive his proposal?

How soon did the notes of the pipe take effect?

Read the report to Rat-land.

What did the Mayor order when the rats had been destroyed?

Whom had he forgotten?

Read the lines which show why the Mayor dared dispute the Piper's claim.

How did the Mayor reward the Piper for his services?

Compare the sound made by the gathering of the children with the noise made by the rats.

Where did the Piper lead the children?

What lines rhyme in each stauza?

What comparison is made in lines 251, 252 and 253?

Words and Phrases for Discussion

"sprats"	"guilders"	"Hock"
"noddy"	"psaltery"	"quaint attire"
"ermine"	"nuncheon"	"doom's tone"
"vermin"	"hostelry"	"Julius Caesar"
"dolts"	"Claret"	"burgher's pate"
"obese"	"Moselle"	"subterranean prison"
"consternation"	"Vin-de-Grave"	"trepanned"

KENTUCKY BELLE

CONSTANCE FENIMORE WOOLSON

Constance Fenimore Woolson (1848-1894), an American writer, was born in Clermont, New Hampshire. She was a grandniece of James Fenimore Cooper, the author of "Leather Stocking Tales." With her parents she removed to Cleveland, O., and afterwards to New York City. She died in Venice, Italy.

1

Summer of 'sixty-three, sir, and Conrad was gone away—
Gone to the country town, sir, to sell our first load of hay:
We lived in the log-house yonder, poor as ever you've seen;
Röschen there was a baby, and I was only nineteen.

2

Conrad he took the oxen, but he left Kentucky Belle.
How much we thought of Kentuck, I couldn't begin to tell—
Came from the Blue-grass country; my father gave her to me
When I rode North with Conrad, away from the Tennessee.

3

Conrad lived in Ohio—a German he is, you know—
The house stood in broad corn-fields, stretching on row after row.
The old folks made me welcome; they were kind as kind could be;
But I kept longing, longing, for the hills of the Tennessee.

4

Oh for a sight of water, the shadowed slope of a hill!
Clouds that hang on the summit, a wind that never is still!

But the level land went stretching away to meet the sky—
Never a rise, from north or south, to rest the weary eye!

5

From east to west, no river to shine out under the moon,
Nothing to make a shadow in the yellow afternoon:
Only the breathless sunshine, as I looked out, all forlorn;
Only the "rustle, rustle," as I walked among the corn.

6

When I fell sick with pining, we didn't wait any more,
But moved away from the corn-lands, out to this river shore—
The Tuscarawas it's called, sir—off there's a hill, you see—
And now I've grown to like it next best to the Tennessee.

7

I was at work that morning. Some one came riding like mad
Over the bridge and up the road—Farmer Routh's little lad
Bareback he rode; he had no hat; he hardly stopped to say:
"Morgan's men are coming, Frau; they're galloping on this way.

8

"I'm sent to warn the neighbors. He isn't a mile behind;
He sweeps up all the horses—every horse that he can find.
Morgan, Morgan the raider, and Morgan's terrible men,
With bowie-knives and pistols, are galloping up the glen!"

9

The lad rode down the valley, and I stood still at the door;
The baby laughed and prattled, playing with spools on the floor;
Kentuck was out in the pasture; Conrad, my man, was gone.
Near, nearer, Morgan's men were galloping, galloping on!

10

Sudden I picked up baby, and ran to the pasture-bar.
"Kentuck!" I called—"Kentucky!" She knew me ever so far!
I led her down the gully that turns off there to the right,
And tied her to the bushes; her head was just out of sight.

11

As I ran back to the log-house, at once there came a sound—
The ring of hoofs, galloping hoofs, trembling over the ground—
Coming into the turnpike out from the White-woman Glen—
Morgan, Morgan the raider, and Morgan's terrible men.

12

As near they drew and nearer, my heart beat fast in alarm;
But still I stood in the door-way with baby on my arm.
They came; they passed; with spur and whip in haste they sped
        along—
Morgan, Morgan the raider, and his band, six hundred strong.

13

Weary they looked and jaded, riding through night and through
        day;
Pushing on east to the river, many long miles away,
To the border-strip where Virginia runs up into the west,
And fording the Upper Ohio before they could stop to rest.

14

On like the wind they hurried, and Morgan rode in advance;
Bright were his eyes like live coals, as he gave me a sidewise
        glance;
And I was just breathing freely, after my choking pain,
When the last one of the troopers suddenly drew his rein.

15

Frightened I was to death, sir; I scarce dared look in his face,
As he asked for a drink of water, and glanced around the place.
I gave him a cup, and he smiled—'twas only a boy, you see,
Faint and worn, with dim-blue eyes; and he'd sailed on the
        Tennessee.

16

Only sixteen he was, sir—a fond mother's only son—
Off and away with Morgan before his life had begun;
The damp drops stood on his temples; drawn was the boyish
    mouth;
And I thought me of the mother waiting down in the South.

17

Oh! pluck was he to the backbone, and clear grit through and
    through;
Boasted and bragged like a trooper; but the big words wouldn't
    do;—
The boy was dying, sir, dying, as plain as plain could be,
Worn out by his ride with Morgan up from the Tennessee.

18

But when I told the laddie that I too was from the South,
Water came in his dim eyes, and quivers around his mouth.
"Do you know the Blue-grass country?" he wistful began to say;
Then swayed like a willow sapling, and fainted dead away.

19

I had him into the log-house, and worked and brought him to;
I fed him, and I coaxed him, as I thought his mother'd do;
And when the lad got better, and the noise in his head was gone,
Morgan's men were miles away, galloping, galloping on.

20

"Oh, I must go!" he muttered; "I must be up and away!
Morgan—Morgan is waiting for me! Oh, what will Morgan
    say?"
But I heard a sound of tramping, and kept him back from the
    door—
The ringing sound of horses' hoofs that I had heard before.

21

And on, on came the soldiers—the Michigan cavalry—
And fast they rode, and black they looked, galloping rapidly;
They had followed hard on Morgan's track; they had followed
    day and night;
But of Morgan and Morgan's raiders they had never caught a
    sight.

22

And rich Ohio sat startled through all those summer days;
For strange, wild men were galloping over her broad highways—
Now here, now there, now seen, now gone, now north, now east,
    now west,
Through river-valleys and corn-land farms, sweeping away her
    best.

23

A bold ride and a long ride! But they were taken at last.
They almost reached the river by galloping hard and fast;
But the boys in blue were upon them ere ever they gained the
    ford,
And Morgan, Morgan the raider, laid down his terrible sword.

24

Well, I kept the boy till evening—kept him against his will—
But he was too weak to follow, and sat there pale and still.
When it was cool and dusky—you'll wonder to hear me tell,
But I stole down to that gully and brought up Kentucky Belle.

25

I kissed the star on her forehead—my pretty, gentle lass—
But I knew that she'd be happy back in the old Blue-grass.
A suit of clothes of Conrad's, with all the money I had,
And Kentuck, pretty Kentuck, I gave to the worn-out lad.

26

I guided him to the southward as well as I knew how;
The boy rode off with many thanks and many a backward bow;
And then the glow it faded, and my heart began to swell,
As down the glen away she went, my lost Kentucky Belle!

27

When Conrad came in the evening, the moon was shining high;
Baby and I were both crying—I couldn't tell him why—
But a battered suit of rebel gray was hanging on the wall,
And a thin old horse, with drooping head, stood in Kentucky's
    stall.

28

Well, he was kind, and never once said a hard word to me;
He knew I couldn't help it—'twas all for the Tennessee.
But, after the war was over, just think what came to pass—
A letter, sir; and the two were safe back in the old Blue-grass.

29

The lad had got across the border, riding Kentucky Belle;
And Kentuck she was thriving, and fat, and hearty, and well;
He cared for her, and kept her, nor touched her with whip or
    spur.
Ah! we've had many horses since, but never a horse like her!

HELPS TO STUDY

Historical: In the summer of 1863, a force of men under the Confederate general, John H. Morgan, dashed across Kentucky into Indiana and Ohio, but they were surrounded and captured while trying to recross the Ohio river. This was called "Morgan's Raid."

Notes and Questions

What great war was going on in the United States at this time?

Where is the Blue Grass country? For what did the woman long in her new home?

Read the lines in the fourth and fifth stanzas which describe the Ohio country.

Where were Morgan and his men going when the woman saw them?

Who were the horsemen who galloped past soon after?

What was the second company of horsemen trying to do?

What did the woman do for the young soldier?

How did she feel after he rode away?

When did she hear from him?

What did he tell her about Kentucky Belle?

What does the repetition of Morgan's name in, ''Morgan, Morgan the raider,'' help you to feel?

What does the repetition of the word ''galloping,'' as ''galloping, galloping on,'' help you to see?

For whom is the story named?

Can you think of any other title which might be given to it?

Words and Phrases for Discussion

''yellow afternoon''

''breathless sunshine''

''swayed like a willow sapling''

''laid down his terrible sword''

THE KING OF THE GOLDEN RIVER; OR, THE BLACK BROTHERS

John Ruskin

John Ruskin (1819-1900) was an English writer. He was born in London. In 1839 he won a prize at Oxford University, where he graduated in 1842. He wrote ''The King of the Golden River,'' ''for a very young lady,'' while he was in college. He was an art critic and his writings on art topics are unsurpassed.

CHAPTER ONE

HOW THE AGRICULTURAL SYSTEM OF THE BLACK BROTHERS WAS INTERFERED WITH BY SOUTH-WEST WIND, ESQUIRE

I

TREASURE VALLEY AND THE BLACK BROTHERS

In a secluded and mountainous part of Stiria there was in old time a valley of the most surprising and luxuriant fertility.

It was surrounded on all sides by steep and rocky mountains, rising into peaks which were always covered with snow, and from which a number of torrents descended in constant cataracts. One of these fell westward over the face of a crag so high that, when the sun had· set to everything else, and all below was darkness, his beams still shone full upon this waterfall, so that it looked like a shower of gold. It was, therefore, called by the people of the neighborhood, the Golden River. It was strange that none of these streams fell into the valley itself. They all descended on the other side of the mountains, and wound away through broad plains and past populous cities. But the clouds were drawn so constantly to the snowy hills, and rested so softly in the circular hollow, that in time of drought and heat, when all the country round was burnt up, there was still rain in the little valley; and its crops were so heavy and its hay so high, and its apples so red, and its grapes so blue, and its wine so rich, and its honey so sweet, that it was a marvel to every one who beheld it, and was commonly called the Treasure Valley.

The whole of this little valley belonged to three brothers called Schwartz, Hans, and Gluck. Schwartz and Hans, the two elder brothers, were very ugly men, with overhanging eyebrows and small dull eyes, which were always half shut, so that you could not see into them, and always fancied they saw very far into you. They lived by farming the Treasure Valley, and very good farmers they were. They killed everything that did not pay for its eating. They shot the blackbirds, because they pecked the fruit; and killed the hedgehogs, lest they should suck the cows; they poisoned the crickets for eating the crumbs in the kitchen; and smothered the cicadas, which used to sing all summer in the lime trees. They worked their servants without any wages, till they would not work any more, and then quarrelled with them, and turned them out of doors without paying them. It would have been very odd if with such a farm and such a system of farming they hadn't got very rich; and very rich they did get. They generally contrived to keep their corn

by them till it was very dear, and then sell it for twice its value; they had heaps of gold lying about on their floors, yet it was never known that they had given so much as a penny or a crust in charity; they never went to mass; grumbled perpetually at
5 paying tithes; and were, in a word, of so cruel and grinding a temper as to receive from all those with whom they had any dealings the nickname of the "Black Brothers."

The youngest brother, Gluck, was as completely opposed, in both appearance and character, to his seniors as could possibly
10 be imagined or desired. He was not above twelve years old, fair, blue-eyed and kind in temper to every living thing. He did not, of course, agree particularly well with his brothers, or rather, they did not agree with him. He was usually appointed to the honorable office of turnspit, when there was anything to
15 roast, which was not often; for, to do the brothers justice, they were hardly less sparing upon themselves than upon other people. At other times he used to clean the shoes, floors, and sometimes the plates, occasionally getting what was left on them, by way of encouragement, and a wholesome quantity of dry blows, by
20 way of education.

II

THE WET WEATHER AND THE STRANGE VISITOR

Things went on in this manner for a long time. At last came a very wet summer, and everything went wrong in the country around. The hay had hardly been got in when the haystacks were floated bodily down to the sea by an inundation;
25 the vines were cut to pieces with the hail; the corn was all killed by a black blight; only in the Treasure Valley, as usual, all was safe. As it had rain when there was rain nowhere else, so it had sun when there was sun nowhere else. Everybody came to buy corn at the farm, and went away pouring maledic-
30 tions on the Black Brothers. They asked what they liked, and got it, except from the poor people, who could only beg, and

several of whom were starved at their very door without the slightest regard.

It was drawing towards winter, and very cold weather, when one day the two elder brothers had gone out with their usual
5 warning to little Gluck, who was left to mind the roast, that he was to let nobody in and give nothing out. Gluck sat down quite close to the fire, for it was raining very hard, and the kitchen walls were by no means dry or comfortable looking. He turned and turned, and the roast got nice and brown. "What
10 a pity," thought Gluck, "my brothers never ask anybody to dinner. I'm sure when they have such a nice piece of mutton as this, and nobody else has so much as a piece of dry bread, it would do their hearts good to have somebody to eat it with them."

15 Just as he spoke there came a double knock at the house door, yet heavy and dull, as though the knocker had been tied up— more like a puff than a knock.

"It must be the wind," said Gluck; "nobody else would venture to knock double knocks at our door."

20 No; it wasn't the wind: there it came again very hard; and what was particularly astounding, the knocker seemed to be in a hurry, and not to be in the least afraid of the consequences. Gluck went to the window, opened it, and put his head out to see who it was.

25 It was the most extraordinary-looking little gentleman he had ever seen in his life. He had a very large nose, slightly brass-colored; his cheeks were very round and very red, and might have warranted a supposition that he had been blowing a refractory fire for the last eight-and-forty hours; his eyes
30 twinkled merrily through long silky eyelashes, his moustaches curled twice round like a corkscrew on each side of his mouth, and his hair, of a curious mixed pepper-and-salt color, descended far over his shoulders. He was about four-feet-six in height, and wore a conical pointed cap of nearly the same altitude,
35 decorated with a black feather some three feet long. His doublet

was prolonged behind into something resembling a violent exaggeration of what is now termed a "swallow-tail," but was much obscured by the swelling folds of an enormous black, glossy-looking cloak, which must have been very much too long in calm
5 weather, as the wind, whistling round the old house, carried it clear out from the wearer's shoulders to about four times his own length.

Gluck was so perfectly paralyzed by the singular appearance of his visitor that he remained fixed without uttering a word,
10 until the old gentleman, having performed another and a more energetic concerto on the knocker, turned round to look after his fly-away cloak. In so doing he caught sight of Gluck's little yellow head jammed in the window, with his mouth and eyes very wide open indeed.

15 "Hollo!" said the little gentleman, "that's not the way to answer the door: I'm wet, let me in."

To do the little gentleman justice, he was wet. His feather hung down between his legs like a beaten puppy's tail, dripping like an umbrella; and from the ends of his moustaches the
20 water was running into his waistcoat pockets, and out again like a mill stream.

"I beg pardon, sir," said Gluck, "I'm very sorry, but I really can't."

"Can't what?" said the old gentleman.

25 "I can't let you in, sir,—I can't indeed; my brothers would beat me to death, sir, if I thought of such a thing. What do you want, sir?"

"Want?" said the old gentleman, petulantly. "I want fire and shelter; and there's your great fire there, blazing, crackling,
30 and dancing on the walls, with nobody to feel it. Let me in, I say; I only want to warm myself."

Gluck had had his head so long out of the window by this time that he began to feel it was really unpleasantly cold, and when he turned and saw the beautiful fire rustling and roaring,
35 and throwing long, bright tongues up the chimney, as if it were

licking its chops at the savory smell of the leg of mutton, his heart melted within him that it should be burning away for nothing. "He does look very wet," said little Gluck; "I'll just let him in for a quarter of an hour." Round he went to the
5 door and opened it; and as the little gentleman walked in there came a gust of wind through the house that made the old chimneys totter.

"That's a good boy," said the little gentleman. "Never mind your brothers. I'll talk to them."

10 "Pray, sir, don't do any such thing," said Gluck. "I can't let you stay till they come; they'd be the death of me."

"Dear me," said the old gentleman, "I'm very sorry to hear that. How long may I stay?"

"Only till the mutton's done, sir," replied Gluck, "and it's
15 very brown."

Then the old gentleman walked into the kitchen, and sat himself down on the hob, with the top of his cap accommodated up the chimney, for it was a great deal too high for the roof.

"You'll soon dry there, sir," said Gluck, and sat down again
20 to turn the mutton. But the old gentleman did not dry there, but went on drip, drip, dripping among the cinders, and the fire fizzed, and sputtered, and began to look very black and uncomfortable. Never was such a cloak; every fold in it ran like a gutter.

25 "I beg pardon, sir," said Gluck at length, after watching for a quarter of an hour the water spreading in long, quicksilver-like streams over the floor; "may I take your cloak?"

"No, thank you," said the old gentleman.

"Your cap, sir?"

30 "I am all right, thank you," said the old gentleman, rather gruffly.

"But,—sir,—I'm very sorry," said Gluck, hesitatingly; "but— really, sir,—you're—putting the fire out."

"It'll take longer to do the mutton, then," replied his visitor,
35 dryly.

Gluck was very much puzzled by the behavior of his guest; it was such a strange mixture of coolness and humility. He turned away at the string meditatively for another five minutes.

"That mutton looks very nice," said the old gentleman at
5 length. "Can't you give me a little bit?"

"Impossible, sir," said Gluck.

"I'm very hungry," continued the old gentleman; "I've had nothing to eat yesterday nor to-day. They surely couldn't miss a bit from the knuckle!"

10 He spoke in so very melancholy a tone that it quite melted Gluck's heart. "They promised me one slice, to-day, sir," said he; "I can give you that, but not a bit more."

"That's a good boy," said the old gentleman again.

III

THE RETURN OF HANS AND SCHWARTZ.

Then Gluck warmed a plate, and sharpened a knife. "I don't
15 care if I do get beaten for it," thought he. Just as he had cut a large slice out of the mutton there came a tremendous rap at the door. The old gentleman jumped off the hob, as if it had suddenly become inconveniently warm. Gluck fitted the slice into the mutton again, with desperate efforts at exactitude, and ran
20 to open the door.

"What did you keep us waiting in the rain for?" said Schwartz, as he walked in, throwing his umbrella in Gluck's face. "Ay! what for, indeed, you little vagabond?" said Hans, administering an educational box on the ear, as he followed his brother into
25 the kitchen.

"Bless my soul!" said Schwartz, when he opened the door.

"Amen," said the little gentleman, who had taken his cap off, and was standing in the middle of the kitchen, bowing with the utmost possible velocity.

30 "Who's that?" said Schwartz, catching up a rolling-pin; and turning to Gluck with a fierce frown.

"I don't know, indeed, brother," said Gluck, in great terror.

"How did he get in?" roared Schwartz.

"My dear brother," said Gluck, deprecatingly, "he was so very wet!"

5 The rolling-pin was descending on Gluck's head; but at the instant the old gentleman interposed his conical cap, on which it crashed with a shock that shook the water out of it all over the room. What was very odd, the rolling-pin no sooner touched the cap than it flew out of Schwartz's hand, spinning 10 like a straw in a high wind, and fell into the corner at the farther end of the room.

"Who are you, sir?" demanded Schwartz, turning upon him.

"What's your business?" snarled Hans.

"I am a poor old man, sir," the little gentleman began very 15 modestly, "and I saw your fire through the window, and begged shelter for a quarter of an hour."

"Have the goodness to walk out again, then," said Schwartz. "We've quite enough water in our kitchen without making it a drying-house."

20 "It is a cold day to turn an old man out in, sir; look at my gray hairs." They hung down to his shoulders, as I told you before.

"Ay!" said Hans, "there are enough of them to keep you warm. Walk!"

25 "I'm very, very hungry, sir; couldn't you spare me a bit of bread before I go?"

"Bread, indeed!" said Schwartz; "do you suppose we've nothing to do with our bread but to give it to such red-nosed fellows as you?"

30 "Why don't you sell your feather?" said Hans, sneeringly. "Out with you!"

"A little bit," said the old gentleman.

"Be off!" said Schwartz.

"Pray, gentlemen—"

35 "Off, and be hanged!" cried Hans, seizing him by the collar.

But he had no sooner touched the old gentleman's collar than away he went after the rolling-pin, spinning round and round, till he fell into the corner on the top of it. Then Schwartz was very angry, and ran at the old gentleman to turn him out; but
5 he also had hardly touched him, when away he went after Hans and the rolling-pin, and hit his head against the wall as he tumbled into the corner. And so there they lay, all three.

Then the old gentleman spun himself round with velocity in the opposite direction; continued to spin until his long cloak
10 was all wound neatly about him; clapped his cap on his head, very much on one side (for it could not stand upright without going through the ceiling), gave an additional twist to his corkscrew moustaches, and replied with perfect coolness: "Gentlemen, I wish you a very good morning. At twelve o'clock tonight
15 I'll call again; after such a refusal of hospitality as I have just experienced, you will not be surprised if that visit is the last I ever pay you."

"If ever I catch you here again," muttered Schwartz, coming, half frightened, out of the corner—but, before he could finish
20 his sentence, the old gentleman had shut the house door behind him with a great bang: and there drove past the window, at the same instant, a wreath of ragged cloud, that whirled and rolled away down the valley in all manner of shapes; turning over and over in the air, and melting away at last in a gush of
25 rain.

"A very pretty business, indeed, Mr. Gluck!" said Schwartz. "Dish the mutton, sir. If ever I catch you at such a trick again—bless me, why, the mutton's been cut!"

"You promised me one slice, brother, you know," said Gluck.
30 "Oh! and you were cutting it hot, I suppose, and going to catch all the gravy. It'll be long before I promise you such a thing again. Leave the room, sir; and have the kindness to wait in the coal-cellar till I call you."

Gluck left the room melancholy enough. The brothers ate as

much mutton as they could, locked the rest into the cupboard, and proceeded to get very drunk after dinner.

Such a night as it was! Howling wind, and rushing rain, without intermission. The brothers had just sense enough left
5 to put up all the shutters, and double bar the door, before they went to bed. They usually slept in the same room. As the clock struck twelve, they were both awakened by a tremendous crash. Their door burst open with a violence that shook the house from top to bottom.

10 "What's that?" cried Schwartz, starting up in his bed.

"Only I," said the little gentleman.

The two brothers sat up on their bolster, and stared into the darkness. The room was full of water; and by a misty moon-beam, which found its way through a hole in the shutter, they
15 could see in the midst of it an enormous foam globe, spinning round, and bobbing up and down like a cork, on which, as on a most luxurious cushion, reclined the little old gentleman, cap and all. There was plenty of room for it now, for the roof was off.

20 "Sorry to incommode you," said their visitor, ironically "I'm afraid your beds are dampish; perhaps you had better go to your brother's room: I've left the ceiling on there."

They required no second admonition, but rushed into Gluck's room, wet through, and in an agony of terror.

25 "You'll find my card on the kitchen table," the old gentleman called after them. "Remember, the last visit."

"Pray Heaven it may!" said Schwartz, shuddering. And the foam globe disappeared.

Dawn came at last, and the two brothers looked out of Gluck's
30 little window in the morning. The Treasure Valley was one mass of ruin and desolation. The inundation had swept away trees, crops, and cattle, and left in their stead a waste of red sand and gray mud. The two brothers crept shivering and horror-struck into the kitchen. The water had gutted the whole

first floor; corn, money, almost every movable thing had been swept away, and there was left only a small white card on the kitchen table. On it, in large, breezy, long-legged letters, were engraved the words:—

5   SOUTHWEST WIND, ESQUIRE.

CHAPTER TWO

OF THE PROCEEDINGS OF THE THREE BROTHERS AFTER
THE VISIT OF SOUTH-WEST WIND, ESQUIRE; AND HOW
LITTLE GLUCK HAD AN INTERVIEW WITH THE
KING OF THE GOLDEN RIVER

I

HOW THE BLACK BROTHERS BECAME GOLDSMITHS

Southwest Wind, Esquire, was as good as his word. After the momentous visit above related, he entered the Treasure Valley no more; and what was worse, he had so much influence
10 with his relations, the West Winds in general, and used it so effectually, that they all adopted a similar line of conduct. So no rain fell in the valley from one year's end to another. Though everything remained green and flourishing in the plains below, the inheritance of the Three Brothers was a desert. What had
15 once been the richest soil in the kingdom became a shifting heap of red sand; and the brothers, unable longer to contend with the adverse skies, abandoned their valueless patrimony in despair, to seek some means of gaining a livelihood among the cities and people of the plains. All their money was gone, and they had
20 nothing left but some curious, old-fashioned pieces of gold plate, the last remnants of their ill-gotten wealth.

"Suppose we turn goldsmiths?" said Schwartz to Hans, as they entered the large city. "It is a good knave's trade; we can put a great deal of copper into the gold without any one's
25 finding it out."

The thought was agreed to be a very good one; they hired a furnace, and turned goldsmiths. But two slight circum-

stances affected their trade: the first, that people did not approve
of the coppered gold; the second, that the two elder brothers
whenever they had sold anything used to leave little Gluck to
mind the furnace, and go and drink out the money in the ale-
5 house next door. So they melted all their gold, without making
money enough to buy more, and were at last reduced to one large
drinking mug, which an uncle of his had given to little Gluck,
and which he was very fond of, and would not have parted with
for the world; though he never drank anything out of it but milk
10 and water. The mug was a very odd mug to look at. The
handle was formed of two wreaths of flowing golden hair, so
finely spun that it looked more like silk than metal, and these
wreaths descended into and mixed with a beard and whiskers of
the same exquisite workmanship, which surrounded and deco-
15 rated a very fierce little face, of the reddest gold imaginable,
right in the front of the mug, with a pair of eyes in it which
seemed to command its whole circumference. It was impossible
to drink from the mug without being subjected to an intense
gaze out of the side of these eyes; and Schwartz positively
20 averred that once after emptying it full of Rhenish seventeen
times he had seen them wink! When it came to the mug's turn
to be made into spoons, it half broke poor little Gluck's heart; but
the brothers only laughed at him, tossed the mug into the melting-pot, and staggered out to the ale-house, leaving him, as usual,
25 to pour the gold into bars, when it was all ready.

When they were gone, Gluck took a farewell look at his old
friend in the melting-pot. The flowing hair was all gone; nothing remained but the red nose and the sparkling eyes, which
looked more malicious than ever. "And no wonder," thought
30 Gluck, "after being treated in that way." He sauntered discon-
solately to the window, and sat himself down to catch the fresh
evening air, and escape the hot breath of the furnace. Now this
window commanded a direct view of the range of mountains,
which, as I told you before, overhung the Treasure Valley, and
35 more especially of the peak from which fell the Golden River.

It was just at the close of the day; and when Gluck sat down at the window, he saw the rocks of the mountain tops all crimson and purple with the sunset. There were bright tongues of fiery cloud burning and quivering about them; and the river, brighter
5 than all, fell in a waving column of pure gold from precipice to precipice, with the double arch of a broad purple rainbow stretched across it, flushing and fading alternately in the wreaths of spray.

"Ah!" said Gluck aloud, after he had looked at it for a while,
10 "if that river were really all gold, what a nice thing it would be."

"No, it wouldn't, Gluck," said a clear metallic voice, close at his ear.

"Bless me! what's that?" exclaimed Gluck, jumping up. There was nobody there. He looked round the room, and under the
15 table, and a great many times behind him, but there was certainly nobody there, and he sat down again at the window. This time he did not speak, but he could not help thinking again that it would be very convenient if the river were really all gold.

"Not at all, my boy," said the same voice, louder than before.
20 "Bless me!" said Gluck again, "what is that?" He looked again into all the corners and cupboards, and then began turning round and round as fast as he could in the middle of the room, thinking there was somebody behind him, when the same voice struck again on his ear. It was singing now very merrily,
25 "Lala-lira-la"; no words, only a soft, running, effervescent melody, something like that of a kettle on the boil. Gluck looked out of the window. No, it was certainly in the house. Upstairs, and downstairs. No, it was certainly in that very room, coming in quicker time and clearer notes every moment.
30 "Lala-lira-la." All at once it struck Gluck that it sounded louder near the furnace. He ran to the opening, and looked in: yes, it seemed to be coming not only out of the furnace, but out of the pot. He uncovered it, and ran back in a great fright, for the pot was certainly singing! He stood in the farthest cor-
35 ner of the room for a minute or two with his hands up and his

mouth open, when the singing stopped, and the voice became clear and distinct.

"Hollo!" said the voice.

Gluck made no answer.

5 "Hollo! Gluck, my boy," said the pot again.

Gluck summoned all his energies, walked straight up to the crucible, drew it out of the furnace and looked in. The gold was all melted, and its surface as smooth and polished as a river; but instead of reflecting little Gluck's head as he looked in, he 10 saw meeting his glance from beneath the gold the red nose and sharp eyes of his old friend of the mug, a thousand times redder and sharper than ever he had seen them in his life.

"Come, Gluck, my boy," said the voice out of the pot again, "I'm all right; pour me out."

15 But Gluck was too much astonished to do anything of the kind.

"Pour me out, I say," said the voice, rather gruffly.

Still Gluck couldn't move.

"*Will* you pour me out?" said the voice, passionately, "I'm 20 too hot."

II

GLUCK AND THE LITTLE GOLDEN DWARF

By a violent effort Gluck recovered the use of his limbs, took hold of the crucible, and sloped it so as to pour out the gold. But instead of a liquid stream there came out, first, a pair of pretty little yellow legs, then some coat-tails, then a pair of 25 arms stuck a-kimbo, and, finally, the well-known head of his friend the mug; all which articles, uniting as they rolled out, stood up energetically on the floor, in the shape of a little golden dwarf about a foot and a half high.

"That's right!" said the dwarf, stretching out first his legs, 30 and then his arms, and then shaking his head up and down, and as far round as it would go, for five minutes without stopping, apparently with the view of ascertaining if he were quite cor-

rectly put together, while Gluck stood contemplating him in speechless amazement. He was dressed in a slashed doublet of spun gold, so fine in its texture that the prismatic colors gleamed over it, as if on a surface of mother of pearl; and over this bril-
5 liant doublet his hair and beard fell full half way to the ground in waving curls, so exquisitely delicate, that Gluck could hardly tell where they ended; they seemed to melt into air. The features of the face, however, were by no means finished with the same delicacy; they were rather coarse, slightly inclined to cop-
10 pery in complexion, and indicative, in expression, of a very pertinacious and intractable disposition in their small proprietor. When the dwarf had finished his self-examination, he turned his small sharp eyes full on Gluck, and stared at him deliberately for a minute or two. "No, it wouldn't, Gluck, my boy," said the
15 little man.

This was certainly rather an abrupt way of commencing conversation. It might indeed be supposed to refer to the course of Gluck's thoughts, which had first produced the dwarf's observations out of the pot; but whatever it referred to, Gluck had
20 no inclination to dispute what he said.

"Wouldn't it, sir?" said Gluck, very mildly and submissively indeed.

"No," said the dwarf, conclusively. "No, it wouldn't." And with that the dwarf pulled his cap hard over his brows, and
25 took two turns, of three feet long, up and down the room, lifting his legs up very high and setting them down very hard. This pause gave time for Gluck to collect his thoughts a little, and seeing no great reason to view his diminutive visitor with dread, and feeling his curiosity overcome his amazement, he ventured
30 on a question of peculiar delicacy.

"Pray, sir," said Gluck, rather hesitatingly, "were you my mug?"

On which the little man turned sharp round, walked straight up to Gluck, and drew himself up to his full height. "I," said
35 the little man, "am the King of the Golden River." Whereupon

he turned about again, and took two more turns some six feet long in order to allow time for the consternation which this announcement produced in his auditor to evaporate. After which he again walked up to Gluck and stood still, as if expecting 5 some comment on his communication.

Gluck determined to say something at all events. "I hope your Majesty is very well," said Gluck.

"Listen!" said the little man, deigning no reply to this polite inquiry. "I am the King of what you mortals call the Golden 10 River. The shape you saw me in was owing to the malice of a stronger king, from whose enchantments you have this instant freed me. What I have seen of you, and your conduct toward your wicked brothers, renders me willing to serve you; therefore, attend to what I tell you. Whoever shall climb to the top of 15 that mountain from which you see the Golden River issue, and shall cast into the stream at its source three drops of holy water, for him, and for him only, the river shall turn to gold. But no one failing in his first can succeed in a second attempt; and if any one shall cast unholy water into the river it will overwhelm 20 him, and he will become a black stone." So saying, the King of the Golden River turned away and deliberately walked into the centre of the hottest flame of the furnace. His figure became red, white, transparent, dazzling,—a blaze of intense light,— rose, trembled, and disappeared. The King of the Golden River 25 had evaporated.

"Oh!" cried poor Gluck, running to look up the chimney after him; "oh, dear, dear, dear me! My mug! my mug! my mug!"

CHAPTER THREE

HOW MR. HANS SET OFF ON AN EXPEDITION TO THE GOLDEN RIVER AND HOW HE PROSPERED THEREIN

I

HOW HANS PREPARED FOR THE JOURNEY

THE King of the Golden River had hardly made the extraordi- nary exit related in the last chapter before Hans and Schwartz

came roaring into the house very savagely drunk. The discovery
of the total loss of their last piece of plate had the effect of
sobering them just enough to enable them to stand over Gluck,
beating him very steadily for a quarter of an hour; at the ex-
5 piration of which period they dropped into a couple of chairs,
and requested to know what he had got to say for himself. Gluck
told them his story, of which, of course, they did not believe a
word. They beat him again, till their arms were tired, and
staggered to bed. In the morning, however, the steadiness with
10 which he adhered to his story obtained him some degree of
credence; the immediate consequence of which was that the two
brothers, after wrangling a long time on the knotty question,
Which of them should try his fortune first, drew their swords
and began fighting. The noise of the fray alarmed the neigh-
15 bors, who, finding they could not pacify the combatants, sent for
the constable.

On hearing this, Hans contrived to escape, and hid himself,
but Schwartz was taken before the magistrate, fined for breaking
the peace, and having drunk out his last penny the evening
20 before, was thrown into prison till he should pay.

When Hans heard this, he was much delighted, and determined to set out immediately for the Golden River. How to
get the holy water was the question. He went to the priest, but
the priest could not give any holy water to so abandoned a char-
25 acter. So Hans went to vespers in the evening for the first time
in his life, and, under pretence of crossing himself, stole a cupful
and returned home in triumph.

Next morning he got up before the sun rose, put the holy
water into a strong flask, and two bottles of wine and some meat
30 in a basket, slung them over his back, took his alpine staff in his
hand, and set off for the mountains.

On his way out of the town he had to pass the prison, and as
he looked in at the windows, whom should he see but Schwartz
himself peeping out of the bars, and looking very disconsolate.

"Good morning, brother," said Hans; "have you any message for the King of the Golden River?"

Schwartz gnashed his teeth with rage, and shook the bars with all his strength; but Hans only laughed at him, and advis-
5 ing him to make himself comfortable till he came back again, shouldered his basket, shook the bottle of holy water in Schwartz's face till it frothed again, and marched off in the highest spirits in the world.

It was indeed a morning that might have made any one happy,
10 even with no Golden River to seek for. Level lines of dewy mist lay stretched along the valley, out of which rose the massy mountains—their lower cliffs in pale gray shadow, hardly distinguishable from the floating vapor, but gradually ascending till they caught the sunlight, which ran in sharp touches of
15 ruddy color along the angular crags, and pierced, in long level rays, through their fringes of spear-like pine. Far above, shot up red splintered masses of castellated rock, jagged and shivered into myriads of fantastic forms, with here and there a streak of sunlit snow, traced down their chasms like a line of forked light-
20 ning; and far beyond and above all these, fainter than the morning cloud, but purer and changeless, slept in the blue sky the utmost peaks of the eternal snow.

The Golden River, which sprang from one of the lower and snowless elevations, was now nearly in shadow; all but the upper-
25 most jets of spray, which rose like slow smoke above the undulating line of the cataract, and floated away in feeble wreaths upon the morning wind.

II

THE DIFFICULTIES ENCOUNTERED AND THE END OF THE JOURNEY

On this object, and on this alone, Hans' eyes and thoughts were fixed. Forgetting the distance he had to traverse, he set
30 off at an imprudent rate of walking, which greatly exhausted him before he had scaled the first range of the green and low

hills. He was, moreover, surprised on surmounting them, to find that a large glacier, of whose existence, notwithstanding his previous knowledge of the mountains, he had been absolutely ignorant, lay between him and the source of the Golden River.
5 He mounted it though, with the boldness of a practised mountaineer; yet he thought he had never in his life traversed so strange or so dangerous a glacier. The ice was excessively slippery, and out of all its chasms came wild sounds of gushing water; not monotonous or low, but changeful and loud, rising
10 occasionally into drifting passages of wild melody, then breaking off into short melancholy tones, or sudden shrieks, resembling those of human voices in distress or pain. The ice was broken into thousands of confused shapes, but none, Hans thought, like the ordinary forms of splintered ice. There seemed a curious
15 *expression* about all their outlines—a perpetual resemblance to living features, distorted and scornful. Myriads of deceitful shadows and lurid lights played and floated about and through the pale blue pinnacles, dazzling and confusing the sight of the traveller; while his ears grew dull and his head giddy with the
20 constant gush and roar of the concealed waters. These painful circumstances increased upon him as he advanced; the ice crashed and yawned into fresh chasms at his feet, tottering spires nodded around him, and fell thundering across his path; and though he had repeatedly faced these dangers on the most ter-
25 rific glaciers, and in the wildest weather, it was with a new and oppressive feeling of panic terror that he leaped the last chasm, and flung himself, exhausted and shuddering, on the firm turf of the mountain.

He had been compelled to abandon his basket of food, which
30 became a perilous incumbrance on the glacier, and had now no means of refreshing himself but by breaking off and eating some of the pieces of ice. This, however, relieved his thirst; an hour's repose recruited his hardy frame, and with the indomitable spirit of avarice, he resumed his laborious journey.
35   His way now lay straight up a ridge of bare red rocks, without

a blade of grass to ease the foot, or a projecting angle to afford
an inch of shade from the south sun. It was past noon, and the
rays beat intensely upon the steep path, while the whole atmosphere was motionless and penetrated with heat. Intense thirst
5 was soon added to the bodily fatigue with which Hans was now
afflicted; glance after glance he cast at the flask of water which
hung at his belt. "Three drops are enough," at last thought he;
"I may at least cool my lips with it."

He opened the flask, and was raising it to his lips, when his
10 eye fell on an object lying on the rock beside him; he thought
it moved. It was a small dog, apparently in the last agony of
death from thirst. Its tongue was out, its jaws dry, its limbs
extended lifelessly, and a swarm of black ants were crawling
about its lips and throat. Its eye moved to the bottle which
15 Hans held in his hand. He raised it, drank, spurned the animal
with his foot and passed on. And he did not know how it was,
but he thought that a strange shadow had suddenly come across
the blue sky.

The path became steeper and more rugged every moment, and
20 the high hill air, instead of refreshing him, seemed to throw his
blood into a fever. The noise of the hill cataracts sounded like
mockery in his ears; they were all distant, and his thirst
increased every moment. Another hour passed, and he again
looked down to the flask at his side; it was half empty, but there
25 were much more than three drops in it. He stopped to open it
and again, as he did so, something moved in the path above him.
It was a fair child, stretched nearly lifeless on the rock, its
breast heaving with thirst, its eyes closed, and its lips parched
and burning. Hans eyed it deliberately, drank, and passed on.
30 And a dark gray cloud came over the sun, and long, snake-like
shadows crept up along the mountain-sides. Hans struggled on.
The sun was sinking, but its descent seemed to bring no coolness; the leaden weight of the dead air pressed upon his brow
and heart, but the goal was near. He saw the cataract of the
35 Golden River springing from the hill-side, scarcely five hundred

feet above him. He paused for a moment to breathe, and sprang on to complete his task.

At this instant a faint cry fell on his ear. He turned, and saw a gray-haired old man extended on the rocks. His eyes 5 were sunk, his features deadly pale, and gathered into an expression of despair. "Water!" he stretched his arms to Hans, and cried feebly, "Water! I am dying."

"I have none," replied Hans; "thou hast had thy share of life." He strode over the prostrate body, and darted on. And a 10 flash of blue lightning rose out of the East, shaped like a sword; it shook thrice over the whole heaven, and left it dark with one heavy impenetrable shade. The sun was setting; it plunged towards the horizon like a red-hot ball.

The roar of the Golden River rose on Hans' ear. He stood 15 at the brink of the chasm through which it ran. Its waves were filled with the red glory of the sunset; they shook their crests like tongues of fire, and flashes of bloody light gleamed along their foam. Their sound came mightier and mightier on his senses; his brain grew giddy with the prolonged thunder. 20 Shuddering, he drew the flask from his girdle and hurled it into the centre of the torrent. As he did so, an icy chill shot through his limbs; he staggered, shrieked, and fell. The waters closed over his cry. And the moaning of the river rose wildly into the night, as it gushed over

25   THE BLACK STONE.

CHAPTER FOUR

HOW MR. SCHWARTZ SET OFF ON AN EXPEDITION TO THE GOLDEN RIVER, AND HOW HE PROSPERED THEREIN

POOR Little Gluck waited very anxiously alone in the house for Hans' return. Finding he did not come back, he was terribly frightened, and went and told Schwartz in the prison all that had happened. Then Schwartz was very much pleased, and said 30 that Hans must certainly have been turned into a black stone, and he should have all the gold to himself. But Gluck was very sorry, and cried all night. When he got up in the morning, there was no bread in the house, nor any money; so Gluck went and hired himself to another goldsmith, and he worked so hard 5 and so neatly and so long every day, that he soon got money enough together to pay his brother's fine. He went then and gave it all to Schwartz, and Schwartz got out of prison. Then Schwartz was quite pleased, and said he should have some of the gold of the river. But Gluck only begged he would go and see 10 what had become of Hans.

Now when Schwartz had heard that Hans had stolen the holy water, he thought to himself that such a proceeding might not be considered altogether correct by the King of the Golden River, and he determined to manage matters better. So he took some 15 more of Gluck's money, and went to a bad priest, who gave him some holy water very readily for it. Then Schwartz was sure it was all quite right. He got up early in the morning before the sun rose, took some bread and wine in a basket, put his holy water in a flask, and set off for the mountains. Like his brother, 20 he was much surprised at the sight of the glacier, and had great difficulty in crossing it, even after leaving his basket behind him. The day was cloudless, but not bright; there was a heavy purple haze hanging over the sky, and the hills looked lowering and gloomy. And as Schwartz climbed the steep rock path the thirst 25 came upon him, as it had upon his brother, until he lifted his flask to his lips to drink. Then he saw the fair child lying near him on the rocks, and it cried to him, and moaned for water.

"Water, indeed," said Schwartz; "I haven't half enough for myself," and passed on. As he went he thought the sunbeams 30 grew more dim, and he saw a low bank of black cloud rising out of the West. When he had climbed for another hour the thirst overcame him again, and he would have drunk. Then he saw the old man lying before him on the path, and heard him cry out for water. "Water, indeed," said Schwartz; "I haven't half 35 enough for myself," and on he went.

Then again the light seemed to fade from before his eyes, and he looked up, and, behold, a mist, of the color of blood, had come over the sun. The bank of black cloud too had risen very high, and its edges were tossing and tumbling like the waves of the 5 angry sea. And they cast long shadows, which flickered over Schwartz's path.

Then Schwartz climbed for another hour, and again his thirst returned. As he lifted his flask to his lips, he thought he saw his brother Hans lying exhausted on the path before him, 10 and, as he gazed, the figure stretched its arms to him, and cried for water. "Ha, ha," laughed Schwartz, "are you there? remember the prison bars, my boy. Water, indeed—do you suppose I carried it all the way up here for you!" And he strode over the figure; yet, as he passed, he thought he saw a strange expression 15 of mockery about his lips. When he had gone a few yards farther he looked back; but the figure was not there.

A sudden horror came over Schwartz, he knew not why; but the thirst for gold prevailed over his fear, and he rushed on. The bank of black cloud rose to the zenith, and out of it came 20 bursts of spiry lightning, and waves of darkness seemed to heave and float between their flashes over the whole heavens. The sky where the sun was setting was all level, like a lake of blood; and a strong wind came out of that sky, tearing its crimson clouds into fragments, and scattering them far into 25 the darkness. And when Schwartz stood by the brink of the Golden River, its waves were black, like thunder clouds, but their foam was like fire; and the roar of the waters below, and the thunder above, met as he cast the flask into the stream. As he did so the lightning glared into his eyes, the earth gave way 30 beneath him, and the waters closed over his cry. And the moaning of the river rose wildly into the night, as it gushed over the

TWO BLACK STONES.

CHAPTER FIVE

HOW LITTLE GLUCK SET OFF ON AN EXPEDITION TO THE
GOLDEN RIVER, AND HOW HE PROSPERED THEREIN;
WITH OTHER MATTERS OF INTEREST.

I

HOW GLUCK MET DIFFICULTIES ENCOUNTERED ON THE WAY

WHEN Gluck found that Schwartz did not come back he was
very sorry, and did not know what to do. He had no money,
so he was obliged to go and hire himself again to the goldsmith,
who worked him very hard, and gave him very little money.
After a month or two, Gluck grew tired, and made up his mind
to go and try his fortune with the Golden River. "The little
king looked very kind," thought he. "I don't think he will turn
me into a black stone." So he went to the priest, and the priest
gave him some holy water as soon as he asked for it. Then Gluck
took some bread in his basket, and the bottle of water, and set off
very early for the mountains.

If the glacier had occasioned a great deal of fatigue to his
brothers, it was twenty times worse for him, who was neither
so strong nor so practiced on the mountains. He had several
bad falls, lost his basket and bread, and was very much frightened at the strange noises under the ice. He lay a long time
to rest on the grass, after he had crossed over, and began to
climb the hill just in the hottest part of the day. When he had
climbed for an hour he became dreadfully thirsty, and was going
to drink as his brothers had done, when he saw an old man
coming down the path above him, looking very feeble, and leaning on a staff. "My son," said the old man, "I am faint with
thirst; give me some of that water." Then Gluck looked at
him, and when he saw that he was pale and weary, he gave him
the water; "Only pray don't drink it all," said Gluck. But the
old man drank a great deal, and gave him back the bottle two-
thirds empty. Then he bade him good speed, and Gluck went
on again merrily. The path became easier to his feet, and two

or three blades of grass appeared upon it; some grasshoppers began singing on the bank beside it, and Gluck thought he had never heard such merry singing.

Then he went on for another hour, and the thirst increased
5 on him so that he thought he should be forced to drink. But as he raised the flask he saw a little child lying panting by the roadside, and it cried out piteously for water. Gluck struggled with himself, and determined to bear the thirst a little longer; and he put the bottle to the child's lips, and it drank it all but
10 a few drops. Having done this it smiled on him, and got up, and ran down the hill; and Gluck looked after it till it became as small as a little star. He then turned and began climbing again. And behold there were all kinds of sweet flowers growing on the rocks, bright green moss, with pale pink starry flowers,
15 and soft belled gentians more blue than the sky at its deepest, and pure white transparent lilies. Crimson and purple butterflies darted hither and thither, and the sky sent down such pure light that Gluck had never felt so happy in his life.

Yet after he had climbed for another hour, his thirst became
20 intolerable again; and when he looked at his bottle he saw that there were only five or six drops left in it, and he could not venture to drink. But just as he was hanging the flask to his belt again, he saw a little dog lying on the rocks, gasping for breath —precisely as Hans had seen it on the day of his ascent. Gluck
25 stopped and looked at it, and then at the Golden River, not five hundred yards above him; and he thought of the dwarf's words, "that no one could succeed, except in his first attempt." He tried to pass the dog, but it whined piteously, and he stopped again. "Poor beastie," said Gluck, "it'll be dead when I come
30 down again, if I don't help it." Then he looked closer and closer at it, and its eye turned on him so mournfully, that he could not stand it. "Confound the King and his gold, too," said Gluck; and he opened the flask, and poured all the water into the dog's mouth.

35 The dog sprang up and stood on its hind legs. Its tail disap-

peared, its ears became long, longer, silky, golden; its nose became very red, its eyes became very twinkling; in three seconds the dog was gone, and before Gluck stood his old acquaintance, the King of the Golden River.

"Thank you," said the monarch; "but don't be frightened, it's all right"; for Gluck showed manifest symptoms of consternation at this unlooked-for reply to his last observation. "Why didn't you come before," continued the dwarf, "instead of sending me those rascally brothers of yours, for me to have the trouble of turning into stones? Very hard stones they make, too."

"Oh, dear me!" said Gluck, "have you really been so cruel?"

"Cruel!" said the dwarf; "they poured unholy water into my stream: do you suppose I'm going to allow that?"

"Why," said Gluck, "I am sure, sir—your Majesty, I mean— they got the water out of the church font."

"Very probably," replied the dwarf; "but," and his countenance grew stern as he spoke, "the water which has been refused to the cry of the weary and dying, is unholy, though it had been blessed by every saint in heaven; and the water which is found in the vessel of mercy is holy, though it had been defiled with corpses."

II

HOW TREASURE VALLEY BECAME A GARDEN AGAIN

So saying, the dwarf stooped and plucked a lily that grew at his feet. On its white leaves there hung three drops of clear dew. And the dwarf shook them into the flask which Gluck held in his hand. "Cast these into the river," he said, "and descend on the other side of the mountains into the Treasure Valley. And so good speed."

As he spoke, the figure of the dwarf became indistinct. The playing colors of his robe formed themselves into a prismatic mist of dewy light; he stood for an instant veiled with them as with the belt of a broad rainbow. The colors grew faint, the mist rose into the air; the monarch had evaporated.

And Gluck climbed to the brink of the Golden River; its waves were as clear as crystal, and as brilliant as the sun. When he cast the three drops of dew into the stream, there opened where they fell a small circular whirlpool, into which the waters de-
5 scended with a musical noise.

Gluck stood watching it for some time, very much disappointed, because not only the river was not turned into gold, but its waters seemed much diminished in quantity. Yet he obeyed his friend the dwarf, and descended the other side of the mountains
10 towards the Treasure Valley; and, as he went, he thought he heard the noise of water working its way under the ground. Now, when he came in sight of the Treasure Valley, behold, a river, like the Golden River, was springing from a new cleft of the rocks above it, and was flowing in innumerable streams
15 among the dry heaps of red sand.

As Gluck gazed, fresh grass sprang beside the new streams, and creeping plants grew and climbed among the moistening soil. Young flowers opened suddenly along the river sides, as stars leap out when twilight is deepening, and thickets of myrtle
20 and tendrils of vine cast lengthening shadows over the valley as they grew. And thus the Treasure Valley became a garden again, and the inheritance which had been lost by cruelty was regained by love.

And Gluck went and dwelt in the valley, and the poor were
25 never driven from his door: so that his barns became full of corn, and his house of treasure. For him the river had, according to the dwarf's promise, become a River of Gold.

And to this day the inhabitants of the valley point out the place where the three drops of holy dew were cast into the stream,
30 and trace the course of the Golden River under the ground, until it emerges in the Treasure Valley. And at the top of the cataract of the Golden River are still to be seen Two Black Stones, round which the waters howl mournfully every day at sunset; and these stones are still called by the people of the valley The Black
35 Brothers.

HELPS TO STUDY

Notes and Questions

From what did the Golden River derive its name?

To what was the fertility of the valley due?

By what name were Hans and Schwartz known?

Why were they given this name?

How did Gluck differ from his brothers?

In what manner did the Southwest wind make his last visit?

What change came over the valley when the west wind ceased to visit it?

What chances to show kindness did Hans have as he climbed the mountain?

Read lines which show how the sky changed each time that he refused to help the suffering.

What opportunities to help others did Schwartz have as he ascended the mountain?

What happened each time that he refused to help?

How did the face of the mountain change after Gluck gave the water to the old man? To the child?

What happened after he gave the water to the dog?

Why was it hard for Gluck to give away all his water?

What chance did he think he was giving up when he gave away the last drop of water?

What words show that he was willing to lose his chance in order to save the dog?

Read lines which show that Gluck's boyhood had been spent in service to others.

Read lines which show how he helped others when he became a man.

Commit to memory the following lines:

"A poor man served by thee shall make thee rich;

A sick man helped by thee shall make thee strong."

Words and Phrases for Discussion

"violent exaggeration"
"ill-gotten wealth"
"intense gaze"
"ungovernable disposition"
"impenetrable shade"
"adverse skies"

"exquisite workmanship"
"prismatic colors"
"fantastic forms"
"circular whirlpool"
"pale blue pinnacles"
"peaks of the eternal snow"

SONG

CELIA THAXTER

Celia Thaxter (1835-1894) was an American poet. Her father was a light-house keeper on one of the rocky isles, known as the "Isles of Shoals," off the coast of New Hampshire. She was familiar with the wild-flowers, the birds, and all sea life, and has written many beautiful poems about them.

1

Sing, little bird, oh sing!
　How sweet thy voice and clear!
How fine the airy measures ring,
　The sad old world to cheer!

2

Bloom, little flower, oh bloom!
　Thou makest glad the day;
A scented torch, thou dost illume
　The darkness of the way.

3

Dance, little child, oh dance!
　While sweet the small birds sing,
And flowers bloom fair, and every glance
　Of sunshine tells of spring.

4

Oh! bloom, and sing, and smile,
　Flower, bird, and child, and make
The sad old world forget awhile
　Its sorrow for your sake!

HELPS TO STUDY

Notes and Questions

What does the song of the bird do for the world?

To what is the flower compared in the second stanza?

Who is addressed in the third stanza?

What time of the year is described in this poem?

To whom is the fourth stanza addressed?

Read the words which tell how the child, the bird, and the flower may help the world. What child can do this?

Words and Phrases for Discussion

"airy measures"

"scented torch"

"illume the darkness"

"Thou makest glad the day"

"MY HEART LEAPS UP"

WILLIAM WORDSWORTH

William Wordsworth (1770-1850) was an English poet. He was born and lived in the beautiful region known as the Cumberland Highlands, in northern England. His father and mother died when he was a mere boy. He attended Cambridge, where he and Coleridge became friends. His poems deal with humble life and are expressed in simple and beautiful language.

> My heart leaps up when I behold
>   A rainbow in the sky:
> So was it when my life began;
> So is it now I am a man;
> So be it when I shall grow old,
>   Or let me die!
> The Child is father of the Man;
> And I could wish my days to be
> Bound each to each by natural piety.

HELPS TO STUDY
Notes and Questions

What feeling causes the heart to leap up?

To what time of his life does the poet refer in the words "when my life began"?

What does he hope will be the same when he grows old?

Can you mention something else in Nature which might cause the heart to leap up?

If Wordsworth had lost his joy in the sight of the rainbow, what other things in Nature would no longer delight him?

What difference do you think this would have made in his life?

How can we keep this joy in our hearts?

Memorize these lines.

Words and Phrases for Discussion

"The Child is father of the Man"

THE SPACIOUS FIRMAMENT

JOSEPH ADDISON

Joseph Addison (1672-1719) was an English writer. He received his education at Oxford College. For a time he was a member of Parliament. As a man he was kind and generous and as a writer he had grace and refinement.

1

The spacious firmament on high,
With all the blue ethereal sky,
And spangled heavens, a shining frame,
Their great Original proclaim:
Th' unwearied Sun, from day to day,
Does his Creator's power display,
And publishes to every land
The work of an Almighty hand.

2

Soon as the evening shades prevail,
The Moon takes up the wondrous tale,
And, nightly, to the listening Earth,
Repeats the story of her birth:
While all the stars that round her burn,
And all the planets in their turn,
Confirm the tidings as they roll,
And spread the truth from pole to pole.

3

What though, in solemn silence, all
Move round the dark terrestrial ball?
What though no real voice nor sound
Amid their radiant orbs be found:
In Reason's ear they all rejoice,
And utter forth a glorious voice,
Forever singing as they shine,
"The Hand that made us is divine."

HELPS TO STUDY
Notes and Questions

Who is the great "Original" of the heavens?

Of what is the poet thinking when he speaks of the sun as "unwearied"?

What is the "wondrous tale" which the moon takes up when the sun is gone?

To whom does the moon tell the "story of her birth"?

Read the "story of her birth" as told in the Book of Genesis: "And God made two great lights; the greater light to rule the day, and the lesser light to rule the night. He made the stars also. And God set them in the firmament of the heaven to give light upon the earth, and to rule over the day and over the night, and to divide the light from the darkness: and God saw that it was good."

What is the "dark terrestrial ball"?

What contrast to this expression is found in the fourth line of the same stanza?

Read the line which tells what the sun, moon, and stars sing as they shine.

How may we hear their song?

Words and Phrases for Discussion

"spacious firmament"
"spangled heavens"
"confirm the tidings"

"pole to pole"
"solemn silence"
"Reason's ear"

THE SEA

Bryan Waller Procter

Bryan Waller Procter (1787-1874) was an English poet. He was born in London. He wrote under the name of Barry Cornwall. "The Sea" is one of his best poems.

1

The sea! the sea! the open sea!
The blue, the fresh, the ever free!
Without a mark, without a bound,
It runneth the earth's wide regions round;
It plays with the clouds; it mocks the skies;
Or like a cradled creature lies.

2

I'm on the sea! I'm on the sea!
I am where I would ever be;
With the blue above, and the blue below,
And silence whereso'er I go;
If a storm should come and awake the deep,
What matter? *I* shall ride and sleep.

3

I love, oh, how I love to ride
On the fierce, foaming, bursting tide,
When every mad wave drowns the moon
Or whistles aloft his tempest tune,
And tells how goeth the world below,
And why the sou'west blasts do blow.

4

I never was on the dull, tame shore,
But I lov'd the great sea more and more,
And backwards flew to her billowy breast,
Like a bird that seeketh its mother's nest;

And a mother she was, and is, to me;
For I was born on the open sea!

5

The waves were white, and red the morn,
In the noisy hour when I was born;
And the whale it whistled, the porpoise roll'd,
And the dolphins bared their backs of gold;
And never was heard such an outcry wild
As welcom'd to life the ocean child!

6

I've liv'd since then in calm and strife,
Full fifty summers, a sailor's life,
With wealth to spend and power to range,
But never have sought nor sighed for change;
And Death, whenever he comes to me,
Shall come on the wild, unbounded sea!

HELPS TO STUDY

Notes and Questions

Who is supposed to tell this story?

Read the lines which answer this question.

When does the sea play with the clouds?

When does it lie "like a cradled creature"?

What is meant by the "blue above"?

What is the "blue below"?

Why does the shore seem tame to the sailor?

To what does the speaker compare himself when he returns from the shore?

Find a line in the poem which speaks of the silence of the ocean.

Find lines which speak of the noise of the ocean.

What caused the noise described in these lines?

Read lines which show that the sailor was not afraid of storms at sea.

Read lines which show his contentment.

Words and Phrases for Discussion

"mad wave"   "outcry wild"
"tempest tune"   "wealth to spend"
"billowy breast"   "power to range"

MARCH

WILLIAM WORDSWORTH*

The Cock is crowing,
The stream is flowing,
The small birds twitter,
The lake doth glitter,
The green field sleeps in the sun;
The oldest and youngest
Are at work with the strongest;
The cattle are grazing,
Their heads never raising;
There are forty feeding like one!
Like an army defeated
The snow hath retreated,
And now doth fare ill
On the top of the bare hill;
The ploughboy is whooping—anon—anon:
There's joy in the mountains;
There's life in the fountains;
Small clouds are sailing,
Blue sky prevailing;
The rain is over and gone!

HELPS TO STUDY

Notes and Questions

What things mentioned in this poem have you noticed in the spring?

What things mentioned in this poem may be seen in the city?

What things can be seen only in the country?

What is meant by "forty feeding like one"?

* For Biography, see p. 89.

From what places has the snow retreated?

Where does it still linger ?

What are the "fountains" of which the poet speaks?

What tells you that the plough-boy feels happy?

What comparison is made in the last stanza?

Words and Phrases for Discussion

"The green field sleeps in the sun"

"Blue sky prevailing"

THE VOICE OF SPRING

MARY HOWITT

Mary Howitt (1804-1888), an English poet, was the wife of William Howitt, the poet and author. She was a Quakeress. She has written many beautiful poems for children.

1

I am coming, little maiden,
With the pleasant sunshine laden;
With the honey for the bee;
With the blossom for the tree;
With the flower and with the leaf;
Till I come the time is brief.

2

I am coming, I am coming!
Hark! the little bee is humming;
See! the lark is soaring high
In the bright and sunny sky,
And the gnats are on the wing:
Little maiden, now is spring.

3

See the yellow catkins cover
All the slender willows over;

And on mossy banks so green
Starlike primroses are seen;
Every little stream is bright;
All the orchard trees are white.

4

Hark! the little lambs are bleating,
And the cawing rooks are meeting
In the elms—a noisy crowd;
And all birds are singing loud;
And the first white butterfly
In the sun goes flitting by.

5

Turn thy eyes to earth and heaven:
God for thee the spring has given,
Taught the birds their melodies,
Clothed the earth and cleared the skies
For thy pleasure or thy food—
Pour thy soul in gratitude.

HELPS TO STUDY

Notes and Questions

Who is speaking in this poem?

What is the voice of Spring?

What promise is made in the first stanza?

Read the line that tells the promise is fulfilled.

What things mentioned in this poem have you seen in the Spring?

What things mentioned may be seen in the city?

What things can be seen only in the country?

Do you think of other evidences (signs) of Spring not mentioned in the poem?

Read the line that tells who gives us Spring.

Read the line that tells why the Spring is given us.

Read the line that tells us we should show gratitude for these things.

Words and Phrases for Discussion

"on the wing"   "flitting by"
"starlike primroses"   "clothed the earth"
               "melodies"

AN APRIL DAY

Caroline B. Southey

Caroline B. Southey (1786-1854), an English poet, was the wife of Robert Southey. She wrote many beautiful poems, "An April Day" being one of her best.

1

All day the low-hung clouds have dropped
  Their garnered fullness down;
All day that soft, gray mist hath wrapped
  Hill, valley, grove, and town.

2

There has not been a sound today
  To break the calm of nature;
Nor motion, I might almost say,
  Of life, or living creature;

3

Of waving bough, or warbling bird,
  Or cattle faintly lowing:
I could have half believed I heard
  The leaves and blossoms growing.

4

I stood to hear—I love it well—
  The rain's continuous sound;
Small drops, but thick and fast they fell,
  Down straight into the ground.

5

For leafy thickness is not yet,
  Earth's naked breast to screen;
Though every dripping branch is set
  With shoots of tender green.

6

Sure, since I looked at early morn,
  Those honeysuckle buds
Have swelled to double growth; that thorn
  Hath put forth larger studs.

7

That lilac's cleaving cones have burst,
  The milk-white flowers revealing;
Even now, upon my senses first
  Methinks their sweets are stealing.

8

The very earth, the steamy air,
  Is all with fragrance rife;
And grace and beauty everywhere
  Are bursting into life.

9

Down, down they come—those fruitful stores,
  Those earth rejoicing drops!
A momentary deluge pours,
  Then thins, decreases, stops.

10

And ere the dimples on the stream
  Have circled out of sight,
Lo! from the west a parting gleam
  Breaks forth, of amber light.

11

But yet behold—abrupt and loud,
 Comes down the glittering rain;
The farewell of a passing cloud,
 The fringes of her train.

HELPS TO STUDY

Notes and Questions

Does this poem describe an April day in the city or in the country? Give reasons for your answer.

What did the clouds drop all day?

Read lines from the third stanza which tell how quiet everything was.

How can you explain this quiet?

Read lines which tell that the leaves were just coming out.

Read the lines which tell the changes which the author noticed in her flowers.

What caused the changes?

What are the "sweets" of the lilac?

What color were the lilac flowers in this garden?

What is meant by the "cones" of the lilacs?

Read the lines which tell of the gleam of sunshine in that day of rain.

Why is it called a "parting" gleam?

What word helps you to know that it was a parting gleam?

If you did not know the title of this poem, what expressions in it would tell you that this was a spring rain?

Read the stanza which you like best.

Words and Phrases for Discussion

"low-hung clouds"
"garnered fullness"
"cleaving cones"
"steamy air"

"with fragrance rife"
"momentary deluge"
"amber light"
"glittering rain"

APPLE BLOSSOMS

WILLIAM WESLEY MARTIN

William Wesley Martin is not a well-known author, but his ''Apple Blossoms'' presents a picture of such rare beauty and charm that his name will long be remembered in literature.

1

Have you seen an apple orchard in the spring?
    In the spring?
An English apple orchard in the spring?
When the spreading trees are hoary
With their wealth of promised glory,
And·the mavis pipes his story
In the spring!

2

Have you plucked the apple blossoms in the spring?
    In the spring?
And caught their subtle odors in the spring?
Pink buds bursting at the light,
Crumpled petals baby-white,
Just to touch them a delight!
In the spring!

3

Have you walked beneath the blossoms in the spring?
    In the spring?
Beneath the apple blossoms in the spring?
When the pink cascades were falling,
And the silver brooklets brawling,
And the cuckoo bird is calling
In the spring?

4

Have you seen a merry bridal in the spring?
>In the spring?
In an English apple country in the spring?
When the bride and maidens wear
Apple blossoms in their hair;
Apple blossoms everywhere,
In the spring?

5

If you have not, then you know not, in the spring,
>In the spring,
Half the color, beauty, wonder of the spring.
No sight can I remember,
Half so precious, half so tender,
As the apple blossoms render
In the spring!

HELPS TO STUDY

Notes and Questions

What is the glory of the apple tree?

What is the wealth of the apple tree in spring?

What is the meaning of "hoary" as used in the first stanza?

How is this word generally used?

What picture does the word "baby-white" bring before you?

Where have you read of cascades before?

How are cascades formed?

How could blossoms falling from a tree make the poet think of a cascade?

What is a brooklet?

What made it look like silver?

What is meant by the "brawling" of the brooklet?

How often are the words "In the spring" used in the first stanza?

In what lines are they used?

In what lines are they used in the second stanza? In the third? In the fourth? In the fifth?

Find three lines in each stanza which rhyme.

What makes this poem so pleasant to read aloud?

DARE TO DO RIGHT

George L. Taylor

George Lansing Taylor (1835-   ) was born at Skaneateles, New York. He graduated from Columbia University. He became a Methodist Episcopal minister and was a well-known lecturer and author.

1

Dare to do right! Dare to be true!
You have a work that no other can do;
Do it so bravely, so kindly, so well,
Angels will hasten the story to tell.

2

Dare to do right! Dare to be true!
Other men's failures can never save you;
Stand by your conscience, your honor, your faith;
Stand like a hero, and battle till death.

HELPS TO STUDY

Notes and Questions

To whom is this poem addressed?

Why are we sometimes afraid to tell the truth?

Why are we sometimes afraid to do what we know is right?

What would you say of a soldier who was afraid and yet obeyed orders and stood at his post?

Why can no one else do your work?

How can you "stand by your conscience"?

Against what enemies must you "battle till death"?

Words and Phrases for Discussion
"faith"   "honor"
"other men's failures"

A PSALM OF LIFE

Henry Wadsworth Longfellow*

1

Tell me not, in mournful numbers,
   "Life is but an empty dream!"
For the soul is dead that slumbers,
   And things are not what they seem.

2

Life is real! Life is earnest!
   And the grave is not its goal;
"Dust thou art, to dust returnest,"
   Was not spoken of the soul.

3

Not enjoyment, and not sorrow,
   Is our destined end or way;
But to act, that each tomorrow
   Find us farther than today.

4

Art is long, and Time is fleeting,
   And our hearts, though stout and brave,
Still, like muffled drums, are beating
   Funeral marches to the grave.

* For Biography, see p. 280.

5

In the world's broad field of battle,
    In the bivouac of Life,
Be not like dumb, driven cattle;
    Be a hero in the strife!

6

Trust no Future, howe'er pleasant!
    Let the dead Past bury its dead!
Act,—act in the living Present!
    Heart within, and God o'erhead!

7

Lives of great men all remind us
    We can make our lives sublime,
And, departing, leave behind us
    Footprints on the sands of time;

8

Footprints, that perhaps another,
    Sailing o'er life's solemn main,
A forlorn and shipwrecked brother,
    Seeing, shall take heart again.

9

Let us, then, be up and doing,
    With a heart for any fate;
Still achieving, still pursuing,
    Learn to labor and to wait.

HELPS TO STUDY
Notes and Questions

Read the line in the second stanza which gives the thought which is carried through the poem. What is a goal?

To what is life compared when we speak of its goal?

Read the words in the second stanza which Longfellow says were not spoken of the soul.

Read the words which Longfellow had in mind when he wrote the second stanza.

"Then shall the dust return to the earth as it was: and the spirit shall return unto God who gave it."—Ecclesiastes, XII, 7.

What was "spoken of the soul"?

What must we constantly do if we want each tomorrow to "find us farther than today"?

In what do you want to be "farther" tomorrow than you are today?

To what is life compared in the fifth stanza?

What does the poet say that the lives of great men teach us?

What has the life of Washington taught the whole world?

Can you find selections in your reader which show this?

To what is life compared in the eighth stanza?

Read a line which makes you feel brave.

Read a line which makes you want to work.

Words and Phrases for Discussion

"Time is fleeting"
"muffled drums"
"bivouac of Life"

"Be a hero in the strife"
"take heart again"
"lives sublime"

"mournful numbers" = sad poetry

FIND A WAY OR MAKE IT

J. G. SAXE

John G. Saxe (1816-1887) was an American poet. He was born in Vermont and graduated from Middlebury College. He became editor of the "Burlington Sentinel." His poems are very popular.

1

It was a noble Roman,
    In Rome's imperial day,
Who heard a coward croaker,
    Before the castle, say,
"They're safe in such a fortress;

There is no way to shake it!"
"*On!* on!" exclaimed the hero,
   "*I'll find a way, or make it!*"

2

Is Fame your aspiration?
   Her path is steep and high;
In vain you seek her temple,
   Content to gaze and sigh:
The shining throne is waiting,
   But he alone can take it,
Who says, with Roman firmness,
   "*I'll find a way, or make it!*"

3

Is Learning your ambition?
   There is no royal road;
Alike the peer and peasant
   Must climb to her abode;
Who feels the thirst for knowledge
   In Helicon may slake it,
If he has still the Roman will,
   To "*find a way, or make it!*"

4

Are Riches worth the getting?
   They must be bravely sought;
With wishing and with fretting,
   The boon can not be bought;
To *all* the prize is open,
   But only *he* can take it,
Who says, with Roman courage,
   "I'll find a way, or make it!"

HELPS TO STUDY

Notes and Questions

What is the castle called in the first stanza?

Where were the hero and the coward?

Read the coward's words.

Read the hero's words.

Where does the poet imagine the temple of Fame to be?

How may it be reached?

Why may the winning of fame be compared to climbing a mountain?

What did Washington do which may be compared to climbing a steep path?

When did Washington take the "shining throne"?

What do you know of the life of Washington which shows that he did not think of fame?

Read the line which tells what everyone must do who wishes to obtain learning.

How does the school help you to climb?

How have men made ways through forests?

How have they made ways through mountains?

Words and Phrases for Discussion

"imperial day"

"aspiration"

"peer and peasant"

"royal road"

Helicon—a mountain range in Greece on the slopes of which were the fountains supposed to give inspiration to poets.

BETTER THAN GOLD

Abram J. Ryan

Abram J. Ryan was born in Norfolk, Va., in 1836, and served as a chaplain in the Civil War. He died in 1886. "Better than Gold" is one of his choice poems.

1

Better than grandeur, better than gold,
Than rank and titles a thousand fold,
Is a healthy body, a mind at ease,

And simple pleasures that always please;—
A heart that can feel for another's woe,
And share his joys with a genial glow,
With sympathies large enough to infold
All men as brothers, is better than gold.

2

Better than gold is a conscience clear,
Though toiling for bread in a humble sphere,
Doubly blessed with content and health,
Untried by the lusts or cares of wealth,
Lowly living and lofty thought
Adorn and ennoble a poor man's cot;
For mind and morals, in Nature's plan
Are the genuine test of a gentleman.

3

Better than gold is the sweet repose
Of the sons of toil when their labors close;
Better than gold is a poor man's sleep,
And the balm that drops on his slumber deep.
Bring sleeping draughts on the downy bed,
Where Luxury pillows his aching head,
His simple opiate labor deems
A shorter road to the land of dreams.

4

Better than gold is a thinking mind,
That, in the realm of books, can find
A treasure surpassing Australian ore,
And live with the great and good of yore.
The sage's lore, and the poet's lay,
The glories of empires passed away
The world's great drama, will thus unfold,
And yield a pleasure better than gold.

5

Better than gold is a peaceful home
Where all the fireside characters come,
The shrine of love, the heaven of life,
Hallowed by mother, or sister, or wife.
However humble the home may be,
Or tried with sorrow by Heaven's decree,
The blessings that never were bought or sold,
And center there, are better than gold.

HELPS TO STUDY
Notes and Questions

How can you share the joys of another?

If you feel for another's trouble what will you try to do?

What kind of thoughts are "lofty" thoughts?

What longer word is generally used for the word cot in the second stanza?

Why does the man who works hard sleep sweetly?

What does the author say such repose is worth?

Who is represented by the word "Luxury"?

What does the author say "Luxury" needs to make him sleep?

What is meant by the "land of dreams"?

Read the words in the fourth stanza which tell how we may live "with the great and good" of past years.

Where can you read of the "glories of empires passed away"?

What Australian ore is meant in this stanza?

What does the last stanza tell us is better than gold?

Words and Phrases for Discussion

"humble sphere"
"genuine test"
"sleeping draughts"
"opiate"

"sage's lore"
"poet's lay"
"fireside characters"
"hallowed"

GRADATIM

Josiah Gilbert Holland

Josiah Gilbert Holland (1819-1881) was an American poet and journalist. He was born on a Massachusetts farm, but studied medicine and afterward became editor of the "Springfield Republican." He was one of the founders of "Scribner's Monthly Magazine" and became its editor.

1

Heaven is not reached at a single bound,
    But we build the ladder by which we rise
    From the lowly earth to the vaulted skies,
And we mount to its summit round by round.

2

I count this thing to be grandly true,
    That a noble deed is a step toward God,
    Lifting the soul from the common clod
To a purer air and a fairer view.

3

We rise by the things that are under our feet,
    By what we have mastered of good or gain;
    By the pride deposed or the passion slain,
And the vanquished ills that we hourly meet.

Abridged.

HELPS TO STUDY

Notes and Questions

Where does the poet imagine the foot of the ladder to be?

How is the ladder built?

By what kind of deeds do we ascend this ladder?

What kind of actions cause us to slip back?

What foes does the third stanza tell us we must conquer, if we wish to mount the ladder?

Mention some noble deed of which you have read in this book.

What opportunities have boys and girls to do noble deeds?

Words and Phrases for Discussion

"vaulted skies"   "pride deposed"
"common clod"   "passion slain"
"vanquished ills"

THOSE EVENING BELLS!

Thomas Moore

Thomas Moore (1779-1852) was an Irish poet. He was born at Dublin and educated at Trinity College. He was a friend and classmate of Robert Emmet. He visited America, spending two years here. His poems are musical.

1

Those evening bells! those evening bells!
How many a tale their music tells,
Of youth, and home, and that sweet time
When last I heard their soothing chime!

2

Those joyous hours are passed away;
And many a heart, that then was gay,
Within the tomb now darkly dwells,
And hears no more those evening bells.

3

And so 't will be when I am gone;
That tuneful peal will still ring on,
While other bards shall walk these dells,
And sing your praise, sweet evening bells!

HELPS TO STUDY
Notes and Questions

For what do you think the bells which the poet praises were ringing?
Of what did they speak to him?

What words in the first stanza tell you that the bells rang sweetly and softly?

| What words in the first stanza tell you that the poet had been away from home? | Was the poet in the city or in the country when he heard the bells? How do you know? |

Words and Phrases for Discussion

"soothing chimes"   "other bards"
"tuneful peal"   "shall walk these dells"

THE BELLS OF SHANDON

FRANCIS MAHONY

Francis Mahony (1804-1866) was an Irish poet and journalist. He was born at Cork and was educated for the priesthood in Paris and Rome. Afterward he gave up his calling and became a magazine writer. He wrote under the name of "Father Prouty."

1

With deep affection
And recollection
I often think of
    Those Shandon bells,
Whose sound so wild would,
In the days of childhood,
Fling round my cradle
    Their magic spells.

2

On this I ponder
Where'er I wander,
And thus grow fonder,
    Sweet Cork, of thee,—
With thy bells of Shandon,
That sound so grand on
The pleasant waters
    Of the river Lee.

3

I've heard bells chiming
Full many a clime in,
Tolling sublime in
    Cathedral shrine,
While at a glib rate
Brass tongues would vibrate;
But all their music
    Spoke naught like thine.

4

For memory, dwelling
On each proud swelling
Of thy belfry, knelling
    Its bold notes free,
Made the bells of Shandon
Sound far more grand on
The pleasant waters
    Of the River Lee.

5

I've heard bells tolling
Old Adrian's Mole in,
Their thunder rolling
    From the Vatican,—
And cymbals glorious
Swinging uproarious
In the gorgeous turrets
    Of Notre Dame;

6

But thy sounds were sweeter
Than the dome of Peter
Flings o'er the Tiber
    Pealing solemnly.

Oh! the bells of Shandon
Sound far more grand on
The pleasant waters
    Of the River Lee.

7

There's a bell in Moscow;
While on tower and kiosk O
In Saint Sophia
    The Turkman gets,
And loud in air
Calls men to prayer,
From the tapering summit
    Of tall minarets.

8

Such empty phantom
I freely grant them;
But there's an anthem
    More dear to me,—
'Tis the bells of Shandon,
That sound so grand on
The pleasant waters
    Of the river Lee.

HELPS TO STUDY

Notes and Questions

Read the lines which tell you in what city the poet lived.

Read the lines which tell you that he heard the bells in early childhood.

Of what does he think wherever he wanders?

Read the line which tells the name of the river which was near his home.

What sound of bells does the first line of the third stanza give?

When are chimes rung?

What sound do the words "tolling sublime" give?

When do bells toll?

What bells do you sometimes hear which sound like the bells described in the fifth and sixth lines of this stanza?

What comparison is made between the music of all these bells and the bells of Shandon?

To what is the sound of the bells in the Vatican compared?

To what musical instruments are the bells of Notre Dame compared?

What does the dome of Peter "fling o'er the Tiber"?

Where is the Tiber River?

To whom does the poet say, "Thy sounds were sweeter"?

Words and Phrases for Discussion

"Old Adrian's Mole"—the massive, towerlike mausoleum or tomb of the Roman Emperor Hadrian.

"Vatican"—the palace of the Popes at Rome.

"Notre Dame"—the great cathedral at Paris.

"dome of Peter"—dome of St. Peter's at Rome—the largest cathedral in the world.

"St. Sophia"—mosque of St. Sophia at Constantinople.

"magic spells"

"gorgeous turrets"

"calls men to prayer".

RING OUT, WILD BELLS*

ALFRED, LORD TENNYSON

Alfred, Lord Tennyson, (1809-1892) was an English poet. He was born in Lincolnshire and studied at Trinity College, Cambridge. He was poet laureate of England, succeeding Wordsworth. He devoted himself to poetry. His poems are noted for their beauty of expression.

1

Ring out, wild bells, to the wild sky,
The flying cloud, the frosty light;
The year is dying in the night:
Ring out, wild bells, and let him die.

* From "In Memoriam."

2

Ring out the old, ring in the new,
　　Ring, happy bells, across the snow;
　　The year is going—let him go;
Ring out the false, ring in the true.

3

Ring out the grief that saps the mind,
　　For those that here we see no more;
　　Ring out the feud of rich and poor,
Ring in redress to all mankind.

4

Ring out a slowly dying cause,
　　And ancient forms of party strife;
　　Ring in the nobler modes of life,
With sweeter manners, purer laws.

5

Ring out the want, the care, the sin,
　　The faithless coldness of the times;
　　Ring out, ring out my mournful rhymes,
But ring the fuller minstrel in.

6

Ring out false pride in place and blood,
　　The civic slander and the spite;
　　Ring in the love of truth and right,
Ring in the common love of good.

7

Ring out old shapes of foul disease,
　　Ring out the narrowing lust of gold,
　　Ring out the thousand wars of old,
Ring in the thousand years of peace.

8

Ring in the valiant man and free,
    The larger heart, the kindlier hand;
Ring out the darkness of the land,
Ring in the Christ that is to be.

HELPS TO STUDY

Notes and Questions

For what were the bells described in this poem ringing?

How are the bells described in the first stanza?

How is the sky described in this stanza?

Read the words in the second line which tell what gave this appearance to the sky.

How can you explain this description of the bells?

How does the poet describe the bells in the second stanza?

Read the line in the second stanza which tells what the poet hopes will go with the old year.

What does he hope will come in with the new year?

How does the poet's beautiful hope explain his description of the bells in this stanza?

Read the lines in the fourth stanza which tell what the poet hopes will come in with the new year.

What do you think the poet meant by "sweeter manners"?

What does the mention of "sweeter manners" and "purer laws" in the same line tell you of the importance of manners?

Read what Tennyson tells us about manners in another poem and see if this will help you to understand:

"For manners are not idle, but the fruit
  Of loyal nature and of noble mind."

How does Tennyson describe his own poetry in the fifth stanza?

What does he mean by a "fuller minstrel"?

What efforts are being made to end war?

What is meant by the "darkness of the land"?

How does the public school help to "ring out" this darkness?

Words and Phrases for Discussion

"party strife"
"nobler modes of life"
"purer laws"
"valiant man and free"

"false pride"
"common love of good"
"lust of gold"
"larger heart"

CHRISTMAS BELLS

Henry W. Longfellow*

1

I heard the bells on Christmas Day
Their old, familiar carols play,
 And wild and sweet
 The words repeat
Of peace on earth, good-will to men!

2

And thought how, as the day had come,
The belfries of all Christendom
 Had rolled along
 The unbroken song
Of peace on earth, good-will to men!

3

Till, ringing, singing on its way,
The world revolved from night to day,
 A voice, a chime,
 A chant sublime
Of peace on earth, good-will to men!

—*Abridged.*

HELPS TO STUDY

Notes and Questions

Who is speaking in this poem?

What words describe the sound of the bells?

What words do these bells repeat?

Who "thought how, as the day had come"?

What day is meant?

What is meant by "The belfries of all Christendom"?

In what sense is it an "unbroken" song?

Why does the poet say "rolled"?

What does the second stanza tell you?

What is meant by "revolved from night to day"?

* For Biography, see p. 280.

THE FIR TREE

Hans Christian Andersen

Hans Christian Andersen (1805-1875) was a Danish novelist and poet. He is best known to children by his fairy tales, from which this selection has been taken.

CHAPTER ONE

IN THE FOREST

Far away in the deep forest there once grew a pretty little Fir Tree. The sun shone full upon him and the breezes played freely round him. Near him grew many other fir trees, some older, some younger, but the little Fir Tree was not happy, for
5 he was always wishing to be tall like the others.

He thought not of the warm sun and the fresh air, and he did not care for the merry country children who came to the forest to look for strawberries and raspberries. Sometimes, after having filled their pitchers, or made the bright berries into a
10 chain with straw, they would sit down near the little Fir Tree and say: "What a pretty little tree this is!" Then the Fir Tree would feel more unhappy than ever.

"Oh, that I were as tall as the other trees!" sighed the little Fir; "then I should spread my branches on every side, and my
15 top should look over the wide world! The birds would build their nests among my branches, and when the wind blew, I should bend my head so grandly, just as the others do!" He had no joy in the sunshine, in the song of birds, or in the rosy clouds that sailed over him every morning and evening.

20 In winter, when the ground was covered with the bright, white snow, a hare would sometimes come running along, and jump right over the little Tree's head; and then how sad he felt. However, two winters passed away, and by the third the Tree was so tall that the hare had to run round it. "Oh, if I
25 could but grow and grow, and become tall and old!" thought the Tree. "That is the only thing in the world worth living for."

The woodcutters came in the autumn and felled some of the

largest of the trees. This took place every year, and our young
Fir, who was by this time a good height, began to shake when
he saw those grand trees fall with a crash to the earth. Their
branches were then cut off. The stems looked so naked and
5 lanky that the Fir Tree hardly knew them. They were laid one
upon another in carts, and horses drew them away, far, far
away from the forest.

Where could they be going? What would happen to them?
The Fir Tree wished very much to know, so in the spring, when
10 the swallows and the storks came back, he asked them if they
knew where the felled trees had been taken.

The swallows knew nothing. But the stork thought for a
moment, then nodded his head and said: "Yes, I think I have
seen them. As I was flying to this country I met many ships.
15 They had fine new masts that smelt like fir. I am sure that
they were the trees that you speak of. They were tall, very
tall, I can tell you."

"Oh, I wish that I too was tall enough to sail upon the sea!
Tell me what is this sea, and what does it look like?" said the
20 Fir Tree.

"That," said the stork, "would take too long a time to tell,"
and away he went.

"Be glad that you are young!" said the sunbeams. "Enjoy
your fresh youth, and the young life that is within you!"

25 The wind kissed the tree, and the dew wept tears over him,
but the Fir Tree did not know what they meant.

When Christmas drew near, many quite young trees were
felled, some of them not so tall as the young Fir Tree who was
always wishing to be away. Their branches were not cut off.
30 They too were laid in a cart, and horses drew them away from
the forest.

"Where are they going?" asked the Fir Tree. "They are no
taller than I; indeed one of them is much less. Why do they
keep all their branches? Where can they be going?

35 "We know! We know!" chirped the sparrows. "We peeped

through the windows in the town below. We know where they are gone. Oh, you cannot think what honor is done to them! We looked through the windows and saw them planted in a warm room, and decked out with such beautiful things: gilded
5 apples, sweets, playthings, and hundreds of bright candles!"

"And then?" asked the Fir Tree, shaking in every branch; "and then? what happened then?"

"Oh, we saw no more! That was beautiful, beautiful beyond anything we have ever seen," chirped the sparrows.

10 "Is such a glorious lot to be mine?" cried the Fir Tree in its great joy. "This is far better than sailing over the sea. How I long for the time! Oh, I wish that Christmas was come! I am now tall and have many branches, like those trees that were taken away last year. Oh, I wish that I was in the warm room,
15 honored and adorned!"

"Enjoy our love!" said the air and the sunshine. "Enjoy your youth and your freedom!"

But be glad he would not. He grew taller every day. In winter and summer he stood there clothed in dark green leaves.
20 The people that saw him said, "That is a beautiful tree!" And next Christmas he was the first that was felled. The axe cut through the wood and pith, and the tree fell to the earth with a deep groan.

CHAPTER TWO

CHRISTMAS EVE

The Tree first came to himself when, in the courtyard to
25 which he had been taken with the other trees, he heard a man say: "This is a beautiful one, the very thing we want!"

Then came two finely dressed servants and took the Fir Tree into a large and beautiful drawing-room. Pictures hung on the walls, and on the mantelpiece stood large vases with lions on the
30 lids. There were rocking-chairs, silken sofas, tables covered with picture books and toys. The Fir Tree was placed in a large tub filled with sand. But no one could know it was a tub, for

it was hung with green cloth and stood on a rich, bright carpet. Oh, how the tree shook! What was to happen next?

Some young ladies, helped by servants, began to deck him. On some branches they hung little nets, cut out of pretty paper,
5 every net filled with sugar plums. From others gilded apples and walnuts were hung, looking just as if they had grown there. And hundreds of little wax tapers, red, blue, and white, were placed here and there among the branches.

Dolls that looked almost like men and women—the Tree
10 had never seen such things before—seemed dancing to and fro among the leaves, and high up, on the top of the tree, was tied a large star of gold tinsel. This was indeed beautiful, beautiful beyond anything the Tree had ever seen.

"This evening," they said, "it will be lighted up."
15   "I wish it was evening," thought the Tree. "I wish that the lights were kindled, for then—what will happen then? Will the trees comes out of the forest to see me? Will the sparrows fly here and look in through the windows? Shall I stand here decked both winter and summer?"

20   All at once, the doors were flung open, and a troop of children rushed in as if they had a mind to jump over him. The older people came after more quietly.

The little ones stood silent, but only for a moment. Then they shouted with joy till the room rang again. They danced
25 round the Tree, and one present after another was torn down.

"What are they doing?" thought the Tree. "What will happen now?" The candles burnt down to the branches, and as each burnt down it was put out. The children were given leave to strip the Tree. They threw themselves on him till all
30 his branches creaked. If he had not been tied with the gold star to the roof he would have been overturned.

The children danced about with their beautiful playthings. No one but the old nurse thought of the Tree any more. She came and peeped among the branches, but it was only to see if
35 by chance a fig or an apple had been left among them.

"A story! a story!" cried the children, pulling a little, fat man toward the Tree. "It is pleasant to sit under the shade of green branches," said he, sitting down. "Besides, the Tree may want to hear my story."

5 The little, fat man told the story of Humpty Dumpty who fell downstairs, and yet came to the throne and won the Princess.

The Fir Tree in the meantime stood quite silent and thinking to himself. The birds in the forest had never told him any story like this.

10 "Who knows but I, too, may fall downstairs and win a Princess?" And he thought with joy of being next day decked out with candles and playthings, gold and fruit. And the Tree thought about this all night.

CHAPTER THREE

WINTER IN A GARRET

In the morning the maids came in. "Now begins my state 15 anew!" thought the Tree. But they dragged him out of the room, up the stairs, and into a garret, and there pushed him into a dark corner where not a ray of light could enter.

"What can be the meaning of this?" thought the Tree. "What am I to do here? What shall I hear in this place?" And 20 he leant against the wall, and thought, and thought.

"It is now winter," thought the Tree. "The ground is hard and covered with snow. They cannot plant me now, so I am to stay here in shelter till the spring. Men are so thoughtful! I only wish it were not so dark and so lonely!"

25 "Squeak! squeak!" cried a little mouse, just then coming forward. Another came after it. They snuffed about the Fir Tree, and then slipped in and out among the branches.

"It is very cold," said a little mouse, "or it would be quite nice up here. Don't you think so, you old Fir Tree?"

30 "I am not old," said the Fir Tree; "there are many who are much older than I."

"How came you here?" asked the mice; "and what do you

know?" They seemed to wish to know all about everything, and they asked the Fir Tree a great many things. "Tell us about the most beautiful place on earth! Have you ever been there? Have you been into the storeroom, where cheeses lie on the
5 shelves, and hams hang from the roof; where one can dance over tallow candles; where one goes in thin and comes out fat?"

"I know nothing about that," said the Tree, "but I know the forest, where the sun shines and where the birds sing." And then he spoke of his youth and its joys. They listened very
10 closely, and said: "Well, to be sure, how much you have seen! How happy you have been!"

"Happy!" said the Fir Tree in surprise, and he thought a moment over all that he had been saying. "Yes, on the whole those were joyful times." He then told them about the Christ-
15 mas Eve when he had been dressed up with cakes and candles.

"Oh," cried the little mouse, "how happy you have been, you old Fir Tree!"

'I am not old at all!" said the Fir. "It was only this winter that I left the forest. I am just at the best time of life."

20 "How well you can talk!" said the little mouse; and the next night they came again, and brought with them four other little mice, who wanted also to hear the Tree's history. And the more the Tree spoke of his youth in the forest, the more clearly he remembered it.

25 "Yes," said he, "those were happy times! But they may come back, they may come back! Humpty Dumpty fell downstairs, and yet for all that he won the Princess. Perhaps I, too, may win a Princess."

CHAPTER FOUR

THE FIR TREE REMEMBERS HAPPY DAYS

The mice never came again. The Tree sighed. "It was nice
30 when those busy little mice sat round me, listening to my words. Now that, too, is past. However, I shall have joy in remembering it, when I am taken from this place."

But when would that be? One morning people came and cleared out the lumber room. The trunks were taken away. The Tree, too, was dragged out of the corner. They threw him on the floor; but one of the servants picked him up and carried him downstairs. Once more he beheld the light of day.

"Now life begins again!" thought the Tree. He felt the fresh air and the warm sunbeams—he was out in the yard. All happened so quickly that the Tree quite forgot to look at himself, there was so much to look at all around. The yard joined a garden. Everything was so fresh and blooming. The roses were so bright and sweet-smelling. The lime trees were in full blossom, and the swallows flew backwards and forwards, twittering.

"I shall live! I shall live!" He was filled with joy and hope. He tried to spread out his branches; but, alas! they were all dried and yellow. He was thrown down on a heap of weeds and nettles.

The star of gold tinsel that had been left on his crown now looked bright in the sunshine. Some children were playing in the yard; they were the same children who had danced round the Tree. One of the youngest of them saw the gold star, and ran to tear it off.

"Look at this, still tied to the ugly old Christmas Tree!" cried he, trampling upon the branches until they broke under his feet.

The Tree looked on the flowers of the garden, now blooming in all the freshness of their beauty. He looked upon himself, and he wished with all his heart that he had been left to wither in the dark corner of the lumber room. He called to mind his happy forest life and the merry Christmas Eve.

"Past, all past!" said the poor Tree. "If I had but been happy, as I might have been! Past, all past!"

The servant came and cut the Tree into small pieces. She then heaped them up, and set fire to them. The Tree groaned deeply. The children all ran up to the place and jumped about

in front of the blaze. But at each of those heavy groans the
Fir Tree thought of a bright summer's day, of Christmas Eve,
or of Humpty Dumpty, the only story that he knew and could
tell. And at last the Tree was burned.

5   The boys played about in the yard. On the breast of the
youngest one shone the golden star that the Tree had worn
on the happiest evening of his life. But that was past, and the
Tree was past, and the story also, past! past! for all stories
must come to an end some time or other.

HELPS TO STUDY

Notes and Questions

Mention some things which the
Fir Tree should have enjoyed in
the forest.

What bird told the tree about the
ships?

How did this bird know?

What birds told about the Christmas trees?

How did they know these things?

Why was the little tree unhappy?

What did the sunbeams say to
him?

When did the Fir Tree receive
great honor?

How long did this last?

Are all Christmas trees treated as
this one was?

What purpose do you think Hans
Andersen had in ending the
story as he did?

Words and Phrases for Discussion

"rosy clouds"   "felled trees"   "glorious lot"

A CHRISTMAS TREE

(Selected)

CHARLES DICKENS

Charles Dickens (1812-1870) was a great English writer. He gained
much of the material for his novels while a reporter on a London
newspaper. "A Christmas Tree" appeared in "Household Words," a
magazine which Dickens edited, in 1850.

A GERMAN CHRISTMAS TREE

I have been looking on, this evening, at a merry company of
children assembled round that pretty German toy, a Christmas
Tree. The tree was planted in the middle of a great round

table, and towered high above their heads. It was brilliantly lighted by a multitude of little tapers; and everywhere sparkled and glittered with bright objects. There were rosy-cheeked dolls, hiding behind the green leaves; and there were real
5 watches (with movable hands, at least, and an endless capacity of being wound up) dangling from innumerable twigs; there were French-polished tables, chairs, bedsteads, wardrobes, eight-day clocks, and various other articles of domestic furniture (wonderfully made, in tin), perched among the boughs, as
10 if in preparation for some fairy housekeeping; there were jolly, broad-faced little men, much more agreeable in appearance than many real men—and no wonder, for their heads took off, and showed them to be full of sugar-plums; there were fiddles and drums; there were tambourines, books, work-
15 boxes, paint-boxes, sweetmeat-boxes, peep-show boxes, and all kinds of boxes; there were trinkets for the elder girls, far brighter than any grown-up gold and jewels; there were baskets and pincushions in all devices; there were guns, swords, and banners; there were humming-tops, needle-cases, pen-wipers,
20 smelling-bottles, conversation-cards, bouquet-holders; real fruit, made artificially dazzling with gold leaf; imitation apples, pears, and walnuts, crammed with surprises; in short, as a pretty child, before me, delightedly whispered to another pretty child, her bosom friend, "There was everything, and
25 more."

Being now at home again, and alone, the only person in the house awake, my thoughts are drawn back, by a fascination which I do not care to resist, to my own childhood. I begin to consider, what do we all remember best upon the branches of
30 the Christmas Tree of our own young Christmas days.

THE TOYS

Straight, in the middle of the room, cramped in the freedom of its growth by no encircling walls or soon-reached ceiling, a shadowy tree arises; and, looking up into the dreamy brightness of its top—for I observe in this tree the singular property that it appears to grow downward towards the earth—I look into my youngest Christmas recollections!

All toys at first, I find. Up yonder, among the green holly
5 and red berries, is the Tumbler with his hands in his pockets, who wouldn't lie down, but whenever he was put upon the floor, persisted in rolling his fat body about, until he rolled himself still, and brought those lobster eyes of his to bear upon me— when I affected to laugh very much, but in my heart of
10 hearts was extremely doubtful of him. Close beside him is that snuff-box, out of which there sprang a Counsellor in a black gown, with a red cloth mouth, wide open, who was not to be endured on any terms, but could not be put away either! for he used suddenly, in a highly mag-
15 nified state, to fly out of Mammoth Snuff-boxes in dreams, when least expected. Nor is the frog with cobbler's wax on his tail, far off; for there was no knowing where he wouldn't jump; and when he flew over the candle, and came upon one's hand with that spotted back—red on a green ground
20 —he was horrible. The cardboard lady in a blue-silk skirt, who was stood up against the candlestick to dance, and whom I see on the same branch, was milder, and was beautiful; but I can't say as much for the larger cardboard man, who used to be hung against the wall and pulled by a string; there was a sinister
25 expression in that nose of his; and when he got his legs round his neck (which he very often did), he was ghastly, and not a creature to be alone with.

I never wondered what the dear old donkey with the panniers —there he is! was made of, then! His hide was real to the
30 touch, I recollect. And the great black horse with the round red spots all over him—the horse that I could even get upon— I never wondered what had brought him to that strange condition, or thought that such a horse was not commonly seen at Newmarket. The four horses of no color, next to him, that
35 went in the wagon of cheeses, and could be taken out and

stabled under the piano, appear to have bits of fur for
their tails, and other bits for their manes, and to stand on pegs
instead of legs, but it was not so when they were brought home
for a Christmas present. They were all right, then; neither
5 was their harness nailed into their chests, as appears to be
the case now. The tinkling works of the music cart, I *did* find
out, to be made of quill toothpicks and wire; and I always
thought that little tumbler in his shirt-sleeves, perpetually
swarming up one side of a wooden frame, and coming down,
10 head foremost, on the other, rather a weak-minded person—
though good-natured; but the Jacob's Ladder, next him, made
of little squares of red wood, that went flapping and clattering
over one another, each developing a different picture, and the
whole enlivened by small bells, was a mighty marvel and a
15 great delight.

THE DOLL'S HOUSE

Ah! The Doll's house!—of which I was not proprietor, but
where I visited. I don't admire the Houses of Parliament half
so much as that stone-fronted mansion with real glass windows,
and doorsteps, and a real balcony—greener than I ever see now,
20 except at watering-places; and even they afford but a poor
imitation. And though it *did* open all at once, the entire
house-front, it was but to shut it up again. Even open,
there were three distinct rooms in it: a sitting-room and
bed-room, elegantly furnished, and, best of all, a kitchen,
25 with uncommonly soft fire-irons, a plentiful assortment of
diminutive utensils, and a tin man-cook in profile, who was
always going to fry two fish. What justice have I done to the
noble feasts wherein the set of wooden platters figured, each
with its own peculiar delicacy, as a ham or turkey, glued
30 tight on to it, and garnished with something green, which
I recollect as moss! Could all the Temperance Societies of
these later days, united, give me such a tea-drinking as I have
had through the means of yonder little set of blue crockery,
which really would hold liquid, and which made tea, nectar?

And if I did once shriek out, as a poisoned child, and strike the fashionable company with consternation, by reason of having drunk a little teaspoon, inadvertently dissolved in too hot tea, I was never the worse for it!

THE BOOKS BEGIN TO COME

5   Upon the next branches of the tree, lower down, hard by the green roller and miniature gardening-tools, how thick the books begin to hang. Thin books, in themselves, at first, but many of them, and with deliciously smooth covers of bright red or green. What fat black letters to begin with! "A was an
10   archer, and shot at a frog." Of course he was. He was an apple-pie also, and there he is! He was a good many things in his time, was A, and so were most of his friends, except X, who had so little versatility that I never knew him to get beyond Xerxes or Xantippe—like Y, who was always confined to a
15   Yacht or a Yew Tree; and Z condemned for ever to be a Zebra or a Zany. But, now, the very tree itself changes, and becomes a bean-stalk—the marvellous bean-stalk up which Jack climbed to the Giant's house! And now, those dreadfully interesting, double-headed giants, with their clubs over their shoulders,
20   begin to stride along the boughs in a perfect throng, dragging knights and ladies home for dinner by the hair of their heads. And Jack—how noble, with his sword of sharpness, and his shoes of swiftness!

          Good for Christmas-time is the ruddy color of the cloak, in
25   which—the tree making a forest of itself for her to trip through, with her basket—Little Red Riding-Hood comes to me one Christmas Eve to give me information of the cruelty and treachery of that dissembling Wolf who ate her grandmother, without making any impression on his appetite, and then ate
30   her, after making that ferocious joke about his teeth. She was my first love. I felt that if I could have married Little Red Riding-Hood, I should have known perfect bliss. But, it was not to be; and there was nothing for it but to look out the Wolf in the Noah's Ark there, and put him late in the procession on

the table, as a monster who was to be degraded. O the wonderful Noah's Ark! It was not found seaworthy when put in a washing-tub, and the animals were crammed in at the roof, and needed to have their legs well shaken down before they could
5 be got in, even there—and then, ten to one but they began to tumble out at the door, which was but imperfectly fastened with a wire latch—but what was *that* against it! Consider the noble fly, a size or two smaller than the elephant: the lady-bird, the butterfly—all triumphs of art! Consider the goose, whose
10 feet were so small, and whose balance was so indifferent, that he usually tumbled forward, and knocked down all the animal creation! Consider Noah and his family, like idiotic tobacco-stoppers; and how the leopard stuck to warm little fingers; and how the tails of the larger animals used gradually to resolve
15 themselves into frayed bits of string!

THE ARABIAN NIGHTS

Hush! Again a forest, and somebody up in a tree—not Robin Hood, not Valentine, but an Eastern King with a glittering scimitar and turban. By Allah! two Eastern Kings; for I see another, looking over his shoulder! Down upon the grass,
20 at the tree's foot, lies the full length of a coal-black Giant, stretched asleep, with his head in a lady's lap; and near them is a glass box, fastened with four locks of shining steel, in which he keeps the lady prisoner when he is awake. I see the four keys at his girdle now. The lady makes signs to the two
25 kings in the tree, who softly descend. It is the setting-in of the bright Arabian Nights.

Oh, now all common things become uncommon and enchanted to me. All lamps are wonderful; all rings are talismans. Common flower-pots are full of treasure, with a little earth
30 scattered on the top; trees are for Ali Baba to hide in; beef-steaks are to throw down into the Valley of Diamonds, that the precious stones may stick to them, and be carried by the eagles to their nests, whence the traders, with loud cries, will scare them.

Any iron ring let into stone is the entrance to a cave which only waits for the magician, and the little fire, that will make the earth shake. All the dates imported come from the same tree as that unlucky date, with whose shell the merchant knocked
5 out the eye of the genie's invisible son. My very rocking-horse,— there he is, with his nostrils turned completely inside-out!— should have a peg in his neck, by virtue thereof to fly away with me, as the wooden horse did with the Prince of Persia, in the sight of all his father's Court. Yes, on every object that I
10 recognize among those upper branches of my Christmas Tree, I see this fairy light!

BOYS AND GIRLS WHO COME HOME AT CHRISTMAS TIME.

On the lower and maturer branches of the Tree, Christmas associations cluster thick. School-books shut up; cricket-bats, stumps, and balls, left higher up, with the smell of trodden
15 grass and the softened noise of shouts in the evening air; the tree is still fresh, still gay. If I no more come home at Christmas-time, there will be boys and girls (thank Heaven!) while the World lasts; and they do! Yonder they dance and play upon the branches of my Tree, God bless them, merrily, and
20 my heart dances and plays too!

HELPS TO STUDY

Notes and Questions

Why does Dickens call the Christmas tree a "German toy"?

What did he begin to think about when he returned home?

How did his "shadowy tree" appear to grow?

On what part of the tree were the toys?

What stories from "The Arabian Nights" have you read?

Read lines which refer to the stories you have read.

Read lines which show the love Dickens felt for children.

To what does he compare life? Read the lines which tell this.

Words and Phrases for Discussion

"multitude of tapers" "endless capacity"   "fairy housekeeping"
"fairy light"   "deliciously smooth" "softened noise"

PART II

STORIES OF GREECE AND ROME

"One cannot always be a hero, but one can always be a man."

GOETHE.

PART II

INTRODUCTION

THE stories gathered together here were handed down in the twilight of history from one generation to another. They were told around the firesides or sung in the market places or chanted in the halls of royal palaces. In time, as a national feeling came to be developed, certain heroes became national heroes and around these, minstrels and priests wove the many myths and legends into an artistic whole. Early writers gave definite form to these stories and to-day we read them in Greek and Latin in much the same form as the early minstrel sang them to the music of his lyre.

The religion of the Greeks owed its origin and growth to their keen and vivid imagination, which was stimulated in turn by the natural beauty of their country, the lofty mountains, beautiful rivers, green fields and groves, and over it all the bluest skies.

For the wonders of nature, which are explained to us by science, they created beautiful stories which often had in them such profound truths that when we read them now we are not only charmed by the beauty of these simple stories, but we are moved by their depth of meaning.

As they looked up at the soft, fleecy clouds, they saw flocks of sheep, driven across the sky by their shepherd, the wind. The rainbow was a beautiful maiden, Here's messenger. Her flight was so rapid that one could never see her; only by the trail which her many colored draperies left behind her could one know that she had passed. Under Mount Ætna was bound with unbreakable chains the giant who dared defy Zeus.

135

From time to time he breathed forth fire and flames and when he changed his position the earth trembled.

Everything about the Greeks was personified and every grove, fountain, and river was the habitation of some nymph or satyr. Pan, the god of woods and fields, was everywhere.

The greater gods dwelt on high Olympus, where all was sunshine and clear air, where neither snow fell nor hail nor rain, nor was it ever shaken by the winds.

The religion of the Romans, as we know it from literature, was largely inherited from the Greeks and therefore was much like the Greek religion. They made gods of the sea, the sun, the lightning, and of all the great materials and forces in nature, but to these they gave names different from those of the Greeks. Like the Greeks, their gods were supposed to have human powers of mind, body, and feeling, but in all cases they were more than human.

Zeus (Jupiter) was the king and father of gods and men. With thunderbolts and lightning flashes he punished the crimes of mortals. His special messenger was the eagle. He presided at the councils held on Mount Olympus and called the gods together at his pleasure.

His brothers were Poseidon (Neptune), who ruled the sea, and Pluto (Orcus), king of the underworld, the abode of the dead.

Here (Juno) the glorious, sister and wife of Zeus, sat at his right, while at his left sat Pallas Athene (Minerva) goddess of wisdom, skilled in all the arts of war and peace.

The most beautiful of all the gods was Apollo (Phœbus), god of the sun, of music and poetry, and leader of the nine muses. His golden shafts often proved fatal to mortal man.

His twin sister was Artemis (Diana), goddess of the moon and of the chase. She is often represented with a stag and a quiver of arrows and wearing upon her forehead her emblem, the crescent moon.

Aphrodite (Venus), born of the sea foam, was the goddess of love and beauty.

Ares (Mars) was the god of war and Hephæstus (Vulcan) was the smith of the gods, who built their dwellings on Olympus and forged their weapons.

Hermes (Mercury), the winged messenger of the gods, doing their bidding, sped through the air with staff and winged cap and sandals.

In these stories we shall see how the will of the gods influences and directs the actions of heroes whose courage knows no bounds when a wrong must be righted or a friend's death avenged, who bravely face death upon the perilous seas or in fighting horrid monsters and yet who show the deepest reverence for customs and traditions and great tenderness for wife and child and friend and home.

Many of the best things in our present life and culture are inherited from the Greeks and Romans. We still find our greatest models in the remains of Grecian art, literature, and architecture. In all these fields we have inherited much from the Romans, but our greatest debt to them is to be found in our codes of law. The reading of stories from Greek and Roman heroes will give us, therefore, greater love for the beautiful and true in art, literature, and life.

The names of the Roman gods are given above in parentheses. The following table gives the pronunciation of the names of both the Greek and Roman gods:

Greek	Latin
Zeus (zūs)	Jupiter (jū′pĭ ter)
Poseidon (po sī′don)	Neptune (nep′tūne)
Pluto (plu′to)	Orcus (or′kus)
Here (hē′re)	Juno (jū′no)
Athene (a thē′nē)	Minerva (mĭ ner′va)
Artemis (ar′te mis)	Diana (dī a′na)
Ares (ā′res)	Mars (märs)
Aphrodite (af′rō dī te)	Venus (vē′nus)
Hephæstus (he fes′tus)	Vulcan (vul′kan)
Hermes (her′mēs)	Mercury (mer′kū ry)
Hestia (hes′tĭ a)	Vesta (ves′ta)

In later times Phœbus Apollo (fē′bus a pŏl′ō) was worshiped in Rome under the Greek name Phœbus.

BOOK I

THE STORY OF ACHILLES

CHAPTER ONE

WHY THE GREEKS SAILED TO TROY

HELEN, daughter of Tyndareus and Leda, was the fairest of all the women in Greece—nay, of all the women on the face of the whole earth. All the princes of Greece were suitors for her in marriage, and assembled at Sparta, of which city Tyndareus
5 was king, that she and her father might make their choice among them.

While they awaited the choosing, Tyndareus said to them, "You do me much honor, my lords, by paying court to my daughter and desiring to have her to wife. Nevertheless, there
10 is something in this matter that makes me afraid. Ye are many, and my daughter can have but one of you for a husband. How, then, will the matter stand when she shall have made her choice? Will it not be that one, indeed, will be pleased and many offended, and that for one friend I shall have
15 a score or so of enemies? Listen, therefore, to me, and be sure that my daughter is of one mind with me. She would rather die unmarried, or even lay hands upon herself, than that she should bring trouble upon my house. And her resolve is this: Ye must all swear a great oath that ye will defend her and her
20 husband, whomsoever she may choose, with all your might, and that if he or she suffer any wrong, ye will avenge them to the very best of your power."

This King Tyndareus did by the counsel of Ulysses; and the reason why Ulysses gave this counsel was this. He thought

tĭn dā'rŭs   lē'da   ū lĭs'ēz

138

to himself, "The choice of the maid will scarce fall upon me, for I have but a poor kingdom, nor can I myself, for strength or beauty, be matched with some that are here. But there are other fair maidens in Greece besides Helen, as Penelope, who
5 is niece to King Tyndareus, and is likely to have a good portion. If, then, I do good service to the king he will speak for me to his brother Icarius, and I shall have an advantage when I present my suit."

The words of Tyndareus pleased the suitors, and they swore
10 a great oath, each man by that which he held most sacred upon earth, that they would defend Helen and her husband against all injury that might be done to them.

Helen chose Menelaus, younger brother to Agamemnon, that was overlord of all the land of Greece. And Ulysses had his
15 wish, for Penelope, daughter of Icarius, was given him to wife.

And now for a time all things went well and prosperously. Menelaus lived happily with his wife Helen, who bare him a daughter, Hermione by name. But when the child was scarce a year old there came a grievous trouble to the house of Mene-
20 laus, and on the whole land of Greece and on Asia also. Now it must be told how this came about.

Across the Ægæan Sea from Greece was the city of Troy, famous in ancient days. Here lived a strong, brave race of people, who had made their city great by their industry in
25 peace and their courage in war.

The king of Troy was Priam, who was much beloved by every one. He had many children, but one day another little son was born to King Priam, even Paris. When now the priest said that he would grow to be a danger and a trouble to his
30 family and his country, King Priam had his servants take the baby, and leave it on a barren mountain-side to die. There some shepherds found the child, and reared him carefully; and he grew to be a tall, beautiful youth, very active and skilful in all sorts of games.

pe nĕl'ō pē   ī kā'rĭ ŭs   men ē lā'ŭs   ag a mĕm'non   her mī'o nē
ē jē'an   prī'am

Peleus, king of Thessaly, married Thetis of the sea. And these two called to their wedding feast all the gods, for Thetis was herself of the race of the gods. One only did they not call, and that one was Discord. But Discord came unbidden, bring-
5 ing with her a golden apple on which she had written these words, "To THE FAIREST." This she threw among the guests, and so departed.

And when these words were read aloud there was scarce woman or goddess in the whole company but thought that the
10 apple belonged of right to her, but three only were so bold as to claim it, and these three were Here, queen of the gods, and Athene, and Aphrodite. And when it was doubted who should judge in such a matter Zeus said to Hermes, the messenger, "There is a shepherd that keeps his sheep on Mount Ida, Paris
15 by name; he is son to Priam, king of Troy, and he is the most beautiful of mortal men. Let him be the judge between these three; for if a god should judge there will be no end to the quarrel; but if a mortal man, then it must needs come to an end with his life. Be thou, therefore, guide to these three, and
20 show them the place, and give also my message to this Paris."

So Hermes took the three to Mount Ida, and they stood before Paris that he might judge which was the fairest of the three. Nor were they content that he judge by looks only. Here said to him, "Give thou thy voice to me, and I will give
25 thee lordship over the whole land of Asia," and Athene said, "I can make thee wise in counsel and skilful in war above all others." Last of all Aphrodite said, "I will give thee to wife the fairest woman in all the world." But whether Paris was moved by this promise, or whether he thought in his heart that
30 Aphrodite was in truth the fairest—as indeed she should have been of right, being queen of love—however this may be, this judgment of Paris was the beginning of many troubles.

It is not agreed among those who have written about these things how Helen was persuaded to leave her husband's house.
35 Some say that Paris carried her away by force, and some that

hĕ′rē   a thē′nē   pē′lus   thē′tis   af rō dī′tē   zūs   her′mēz

Aphrodite, that she might keep her promise, touched her soul with madness, so that she knew not what she did. But this one thing is certain, that Menelaus was bereft of his wife, and that he called upon all the princes that had sworn to defend
5 him that they should perform their promise.

Now this call was but little to their liking. Some would have had it that they were not bound to obey it. And Ulysses feigned madness, ploughing the sands of the sea that men might say, "It is no profit to take this fool, who knows no dif-
10 ference between cornfields and the sand of the sea." But there was one of the counsellors of Menelaus who discerned the truth. He said to the king, "Let me see whether this man be really mad or no." So he took the young child Ulysses, and set him in the way of the plough, and when Ulysses saw the child
15 he turned aside. Other chiefs also made excuses for themselves; but at the last a great army was gathered together, greater by far than had ever been seen in the land of Greece, and the place where they were gathered was Aulis.

CHAPTER TWO

THE QUARREL BETWEEN AGAMEMNON AND ACHILLES

For nine years and more the Greeks had besieged the city of
20 Troy, and being many in number and better ordered, and having very strong and valiant chiefs, they had pressed the men of the city very hard, so that these dared not go outside the walls. And, indeed, they might have taken it without further loss, but that there arose a deadly strife between two of the chiefs, even be-
25 tween Agamemnon, who was sovereign lord of all the host, and Achilles, who was the bravest and most valiant man therein. Now the strife chanced in this wise.

The Greeks had offended the Priest of Apollo because of a prize of war which Agamemnon had taken for himself. Apollo
30 was angered by this and sent swift death first among the dogs and mules and then among the men of the Greeks. Achilles

aw'lis   a kǐl'ēz

learning the cause of this misfortune, braved the wrath of Agamemnon and required him to give up the prize.

And Agamemnon in his wrath said, "Though I send back my prize, Achilles, be sure that I shall take for myself another 5 and that, too, from thee, or from Ajax, or from Ulysses."

Then cried Achilles, and his face was black as a thunder-storm, "Surely thou art altogether shameless and greedy, and in truth, an ill ruler of men. No quarrel have I with the Trojans. They never harried oxen or sheep of mine. But I 10 have been fighting in thy cause, and that of thy brother Mene-laus. Naught carest thou for that. Thou leavest me to fight, and sittest in thy tent at ease. But when the spoil is divided, thine is always the lion's share. Small indeed is my part. And this, forsooth, thou wilt take away! Now am I resolved to go 15 home. Small booty wilt thou get then, methinks!"

And King Agamemnon answered, "Go and thy Myrmidons with thee! I have other chieftains as good as thou art, and ready, as thou art not, to pay me due respect."

Then Achilles was mad with anger, and he thought in his 20 heart, "Shall I arise and slay this caitiff, or shall I keep down the wrath in my breast?" And as he thought he laid his hand on his sword-hilt, and had half drawn his sword from the scab-bard, when lo! the goddess Athene stood behind him—for Here, who loved these chieftains, had sent her—and caught him by 25 the long locks of his yellow hair. But Achilles marvelled much to feel the mighty grasp, and turned, and looked, and knew the goddess, but no one else in the assembly might see her. Then his eyes flashed with fire, and he cried, "Art thou come, child of Zeus, to see the insolence of Agamemnon? Of a 30 truth, I think that he will perish for his folly."

But Athene said, "Nay, but I am come to stay thy wrath. Use bitter words, if thou wilt, but put up thy sword in its sheath, and strike him not. Of a truth, I tell thee that for this insolence of today he will bring thee hereafter splendid gifts, 35 threefold and fourfold for all that he may take away."

myr'mĭ donz   trō'jans

Then Achilles answered, "I shall abide by thy command, for it is ever better for a man to obey the immortal gods." As he spake he laid his heavy hand upon the hilt, and thrust back the sword into the scabbard, and Athene went her way to Olympus.

5 Then he turned him to King Agamemnon, and spake again. "Drunkard, with the eyes of a dog and the heart of a deer! never fighting in the front of the battle, nor daring to lie in the ambush! 'Tis a puny race thou rulest, or this had been thy last wrong. And as for me, here is this scepter: once it was the
10 branch of a tree, but a cunning craftsman bound it with bronze to be the sign of the lordship which Zeus gives to kings; as surely as it shall never again have bark or leaves or shoot, so surely shall the Greeks one day miss Achilles, when they fall in heaps before the dreadful Hector, and thou shalt eat thy heart to
15 think that thou hast wronged the bravest of thy host."

And as he spake he dashed his scepter on the ground and sat down. And on the other side Agamemnon sat in furious anger. Then Nestor rose, an old man of a hundred years and more, and counseled peace. But he spake in vain. For Aga-
20 memnon answered—

"Nestor, thou speakest well, and peace is good. But this fellow would lord it over all, and he must be taught that there is one here, at least, who is better than he."

And Achilles said, "I were a slave and a coward if I owned
25 thee as my lord. Not so: play the master over others, but think not to master me."

Then Achilles went apart from his comrades and sat upon the seashore, falling into a great passion of tears, and stretching out his hands with loud prayer to his mother, who indeed was a
30 goddess of the sea, Thetis by name. She heard him where she sat in the depths by her father, the old god of the sea, and rose— you would have thought it a mist rising—from the waves, and came to where he sat weeping, and stroked him with her hand, and called him by his name.

35 "What ails thee, my son?" she said.

nes'tor   ō lim'pus   hek'tor

Then he told her the story of his wrong, and when he had
ended he said—

"Go, I pray thee, to the top of Olympus, to the palace of Zeus.
Often have I heard thee boast how, long ago, thou didst help him
5 when the other gods would have bound him. Go now and call
these things to his mind, and pray him that he help the sons of
Troy and give them victory in the battle, so that the Greeks, as
they flee before them, may have joy of this king of theirs, who
has done such wrong to the bravest of his host."

10 And his mother answered him, "Surely thine is an evil lot,
my son! Thy life is short, and it should of right be without tears
and full of joy; but now it seems to me to be both short and sad.
But I will go as thou sayest to Olympus, to the palace of Zeus,
but not now, for he has gone, and the other gods with him, to a
15 twelve days' feast with the pious Ethiopians. But when he comes
back I will entreat and persuade him. And do thou sit still, nor
go forth to battle."

When the twelve days were past, Thetis went to the top of
Olympus, to the palace of Zeus, and made her prayer to him.
20 He was loath to grant it, for he knew that it would anger his
wife, Here, who loved the Greeks and hated the sons of Troy.
Yet he could not refuse her, but promised that it should be as she
wished. And to make his word the surer, he nodded his awful
head, and with the nod all Olympus was shaken.

25 That night Zeus took counsel with himself how he might best
work his will. And he called to him a dream, and said, "Dream,
go to the tent of Agamemnon, and tell him to set his army in
array against Troy, for that the gods are now of one mind, and
the day of doom is come for the city, so that he shall take it, and
30 gain eternal glory for himself."

So the dream went to the tent of Agamemnon, and it took
the shape of Nestor, the old chief whom the king honored more
than all beside.

Then Nestor spake: "Sleepest thou, Agamemnon? It is not
35 for kings to sleep all through the night, for they must take

e thǐ ō'pi anz

thought for many, and have many cares. Listen now to the words of Zeus: 'Set the battle in array against Troy, for the gods are now of one mind, and the day of doom is come for the city, and thou shalt take it, and gain eternal glory for thyself.'"

5 And Agamemnon believed the dream, and knew not the purpose of Zeus in bidding him go forth to battle, how that the Trojans should win the day, and great shame should come to himself, but great honor to Achilles, when all the Greeks should pray him to deliver them from death. So he rose from his bed

10 and donned his tunic, and over it a great cloak, and fastened the sandals on his feet, and hung from his shoulders his mighty silver-studded sword, and took in his right hand the great scepter of his house, which was the token of his sovereignty over all the Greeks. Then he went forth, and first took counsel with the

15 chiefs, and afterwards called the people to the assembly. And after the assembly the shrill-voiced heralds called the host to the battle. As is the flare of a great fire when a wood is burning on a hill-top, so was the flash of their arms and their armor as they thronged to the field. And as the countless flocks of wild geese

20 or cranes or swans now wheel and now settle in the great Asian fen by the stream of Cayster, or as the bees swarm in the spring, when the milk-pails are full, so thick the Greeks thronged to the battle in the great plain by the banks of the Scamander. Many nations were there, and many chiefs. But the most famous

25 among them were these: Agamemnon, King of Mycenæ, and his brother, the yellow-haired Menelaus, King of Sparta, and husband of the beautiful Helen; Ajax Oileus, or, as men called him, the lesser Ajax, swiftest of foot among the Greeks after the great Achilles; Ajax Telamon, from Salamis; Diomed, son of Tydeus,

30 King of Argos; Nestor, King of Pylos, oldest and wisest among the Greeks; Ulysses, King of Ithaca, than whom there was no one more crafty in counsel. All these were there that day and many more; and the bravest and strongest of all was Ajax, son of Telamon; but there was none that could compare with Achilles

| kă is'ter | ska măn'der | mi sē'nē | ō ī'lŭs | tĕl'a mon | săl'a mis |
| di'ō mēd | tī'dūs | pī'los | ā'jaks | är'gos | ĭth'a ka |

and the horses of Achilles, bravest man and swiftest steeds. Only Achilles sat apart, and would not go to the battle.

And on the other side the sons of Troy and their allies came forth from the gates of the city and set themselves in array.
5 The most famous of their chiefs were these: Hector, son of King Priam, bravest and best of all; Æneas, son of Anchises and the goddess Aphrodite; and Sarpedon from Lycia, whom men affirmed to be the son of Zeus himself, and with him Glaucus.

So the battle was set in array, and the two hosts stood over
10 against each other.

They were now about to fight, when from the ranks of the Trojans Paris rushed forth. He had a panther's skin over his shoulders, and a bow and sword, and in either hand a spear, and he called aloud to the Greeks that they should send forth their
15 bravest to fight with him. But when Menelaus saw him he was glad, for he said that now he should avenge himself on the man who had done him such wrong. He leapt from his chariot and rushed to meet his enemy; but Paris, having done evil, and being therefore a coward in his heart, was afraid when he saw
20 Menelaus, and fled back into the ranks of his comrades. But Hector saw him and rebuked him. "Fair art thou to look upon, Paris, but nothing worth. Surely the Greeks will scorn us if they think that thou art our bravest warrior, because thou art of stately presence. But thou art a coward; and yet thou darest
25 to go across the sea and carry off the fair Helen. Why dost thou not stand and abide the onset of her husband, and see what manner of man he is? Little, I ween, would thy harp and thy long locks and thy fair face avail when thou wert lying in the dust!"

30 Then Paris answered, "Thou speakest well, Hector, and thy rebuke is just. As for thee, thy heart is like iron, ever set on battle; yet are beauty and love also the gifts of the gods, and not to be despised. But now set Menelaus and me in the midst, and let us fight, man to man, for the fair Helen and for all her
35 possessions. And if he prevail over me, let him take her and

ē nē′as   an kī′sēz   sar pē′don   lis′ĭ a   glaw′kus

them and depart, and the Greeks with him, but ye shall dwell in peace; but if I prevail they shall depart without her."

So King Priam, on the one side, for the Trojans, and King Agamemnon for the Greeks, made a covenant with sacrifice that Paris and Menelaus should fight together, and that the fair Helen, with all her treasures, should go with him who should prevail. And afterwards Hector and Ulysses marked out a space for the fight, and Hector took two pebbles in a helmet, looking away as he shook them, that he whose pebble leapt forth the first should be the first to throw his spear. And it so befell that the lot of Paris leapt forth first.

Then the two warriors armed themselves and came forth into the space, and stood over against each other, brandishing their spears, with hate in their eyes. Then Paris threw his spear. It struck the shield of Menelaus, but pierced it not, for the spear point was bent back. Then Menelaus prayed to Zeus, "Grant, father Zeus, that I may avenge myself on Paris, who has done me this wrong; so shall men in after time fear to do wrong to their host." So speaking, he cast his long-shafted spear; but Paris shrank aside, and the spear wounded him not. Then he rushed forward and seized Paris by the helmet, and dragged him toward the host of the Greeks. And truly he had taken him, but Aphrodite loosed the strap that was beneath the chin, and the helmet came off in his hand. And Menelaus whirled it among the Greeks and charged with another spear in his hand. But Aphrodite snatched Paris away, covering him with a mist, and put him down in his chamber in Troy. Then Menelaus looked for him everywhere, but no one could tell him where he might be. No son of Troy would have hidden him out of kindness, for all hated him as death.

Then King Agamemnon said, "Now, ye sons of Troy, it is for you to give back the fair Helen and her wealth, and to pay me besides so much as may be fitting for all my cost and trouble."

But it was not the will of the gods that the sons of Troy should do this thing, but rather that their city should perish.

Then King Agamemnon went throughout the host, and if he saw any one stirring himself to get ready for battle he praised him and gave him good encouragement; but whomsoever he saw halting and lingering and slothful, him he blamed and
5 rebuked whether he were common man or chief.

And the Greeks went forward to the battle, as the waves that curl themselves and then dash upon the shore, throwing high the foam. In order they went after their chiefs; you had thought them dumb, so silent were they. But the Trojans were
10 like a flock of ewes which wait to be milked, and bleat hearing the voice of their lambs, so confused a cry went out from their army, for there were men of many tongues gathered together. And on either side the gods urged them on, but chiefly Athene the Greeks and Ares the sons of Troy. Then, as two streams in
15 flood meet in some chasm, so the armies dashed together, shield on shield and spear on spear.

Hector with Ares at his side dealt death and destruction through the ranks of the Greeks. Here and Athene saw him where they sat on the top of Olympus and were wroth. They
20 passed down to earth and brought victory to the Greeks. At last Helenus, the wise seer, urged Hector to go to the city and bid the mothers of Troy assemble in the temple of Athene to see if perchance her wrath might not be stayed.

Hector came into the city by the Scæan gates, and as he
25 went wives and mothers crowded about him, asking how it had fared with their husbands and sons. But he said naught, save to bid them pray; and indeed there was sore news for many, if he had told that which he knew. Then he came to the palace of King Priam, and there he saw Hecuba, his mother. She
30 caught him by the hand and said—

"Why hast thou come from the battle, my son? Do the Greeks press thee hard, and art thou minded to pray to Father Zeus from the citadel? Let me bring thee honey-sweet wine, that thou mayest pour out before him, aye, and that thou mayest
35 drink thyself, and gladden thy heart."

ā'rēz   hel'e nus   sē'an   hĕk'ū ba

But Hector said, "Give me not wine, my mother, lest thou weaken my knees and make me forget my courage. Nor must I pour out an offering with Zeus thus, with unwashed hands. But do thou gather the mothers of Troy together, and go to the temple of Athene, and take a robe, the one that is the most precious and beautiful in thy stores, and lay it on the knees of the goddess, and pray her to keep the Greeks from the walls of Troy; and forget not to vow therewith twelve heifers as a sacrifice."

So Queen Hecuba and the mothers of Troy did as Hector had bidden them. But when they laid the robe on the knees of the goddess, she would not hear them.

Meanwhile Hector departed and went to his own home seeking his wife Andromache, but found her not, for she was on a tower of the wall with her child and her child's nurse, weeping sore for fear.

So Hector ran through the city to the Scæan gates, and there Andromache spied him, and hastened to meet him. And with her was the nurse, bearing the young child on her bosom—Hector's only child, beautiful, headed as a star. Silently he smiled when he saw the child, but Andromache clasped his hand and wept, and said—

"O Hector, thy courage will bring thee to death. Thou hast no pity on thy wife and child, but sparest not thyself, and all the Greeks will rush on thee and slay thee. It were better for me, losing thee, to die; for I have no comfort but thee. My father is dead, for Achilles slew him—slew him but spoiled him not, so much he reverenced him. With his arms he burnt him, and the mountain-nymphs planted poplars about his grave. Seven brethren I had, and lo! they all fell in one day by the hand of the great Achilles. And my mother, she is dead. But thou art father to me, and mother and brother and husband also. Have pity, then, and stay here upon the wall, lest thou leave me a widow and thy child an orphan. And set the people

an drŏm'a kē

here in array by this fig-tree, where the city is easiest to be taken."

But Hector said, "Nay, let these things be my care. I would not that any son or daughter of Troy should see me sulk-
5 ing from the war. And my own heart loathes the thought, and bids me fight in the front. Well I know, indeed, that Priam and the people of Priam, and holy Troy, will perish. Yet it is not for Troy, or for the people, or even for my father or my mother that I care so much, as for thee in the day when some
10 Greek shall carry thee away captive, and thou shalt ply the loom or carry the pitcher in the land of Greece. And some one shall say when he sees thee, 'This was Hector's wife, who was the bravest of the sons of Troy.' May the earth cover me before that day!"

15 Then Hector stretched out his arm to his child. But the child drew back into the bosom of his nurse with a loud cry, fearing the shining bronze and the horse-hair plume which nodded awfully from his helmet top. Then father and mother laughed aloud. And Hector took the helmet from his head and
20 laid it on the ground, and caught his child in his hands, and kissed him and dandled him, praying aloud to Father Zeus and all the gods—

"Grant, Father Zeus and all ye gods, that this child may be as I am, great among the sons of Troy; and may they say some
25 day, when they see him carrying home the bloody spoils from the war, 'A better man than his father, this,' and his mother shall be glad at heart."

Then he gave the child to his mother, and she clasped him to her breast and smiled a tearful smile. And her husband had
30 pity on her, and stroked her with his hand, and spake—

"Be not troubled overmuch. No man shall slay me against the ordering of fate; but as for fate, that, I trow, no man may escape, be he coward or brave. But go, ply thy tasks, the shuttle and the loom, and give their tasks to thy maidens, and let men
35 take thought for the battle."

Then Hector took up his helmet from the ground, and Andromache went her way to her home, oft turning back her eyes. And when she was come, she and all her maidens wailed for the living Hector as though he were dead, for she thought that she
5 should never see him any more returning safe from the battle.

CHAPTER THREE

THE DEATH OF PATROCLUS

Now Achilles was standing on the stern of his ship, looking at the war, and he saw Nestor carrying a wounded soldier in his chariot to the ships. Then he called to Patroclus, and Patroclus, who was in the tent, came forth; but it was an evil hour for
10 him. Then said Achilles—

"Now will the Greeks soon come, methinks, praying for help, for their need is sore. But go and see who is this whom Nestor is taking to the ships."

Then Patroclus ran. And as he stood in the tent door old
15 Nestor saw him, and went and took him by the hand, and would have had him sit down. Patroclus would not, saying—

"Stay me not. I came but to see who is this that thou hast brought wounded from the battle."

Then said Nestor, "But what cares Achilles for the Greeks?
20 or why does he ask who are wounded? Hear, then, what I say. It may be that Achilles will not go forth to the battle. But let him send thee forth, and the Myrmidons with thee, and let him put his arms upon thee, so that the sons of Troy be affrighted, thinking that he is in the battle, and we shall have breathing
25 space."

So Patroclus ran to the tent of Achilles and stood by him, weeping bitterly. Then said Achilles, "What ails thee, Patroclus, that thou weepest like a girl-child that runs along by her mother's side and would be taken up, holding her gown, and
30 looking at her with tearful eyes till she lift her in her arms?"

pa trō′klus

Then said Patroclus, "Be not wroth with me, great Achilles, for indeed the Greeks are in grievous straits, and all their bravest are wounded, and still thou cherishest thy wrath. Surely Peleus was not thy father, nor Thetis thy mother; but the rocks begat

5 thee, and the sea brought thee forth. Or if thou goest not to the battle, fearing some warning from the gods, yet let me go, and thy Myrmidons with me. And let me put thy armor on me; so shall the Greeks have breathing space from the war."

So he spake, entreating, nor knew that for his own doom he

10 entreated. And Achilles made reply—

"It is no warning that I heed, that I keep back from the war. But these men took from me my prize, which I won with my own hands. But let the past be past. I said that I would not rise up till the battle should come nigh to my own ships. But thou may-

15 est put my armor upon thee, and lead my Myrmidons to the fight. For in truth the men of Troy are gathered as a dark cloud about the ships, and the Greeks have scarce standing-ground between them and the sea. For they see not the gleam of my helmet. And Diomed is not there with his spear; nor do

20 I hear the voice of Agamemnon, but only the voice of Hector, as he calls the men of Troy ·to the battle. Go, therefore, Patroclus, and drive the fire from the ships. And then come thou back, nor fight any more with the Trojans, lest thou take my glory from me. And go not near, in the delight of battle,

25 to the walls of Troy, lest one of the gods meet thee to thy hurt; and, of a truth, the keen archer Apollo loves them well."

But as they talked the one to the other, Ajax could hold out no longer. For swords and javelins came thick upon him, and clattered on his helmet, and his shoulder was weary with the

30 great shield which he held; and he breathed heavily and hard, and the great drops of sweat fell upon the ground. Then at the last Hector came near and smote his spear with a great sword, so that the head fell off. Then was Ajax sore afraid, and gave way, and the men of Troy set torches to the ship's

stem, and a great flame shot up to the sky. And Achilles saw
it, and smote his thigh and spake—

"Haste thee, Patroclus, for I see the fire rising up from the
ships. Put thou on the armor, and I will call my people to the
war."

So Patroclus put on the armor—corselet and shield and helmet—and bound upon his shoulder the silver-studded sword,
and took a mighty spear in his hand. But the great Pelian
spear he took not, for that no man but Achilles might wield.
Then Automedon yoked the horses to the chariot, Bayard and
Piebald, and with them in the side harness, Pedasus; and they
two were deathless steeds, but he was mortal.

Meanwhile Achilles had called the Myrmidons to battle.
Fifty ships had he brought to Troy, and in each there were fifty
men. Five leaders they had, and the bravest of the five was
Pisander.

Then Achilles said, "Forget not, ye Myrmidons, the bold
words that ye spake against the men of Troy during the days
of my wrath, making complaint that I kept you from the battle
against your will. Now, therefore, ye have that which you desired."

So the Myrmidons went to the battle in close array, helmet
to helmet and shield to shield, close as the stones with which a
builder builds a wall. And in front went Patroclus, and
Automedon in the chariot beside him. Then Achilles went to
his tent and took a great cup from the chest which Thetis his
mother had given him. Now no man drank of that cup but he
only, nor did he pour out of it libations to any of the gods but
only to Zeus. This first he cleansed with sulphur, and then with
water from the spring. And after this he washed his hands, and
stood in the midst of the space before his tent, and poured out
of it to Zeus, saying—

"O Zeus, I send my comrade to this battle; make him strong
and bold, and give him glory, and bring him home safe to the
ships, and my people with him."

aw tŏm′e don   bā′yard   pī′bald   pĕd′a sus   pi săn′der

So he prayed, and Father Zeus heard him, and part he granted and part denied.

But now Patroclus with the Myrmidons had come to where the battle was raging and when the men of Troy beheld him,
5 they thought that Achilles had forgotten his wrath, and was come forth to the war. Then the men of Troy turned to flee, and many chiefs of fame fell by the spears of the Greeks. So the battle rolled back to the trench, and in the trench many chariots of the Trojans were broken, but the horses of Achilles
10 went across it at a stride, so nimble were they and strong. And the heart of Patroclus was set to slay Hector; but he could not overtake him, so swift were his horses. Then did Patroclus turn his chariot and keep back those that fled, that they should not go to the city, and rushed hither and thither, still slaying as
15 he went.

But Sarpedon, when he saw the Lycians dismayed and scattered, leapt down from his chariot, and Patroclus also leapt down, and they rushed at each other as two eagles rush together. But Patroclus missed not his aim, driving his spear into Sar-
20 pedon's heart. Then fell the great Lycian chief, as an oak, or a poplar, or a pine falls upon the hills before the axe.

Then did Patroclus forget the word which Achilles had spoken to him, that he should not go near to Troy, for he pursued the men of the city even to the wall. Thrice he mounted on the
25 angle of the wall, and thrice Apollo himself drove him back, pushing his shining shield. But the fourth time the god said, "Go thou back, Patroclus. It is not for thee to take the city of Troy; no, nor for Achilles, who is far better than thou art."

So Patroclus went back, fearing the wrath of the archer-god.
30 Then Apollo stirred up the spirit of Hector, that he should go against Patroclus. Therefore he went, with his brother for driver of his chariot. But when they came near, Patroclus cast a great stone which he had in his hand, and smote the driver on the forehead, crushing it in, so that he fell headlong from
35 the chariot. And Patroclus mocked him, saying—

"How nimble is this man! how lightly he dives! What spoil he would take of oysters, diving from a ship, even in a stormy sea! Who would have thought that there were such skilful divers in Troy!"

5　　Then again the battle waxed hot about his body and this too, at the last, the Greeks drew unto themselves, and spoiled it of the arms. And this being accomplished, Patroclus rushed against the men of Troy. Thrice he rushed, and each time he slew nine chiefs of fame. But the fourth time Apollo stood

10 behind him and struck him on the head and shoulders, so that his eyes were darkened. And the helmet fell from off his head, so that the horsehair plumes were soiled with dust. Never before had it touched the ground, for it was the helmet of Achilles. And also the god brake the spear in his hand, and

15 struck the shield from his arms, and loosed his corselet. All amazed he stood, and then Euphorbus smote him on the back with his spear, but slew him not. Then Patroclus sought to flee to the ranks of his comrades. But Hector saw him, and thrust at him with his spear, smiting him in the groin, so that

20 he fell. And when the Greeks saw him fall, they sent up a terrible cry. Then Hector stood over him and cried—

"Didst thou think to spoil our city, Patroclus, and to carry away our wives and daughters in the ships? But, lo! I have slain thee, and the fowls of the air shall eat thy flesh; nor shall

25 the great Achilles help thee at all—Achilles, who bade thee, I trow, strip the tunic from my breast, and thou thoughtest in thy folly to do it."

But Patroclus answered, "Thou boasteth much, Hector. Yet *thou* didst not slay me, but Apollo, who took from me my arms,

30 for had twenty such as thou met me, I had slain them all. And mark thou this: death and fate are close to thee by the hand of the great Achilles."

And Hector answered, but Patroclus was dead already—

"Why dost thou prophesy death to me? Maybe the great

35 Achilles himself shall fall by my hand."

ū for′bus

Then he drew his spear from the wound, and went after Automedon, to slay him, but the swift horses of Achilles carried him away.

CHAPTER FOUR

THE ROUSING OF ACHILLES

FIERCE was the fight about the body of Patroclus, and many
5 heroes fell, both on this side and on that, and first of them all
Euphorbus who, indeed, had wounded him. For as he came near
to strip the dead man of his arms, Menelaus slew him with his
spear. He slew him, but took not his arms, for Hector came
through the battle; nor did Menelaus dare to abide his coming,
10 but went back into the ranks of his own people. Then did
Hector strip off the arms of Patroclus, the arms which the great
Achilles had given him to wear. Then he laid hold of the body,
and would have dragged it into the host of the Trojans, but
Ajax Telamon came forth, and put his broad shield before it, as
15 a lion stands before its cubs when the hunters meet it in the
woods, drawing down over its eyes its shaggy brows. Then
Hector gave place, but Glaucus saw him and said—

"Now is this a shame to thee, that thou darest not to stand
against Ajax. How wilt thou and thy countrymen save the city
20 of Troy? For surely no more wilt thy allies fight for it. Small
profit have they of thee. Did not Sarpedon fall, and didst thou
not leave him to be a prey to the dogs? And now, if thou hadst
stood firm and carried off Patroclus, we might have made
exchange, and gained from the Greeks Sarpedon and his arms.
25 But it may not be, for thou fearest Ajax, and fleest before him."

But Hector said, "I fear him not, nor any man. Only Zeus
gives victory now to one man and now to another. But wait
thou here, and see whether I be a coward, as thou sayest."

Now he had sent the armor of Patroclus to the city. But
30 now he ran after those that were carrying it, and overtook

them, and put on the armor himself—but Zeus saw him doing it, and liked it not—and came back to the battle; and all who saw him thought that it had been the great Achilles himself. Then they all charged together, and fiercer grew the battle and fiercer

5 as the day went on. For the Greeks said one to another, "Now had the earth better yawn and swallow us up alive, than we should let the men of Troy carry off Patroclus to their city;" and the Trojans said, "Now if we must all fall by the body of this man, be it so, but we will not yield."

10 But the horses of Achilles stood apart from the battle, when they knew that Patroclus was dead, and wept. Nor could Automedon move them with the lash, nor with gentle words, nor with threats. They would not return to the ships, nor would they go into the battle; but as a pillar stands on the tomb of some

15 dead man, so they stood, with their heads drooped to the ground, with the big tears dropping to the earth, and their long manes trailing in the dust.

But Father Zeus beheld them, and pitied them, and said—

"It was not well that we gave you, immortal as ye are, to a

20 mortal man; for of all things that move on earth, mortal man is the fullest of sorrow. But Hector shall not possess you. It is enough for him, yea, and too much, that he has the arms of Achilles."

Then did the horses move from their place and obey their

25 charioteer as before. Nor could Hector take them, though he desired them very much. And all the while the battle raged about the dead Patroclus. And at last Ajax said to Menelaus —now these two had borne themselves more bravely in the fight than all others—

30 "See if thou canst find Antilochus, Nestor's son, that he may carry the tidings to Achilles, how that Patroclus is dead."

So Menelaus went and found Antilochus on the left of the battle, and said to him, "I have ill news for thee. Thou seest, I trow, that the men of Troy have the victory to-day. And also

35 Patroclus lies dead. Run, therefore, to Achilles, and tell him,

an til'o kus

if haply he may save the body; but as for the arms, Hector has them already."

Sore dismayed was Antilochus to hear such tidings, and his eyes were filled with tears and his voice was choked. Yet did 5 he give heed to the words of Menelaus, and ran to tell Achilles of what had chanced. But Menelaus went back to Ajax, where he had left him by Patroclus, and said—

"Antilochus, indeed, bears the tidings to Achilles. Yet I doubt whether he will come, for all his wrath against Hector, 10 seeing that he has no armor to cover him. Let us think, then, how we may best carry Patroclus away from the men of Troy."

Then said Ajax, "Do thou and Meriones run forward and raise the body in your arms, and I and the son of Oileus will keep off meanwhile the men of Troy."

15 So Menelaus and Meriones ran forward and lifted up the body. And the Trojans ran forward with a great shout when they saw them, as dogs run barking before the hunters when they chase a wild boar; but when the beast turns to bay, lo! they flee this way and that. So did the men of Troy flee when Ajax 20 the Greater and Ajax the Less turned to give battle. But still the Greeks gave way, and still the Trojans came on, and, ever in the front were Hector, the son of Priam and Æneas, the son of Anchises. But in the meantime Antilochus came near to Achilles, who, indeed, seeing that the Greeks fled and the 25 men of Troy pursued, was already sore afraid. And he said, weeping as he spake—

"I bring ill news—Patroclus lies low. The Greeks fight for his body, but Hector has his arms."

Then Achilles took of the dust of the plain in his hands, 30 and poured it on his head, and lay at his length upon the ground, and tore his hair. And all the women wailed. And Antilochus sat weeping; but ever he held the hands of Achilles, lest he should slay himself in his great grief.

Then came his mother, hearing his cry from where she sat in 35 the depths of the sea, and laid her hand on him and said—

me rī′o nes

"Why weepest thou, my son? Hide not the matter from me, but tell me."

And Achilles answered, "All that Zeus promised thee for me he hath fulfilled. But what profit have I, for lo! my friend Patroclus is dead, and Hector has the arms which I gave him to wear. And as for me, I care not to live, except I can avenge me upon him."

Then said Thetis, "Nay, my son, speak not thus. For when Hector dieth, thy doom also is near."

And Achilles spake in great wrath: "Would that I might die this hour, seeing that I could not help my friend, but am a burden on the earth—I, who am better in battle than all the Greeks besides. Cursed be the wrath that sets men to strive the one with the other, even as it set me to strive with King Agamemnon! But let the past be past. And as for my fate—let it come when it may, so that I first avenge myself on Hector. Wherefore seek not to keep me back from the battle."

Then Thetis said, "Be it so; only thou canst not go without thy arms, which Hector hath. But to-morrow will I go to Hephæstus, that he may furnish thee anew."

But while they talked the men of Troy pressed the Greeks more and more, and the two heroes, Ajax the Greater and Ajax the Less, could no longer keep Hector back, but that he should lay hold of the body of Patroclus. And indeed he would have taken it, but that Zeus sent Iris to Achilles, who said—

"Rouse thee, son of Peleus, or Patroclus will be a prey for the dogs of Troy!"

But Achilles said, "How shall I go?—for arms have I none, nor know I whose I might wear. Haply I could shift with the shield of Ajax, son of Telamon, but he, I know, is carrying it in the front of the battle."

Then answered Iris, "Go only to the trench and show thyself; so shall the men of Troy tremble and cease from the battle, and the Greeks shall have breathing space."

So he went, and Athene put her ægis about his mighty shoul-

he fes'tus   i'ris

ders, and a golden halo about his head, making it shine as a flame of fire, even as the watch-fires shine at night from some city that is besieged. Then went he to the trench; with the battle he mingled not, heeding his mother's commands, but he
5 shouted aloud, and his voice was as the sound of a trumpet. And when the men of Troy heard, they were stricken with fear, and the horses backed with the chariots, and the drivers were astonished when they saw the flaming fire above his head which Athene had kindled. Thrice across the trench the great Achilles shouted,
10 and thrice the men of Troy fell back. And that hour there perished twelve chiefs of fame, wounded by their own spears or trampled by their own steeds, so great was the terror among the men of Troy.

Right gladly did the Greeks take Patroclus out of the press.
15 Then they laid him on a bier and carried him to the tent, Achilles walking with many tears by his side.

And in the camp of the Greeks they mourned for Patroclus. And Achilles stood among his Myrmidons and said—

"Vain was the promise that I made to Menœtius that I
20 would bring back his son with his portion of the spoils of Troy. But Zeus fulfils not the thoughts of man. For he lies dead, nor shall I return to the house of Peleus, my father, for I, too, must die in this land. But thee, O Patroclus, I will not bury till I bring hither the head and the arms of Hector, and twelve men
25 of Troy to slay at thy funeral pile."

So they washed the body of Patroclus and anointed it, putting ointment into the wounds, and laid it on a bed, and covered it with a veil from the head to the feet.

Then went Thetis to the palace of Hephæstus, to pray him
30 that he would make arms for her son.

Then did Thetis tell him of her son Achilles, and of the wrong that had been done to him, and of his wrath, and of how Patroclus was dead, and the arms that he had had were lost.

Then said Hephæstus, "Be of good cheer: I will make what

thou askest. Would that I could as easily keep from him the doom of death."

Then Hephæstus wrought at his forge. And first of all he made a mighty shield. On it he wrought the earth, and the sky, and the sea, and the sun, and the moon, and all the stars. He wrought also two cities. In the one there was peace, and about the other there was war.

But all the while Achilles sat mourning for Patroclus, and his comrades wept about him. And at dawn Thetis brought him the arms and laid them before him. Loud they rattled on the ground, and all the Myrmidons trembled to hear but when Achilles saw them his eyes blazed with fire, and he rejoiced in his heart.

Then Achilles went along the shore and called the Greeks to an assembly, shouting mightily; and all, even those who were wont to abide in the ships, listened to his voice and came. And Achilles would have led the Greeks straightway to battle, but the wise Ulysses hindered him, saying that it was not well that he should send them to the fight fasting.

But after this the Greeks were gathered to the battle, and Achilles shone in the midst with the arms of Hephæstus upon him, and he flashed like fire.

Then he rushed into the battle, slaying as he went. And Hector would have met him, but Apollo stood by him and said, "Fight not with Achilles, lest he slay thee." Therefore he went back among the men of Troy. Many did Achilles slay, and among them the youngest son of Priam. When Hector saw this he could not bear any more to stand apart. Therefore he rushed at Achilles, and Achilles rejoiced to see him, saying, "This is the man who slew my comrade." But they fought not then, for when Hector cast his spear Athene turned it aside, and when Achilles charged, Apollo bore Hector away.

Then Achilles turned to the others, and slew multitudes of them, so that they fled, part across the plain, and part to the river, the eddying Xanthus. And these leapt into the water

as locusts leap into a river when the fire which men light drives
them from the fields. And all the river was full of horses and
men. Many of the Trojans hid themselves under the banks of
the river. And that hour would the Greeks have taken the
5 city of Troy, but that Apollo saved it by taking the form of a
Trojan chief whom Achilles pursued far from the walls of Troy.

CHAPTER FIVE

THE DEATH OF HECTOR

THE Trojans were now safe in the city, refreshing themselves after all their grievous toil. Only Hector remained outside the walls, standing in front of the great Scæan gates. But
10 all the while Achilles was fiercely pursuing till at last Apollo
turned and spake to him—

"Why dost thou pursue me, swift-footed Achilles? Hast
thou not yet found out that I am a god, and that all thy fury
is in vain? And now all the sons of Troy are safe in their city,
15 and thou art here, far out of the way, seeking to slay me, who
cannot die."

In great wrath Achilles answered him, "Thou hast done me
wrong in so drawing me away from the wall, great archer, most
mischief-loving of all the gods that are. Had it not been for
20 this, many a Trojan more had bitten the ground. Thou hast
robbed me of great glory, and saved thy favorites. O that I
had the power to take vengeance on thee! Thou hadst paid
dearly for thy cheat!"

Then he turned and rushed towards the city, swift as a race-
25 horse whirls a chariot across the plain. Old Priam spied him
from the wall, with his glittering armor, bright as that brightest
of the stars—men call it Orion's dog—which shines at vintage-
time, baleful light bringing the fevers of autumn to men. And
the old man groaned aloud when he saw him, and stretching out
30 his hands, cried to his son Hector, where he stood before the

o rī'on

gates, eager to do battle with this dread warrior and urged him to come within the walls.

Old Priam spake, but could not turn the heart of his son. And from the wall on the other side of the gate his mother
5 called to him, weeping sore, and said —

"Pity me, my son; come within the walls; wait not for this man, nor stand in battle against him. If he slay thee, nor I, nor thy wife, shall pay thee the last honors of the dead, but far away by the ships of the Greeks thy body shall lie unburied and
10 dishonored."

So father and mother besought their son, but all in vain. He was still minded to abide the coming Achilles; and as he waited he thought thus within himself—

"Woe is me if I go within the walls! I fear the sons and
15 daughters of Troy, what they may say; I fear lest some coward reproach me: 'Hector trusted in his strength, and lo! he has destroyed the people.' Better were it for me either to slay Achilles or to fall by his hand with honor here before the walls. Or, stay: shall I put down my shield, and lay aside my
20 helmet; and lean my spear against the wall and go to meet the great Achilles, and promise that we will give back the fair Helen, and all the wealth that Paris carried off with her; ay, and render up all the wealth that there is in the city, that the Greeks may divide it among themselves, binding the sons of Troy with
25 an oath that they keep nothing back? But this is idle talk: he will have no shame or pity, but will slay me while I stand without arms or armor before him. It is not for us to talk as a youth and a maiden talk together. It is better to meet in arms, and see whether the ruler of Olympus will give victory
30 to him or to me."

Thus he thought in his heart; and Achilles came near, brandishing over his right shoulder the great Pelian spear, and the flash of his arms was as the flame of fire, or as the rising sun. And Hector trembled when he saw him, nor dared to
35 abide his coming. Fast he fled from the gates, and fast Achilles

pursued him, as a hawk, fastest of all the birds of air, pursues a
dove upon the mountains. Past the watch-tower they ran, past
the wind-blown fig-tree, along the wagon-road which went about
the walls, and they came to the fair-flowing fountain where
5 from two springs rises the stream of eddying Scamander. Hot
is one spring, and a steam ever goes up from it, as from a
burning fire; and cold is the other, cold, even in the summer
heats, as hail or snow or ice. There are fair basins of stone,
where the wives and fair daughters of Troy were wont to wash
10 their garments, but that was in the old days of peace, or ever
the Greeks came to the land. Past the springs they ran, one
flying, the other pursuing: brave was he that fled, braver he
that pursued; it was no sheep for sacrifice or shield of ox-hide
for which they ran, but for the life of Hector, the tamer of
15 horses. Thrice they ran round the city, and all the gods
looked on.

And Zeus said, "This is a piteous sight that I behold. My
heart is grieved for Hector—Hector, who has ever worshiped me
with sacrifice, now on the heights of Ida, and now in the citadel
20 of Troy; and now the great Achilles is pursuing him round the
city of Priam. Come, ye gods, let us take counsel together. Shall
we save him from death, or let him fall beneath the hand of
Achilles?"

Then Athene said, "What is this that thou sayest, great sire?
25 —to rescue a man whom fate has appointed to die? Do it, if
it be thy will; but we, the other gods, approve it not."

Zeus answered her, "My heart is loath; yet I would do thee
pleasure. Be it as thou wilt."

Then Athene came down in haste from the top of Olympus,
30 and still Hector fled and Achilles pursued, just as a dog pursues
a fawn upon the hills. And ever Hector made for the gates, or
to get shelter beneath the towers, if haply those that stood upon
them might defend him with their spears; and ever Achilles
would get before him, and drive him towards the plain. So they

ran, one making for the city, and the other driving him to the plain. Just as in a dream, when one seems to fly and another seems to pursue, and the one cannot escape and the other cannot overtake, so these two ran together. But as for Hector, Apollo 5 even yet helped him, and gave him strength and nimble knees, else could he not have held out against Achilles, who was swiftest of foot among the sons of men.

Now Achilles had beckoned to the Greeks that no man should throw his spear at Hector, lest, perchance, he should 10 be robbed of his glory. And when the two came in their running for the fourth time to the springs of Scamander, Zeus held out the great balance of doom, and in one scale he put the fate of Achilles, and in the other the fate of Hector; and lo! the scale of Hector sank down to the realms of death, and Apollo 15 left him.

Then Athene lighted down from the air close to Achilles and said, "This, great Achilles, is our day of glory, for we shall slay Hector, mighty warrior though he be. For it is his doom to die, and not Apollo's self shall save him. But stand thou still 20 and take breath, and I will give this man heart to meet thee in battle."

Then the two chiefs came near to each other, and Hector with a waving plume spake first and said, "Thrice, great Achilles, hast thou pursued me round the walls of Troy, and I dared not 25 stand up against thee; but now I fear thee no more. Only let us make this covenant between us: if Zeus give me the victory, I will do no dishonor to thy body; thy arms and armor will I take, and give back thy body to the Greeks; and do thou promise to do likewise."

30 But Achilles scowled at him and said, "Hector, talk not of covenants to me. Men and lions make no oaths between each other, neither is there any agreement between wolves and sheep. So there shall be no covenant between me and thee. One of us two shall fall; and now is the time for thee to show thyself

a warrior, for of a truth Athene will slay thee by my spear, and thou shalt pay the penalty for all my comrades whom thou hast slain."

Then he threw the mighty spear, but Hector saw it coming 5 and avoided it, crouching on the ground, so that the mighty spear flew above his head and fixed itself in the earth. But Athene snatched it from the ground and gave it back to Achilles, Hector not perceiving.

Then Hector spake to Achilles: "Thou hast missed thy 10 aim, great Achilles. It was no word of Zeus that thou spakest, prophesying my doom, but thou soughtest to cheat me, terrifying me by thy words. Thou shalt not drive thy steel into my back, but here into my breast, if the gods will it so. But now look out for my spear. Would it might bury itself in thy flesh. The 15 battle would be easier for the men of Troy were thou only out of the way."

And as he spake he threw his long-shafted spear. True aim he took, for the spear struck the very middle of Achilles's shield. It struck, but pierced it not, but bounded far away, for the 20 shield was not of mortal make. And Hector stood dismayed, for he had not another spear. Then he knew that his end was come, and he said to himself, "Now have the gods called me to my doom. Zeus and Apollo are with me no more; but, if I must die, let me at least die in such a deed as men of after time may 25 hear of."

So he spake, and drew the mighty sword that hung by his side: then, as an eagle rushes through the clouds to pounce on a lamb, rushed on the great Achilles. But he dealt never a blow; for Achilles charged to meet him, his shield before his breast, 30 his helmet bent forward as he ran, with the long plumes streaming behind, and the gleam of his spear-point was as the gleam of the evening star, which is the fairest of all the stars in heaven. One moment he thought where he should drive it home, for the armor which Hector had won from Patroclus guarded him well; 35 but one spot there was, where by the collar-bone the neck joins the shoulder. There he drave in the spear, and the point stood out behind the neck, and Hector fell in the dust.

Then Achilles cried aloud, "Hector, thou thoughtest in the day when thou didst spoil Patroclus of his arms that thou
5 wouldst be safe from vengeance, taking, forsooth, no account of me. And lo! thou art fallen before me, nor shall thy body be given honorable burial, but to him all the Greeks shall give due rites."

But Hector, growing faint, spake to him. "Nay, great
10 Achilles, by thy life, and by thy knees, and by thy parents dear, I pray thee, let not my fallen body suffer this disgrace. Take rather the ransom, gold and bronze, that my father and mother shall pay thee, and let the sons and daughters of Troy give me burial rites."

15 But Achilles scowled at him, and cried, "Dog, seek not to entreat me! No ransom, though it were ten times told, should buy thee back; no, not though Priam should offer thy weight in gold."

Then Hector, who was now at the point to die, spake to him.
20 "I know thee well, what manner of man thou art, that the heart in thy breast is iron only. Only beware lest some vengeance from the gods come upon thee in the day when Paris and Apollo shall slay thee, for all thy valor by the Scæan gates."

So speaking, he died. But Achilles said, "Die, hound; but
25 my fate I meet when Zeus and the other gods decree."

Then he drew his spear out of the corpse and stripped off the arms; and all the Greeks came about the dead man, marvelling at his stature and beauty, and no man came but gloried over the corpse. And one would say to another, "Surely this Hector
30 is less dreadful now than in the day when he would burn our ships with fire."

Then Achilles devised a ruthless thing in his heart. He yearned for vengeance upon Hector, and so bound the body with thongs of ox-hide to the chariot, letting the head drag
35 behind, the head that once was so fair, and now was so disfigured in the dust.

So he dragged Hector to the ships. And Priam saw him from the walls, and scarce could his sons keep him back, but that he should go forth and beg the body of his dear son from him who had slain him. And Hecuba his mother also bewailed him, 5 but Andromache knew not as yet of what had befallen. For she sat in her dwelling, wearing a great purple mantle broidered with flowers. And she bade her maidens make ready a bath for Hector, when he should come back from the battle, nor knew that he should never need it more. But the voice of wailing 10 from the town came to her, and she rose up hastily in great fear, and dropped the shuttle from her hand and called to her maidens—

"Come with me, ye maidens, that I may see what has befallen, for I heard the voice of Queen Hecuba, and I fear me 15 much that some evil has come to the children of Priam. For it may be that Achilles has run between Hector and the city, and is pursuing him to the plain, for never will Hector abide with the army, but will fight in the front, so bold is he."

Then she hastened through the city as if she were mad. And 20 when she came to the wall she stood and looked; and lo! the horses of Achilles were dragging Hector to the ships. Then did darkness come on her, and she fell back fainting, and from her fair head dropped the net and the wreath and the diadem which golden Aphrodite gave her on the day when Hector of the 25 waving plume took her to be his wife.

And after a while, at the bidding of Zeus, Thetis went to Achilles and found him weeping softly for his dead friend, for the strength of his sorrow was now spent, and she said to him, "It is the will of the gods that thou give up the body of Hector, 30 and take in exchange the ransom of gold and precious things which his father will give thee for him."

And her son answered, "Be it so, if the gods will have it."

Then Zeus sent Iris, who was his messenger, to King Priam, where he sat with his face wrapped in his mantle, and his sons weeping about him, and his daughters wailing through the chambers of his palace.

Then Iris spake. "Be of good cheer, Priam, son of Dardanus; Zeus has sent me to thee. Go, taking with thee such gifts as
5 may best please the heart of Achilles, and bring back the body of thy dear son Hector. Go without fear of death or harm, and go alone. Only let an aged herald be with thee, to help thee when thou bringest back the body of the dead."

Then Priam rose with joy, and bade his sons bring forth his
10 chariot; but first he went to his chamber, and called to Hecuba, his wife, and told her of his purpose, nor heeded when she sought to turn him from it, but said, "Seek not to hold me back, nor be a bird of evil omen in my house. If any prophet or seer had bidden me do this thing, I should have held it a deceit; but now
15 have I heard the very voice of the messenger of Zeus. Wherefore, I shall go. And if I die, what care I? Let Achilles slay me, so that I embrace once more the body of my son."

Then Hecuba came near, and bade a woman-servant come and pour water on his hands. And when she had poured, King
20 Priam took a great cup from the hands of his wife, and made a libation to Zeus, and prayed—

"Hear me, Father Zeus, and grant that Achilles may pity me. And do thou send me now a lucky sign, that I may go with a good heart to the ships of the Greeks."

25 And Zeus heard him, and sent an eagle, a mighty bird, whose wings spread out on either side as wide as is the door of some spacious chamber in a rich man's house. On his right hand it flew high above the city, and all rejoiced when they saw the sign.

Then the old man mounted his chariot in haste, and drove
30 forth from the palace. Before him the mules drew the four-wheeled wagon, and these the herald guided. But his chariot the old king drove himself. And all his kinsfolk went with him, weeping as for one who was going to his death. But when they came down from the city to the plain, Priam and the herald

dar′da nus

went towards the ships of the Greeks, but all the others' returned
to Troy.

But Zeus saw him depart, and said to Hermes, "Hermes, go,
guide King Priam to the ships of the Greeks, so that no man
5 see him before he comes to the tents of Achilles."

Then Hermes fastened on his feet the fair sandals of gold
with which he flies, fast as the wind, over sea and land, and
in his hand he took the rod with which he opens and closes, as
he wills, the eyes of men. And he flew down and lighted on the
10 plain of Troy, taking on him the likeness of a fair youth.

Then he leapt into the chariot of the king and caught the
reins in his hand, and gave the horses and the mules a strength
that was not their own. And when they came to the ditch and
the trench that guarded the ships, lo! the guards were busy with
15 their meal; but Hermes made sleep descend upon them, and
opened the gates and brought in Priam with his treasures. And
when they came to the tent of Achilles, Hermes lighted down
from the chariot and said—

"Lo! I am Hermes, whom my father, Zeus, hath sent to be thy
20 guide. And now I shall depart, for I would not that Achilles
should see me. But go thou in, and clasp his knees, and beseech
him by his father and his mother and his child. So shalt thou
move his heart with pity."

So Hermes departed to Olympus, and King Priam leapt down
25 from the chariot, leaving the herald to care for the horses and
the mules, and went to the tent. There he found Achilles sitting;
his comrades sat apart, but two waited on him, for he had but
newly ended his meal, and the table was yet at his hand. But
no man saw King Priam till he was close to Achilles, and caught
30 his knees and kissed his hands, the dreadful, murderous hands
that had slain so many of his sons. As a man who slays another
by mishap flies to some stranger land, to some rich man's home,
and all wonder to see him, so Achilles wondered to see King
Priam, and his comrades wondered, looking one at another. Then
35 King Priam spake—

"Think of thy father, godlike Achilles, and pity me. He is old, as I am, and it may be, his neighbors trouble him, seeing that he has no defender; yet so long as he knows that thou art alive, it is well with him, for every day he hopes to see his dear
5 son returned from Troy. But as for me, I am altogether wretched. Many a valiant son I had—nineteen born to me of one mother— and most of them are dead, and he that was the best of all, who kept our city safe, he has been slain by thee. He it is whom I have come to ransom. Have pity on him and on me, thinking of
10 thy father. Never, surely, was lot so sad as this, to kiss the hands that slew a son."

But the words so stirred the heart of Achilles that he wept, thinking now of Patroclus, and now of his old father at home; and Priam wept, thinking of his dead Hector. But at last Achil-
15 les stood up from his seat and raised King Priam, having pity on his white hair and his white beard, and spake—

"How didst thou dare to come to the ships of the Greeks, to the man who slew thy sons? Surely thou must have a heart of iron. But sit thou down: let our sorrows rest in our hearts, for
20 there is no profit in lamentation. It is the will of the gods that men should suffer woe, but they are themselves free from care. Two chests are set by the side of Father Zeus, one of good and one of evil gifts, and he mixes the lot of men, taking out of both. Many noble gifts did the gods give to King Peleus: wealth and
25 bliss beyond that of other men, and kingship over the Myrmidons. Aye! and they gave him a goddess to be his wife. But they gave also this evil, that he had no stock of stalwart children in his house, but one son only, and I cannot help him at all in his old age, for I tarry here far away in Troy. Thou, too, old man
30 hadst wealth and power of old, and lordship over all that lies between Lesbos and Phrygia and the stream of Hellespont. And to thee the gods have given this ill, that there is ever battle and slaughter about thy city walls. But as for thy son, wail not for him, for thou canst not raise him up."

35 But Priam answered, "Make me not to sit, great Achilles,

lĕs'bos   frĭj'i a   hĕl'es pont

while Hector lies unhonored. Let me ransom him, and look upon him with my eyes, and do thou take the gifts. And the gods grant thee to return safe to thy fatherland."

Then Achilles hastened from his tent, and two comrades with
5 him. First they loosed the horses from the chariot and the mules from the wagon; then they brought in the herald and took the gifts. Only they left of them two cloaks and a tunic, wherein they might wrap the dead. And Achilles bade the women wash and anoint the body, but apart from the tent, lest, perchance,
10 Priam should see his son and cry aloud, and so awaken the fury in his heart. But when it was washed and anointed, Achilles himself lifted it in his arms and put it on the litter, and his comrades lifted the litter on the wagon.

And when all was finished Achilles groaned and cried to his
15 dead friend, saying—

"Be not wroth, Patroclus, if thou shouldst hear in the unknown land that I have ransomed Hector to his father: a noble ransom hath he paid me, and of this, too, thou shalt have thy share, as is meet."

20 Then Priam said, "If thou art minded to let me bury Hector, let there be a truce between my people and the Greeks. For nine days let us mourn for Hector, and on the tenth will we bury him and feast the people, and on the eleventh raise a great tomb above him, and on the twelfth we will fight again, if
25 fight we must."

And Achilles answered, "Be it so: I will stay the war for so long."

So for nine days the people gathered much wood, and on the tenth they laid Hector upon the pile, and lit fire beneath it. And
30 when it was burnt they quenched the embers with wine. Then his brethren and comrades gathered together the white bones, and laid them in a chest of gold; and this they covered with purple robes and put in a great coffin, and laid upon it stones many and great. And over all they raised a mighty mound; and all the
35 while the watchers watched, lest the Greeks should arise and slay

them. Last of all was a great feast held in the palace of King Priam.

So they buried Hector, the tamer of horses.

HELPS TO STUDY

Historical and Biographical: The story of Achilles is found in "The Iliad," one of the oldest poems in existence. The poem takes its name from Ilium, the Greek name of the city of Troy where the war, with which the poem deals, was fought. There is much doubt about the date and authorship of both this poem and the Odyssey, but it is commonly believed that they are the work of Homer, a blind poet who lived in the eighth century B. C. The events which they celebrate occurred about 1000 B. C. It is generally supposed that Homer earned his living as a minstrel, traveling from town to town reciting his poems to the music of his harp. There is much uncertainty as to his birth-place, as the following epigram shows—

> "Seven wealthy towns contend for Homer dead
> Through which the living Homer begged for bread."

After the birth of Achilles, his mother, who was a sea nymph, returned to the sea but was nevertheless deeply concerned for the welfare of her son. She wished for him a long, even if inglorious, life rather than, as the Fates decreed, a short and glorious one. For this reason she tried to make him invulnerable, by dipping him, when an infant, in the river Styx, from which he came out, all but the heel by which she held him, proof against all wounds.

While Achilles was in the temple of Apollo arranging for his marriage to one of the daughters of King Priam, Paris discharged at him a poisoned arrow which, guided by Apollo, fatally wounded him in the heel, his only vulnerable spot.

Hector was the son of King Priam and Hecuba. He was the great hero on the Trojan side just as Achilles was on the Greek. Though less is known of Hector's life, yet in the story we find him a very admirable character.

Notes and Questions

A few rules that will be found helpful in pronouncing Greek and Roman names:

C is soft before e, i, and y and hard before all other sounds.

The vowel in an accented closed syllable is generally short and in an accented open syllable, is generally long: i. e., Agamem′non, Menela′us.

Final eus is generally one syllable and pronounced like long u. Peleus, pelūs; Zeus, zūs.

Chapter One: What do you think

of the counsel of Ulysses? Notice this characteristic of shrewdness which he displays throughout the story. What promise did the princes make regarding Helen? Did they consider it binding? What did Ulysses pretend? How was his sanity tested?

Aulis was a city on the eastern coast of Greece.

"The Iliad" is full of beautiful comparisons or similes. Discuss those on p. 145. Another characteristic of "The Iliad" is the d o u b l e adjective; "shrill-voiced," "honey-sweet." Make a list of these as you meet them and notice, too, how the same descriptive words occur again and again in describing the same people or places.

Mycenae was a very ancient Greek city.

Ares favored the Trojans, being the husband of Aphrodite.

In what scenes do you especially admire Hector?

Chapter Three: The Greeks and Romans poured wine, or other liquids, upon the ground or upon a sacrifice. This sacred ceremony to some deity was called "pouring a libation."

Tell in your own words the story of Sarpedon.

What reply did Patroclus make to Hector's boast?

Chapter Four: Why did Glaucus speak to Hector as he did?

What do you think of the story of the horses of Achilles?

What was the promise referred to in l. 3, p. 159? What did the fulfilment of this promise cost Achilles?

Chapter Five: How did the Greeks regard the paying of the "last honors of the dead"?

Discuss the thoughts of Hector as he stands waiting for Achilles.

Read the passage that shows that even Zeus had to abide by the decree of the Fates.

In what incidents do you admire Achilles most?

BOOK II

THE STORY OF ULYSSES

CHAPTER ONE

THE LOTUS EATERS—THE CYCLOPES

WHEN the great city of Troy was taken, all the chiefs who had fought against it set sail for their homes. But there was wrath in heaven against them, for indeed they had borne themselves haughtily and cruelly in the day of their victory. There-
5 fore they did not all find a safe and happy return. For one was shipwrecked, and another was shamefully slain by his false wife in his palace, and others found all things at home troubled and changed, and were driven to seek new dwellings elsewhere. And some, whose wives and friends and people had been still true to
10 them through those ten long years of absence, were driven far and wide about the world before they saw their native land again. And of all, the wise Ulysses wandered farthest and suffered most.

He was well-nigh the last to sail, for he had tarried many
15 days to do pleasure to Agamemnon, lord of all the Greeks. Twelve ships he had with him—twelve he had brought to Troy —and in each there were some fifty men, being scarce half of those that had sailed in them in the old days, so many valiant heroes slept the last sleep, in the plain and on the seashore,
20 slain in battle or by the shafts of Apollo.

First they sailed north-west to the Thracian coast, where the Ciconians dwelt, who had helped the men of Troy. Their city they took, and in it much plunder, slaves and oxen, and jars of fragrant wine, and might have escaped unhurt, but that
25 they stayed to hold revel on the shore. For the Ciconians gathered their neighbors, being men of the same blood, and did battle with the invaders, and drove them to their ships. And

sī klō′pēz   sĭ kō′nĭ anz

when Ulysses numbered his men, he found that he had lost six out of each ship.

Scarce had he set out again when the wind began to blow fiercely; so, seeing a smooth sandy beach, they drove the ships
5 ashore and dragged them out of reach of the waves, and waited till the storm should abate. And the third morning being fair, they sailed again, and journeyed prosperously till they came to the very end of the great Peloponnesian land, where Cape Malea looks out upon the southern sea. But contrary currents baffled
10 them, so that they could not round it, and the north wind blew so strongly that they must fain drive before it.

On the tenth day they came to the land where the lotus grows —a wondrous fruit, of which whosoever eats cares not to see country or wife or children again. Now the Lotus-eaters, for
15 so they call the people of the land, were a kindly folk, and gave of the fruit to some of the sailors, not meaning them any harm, but thinking it to be the best that they had to give. These, when they had eaten, said that they would not sail any more over the sea; which, when the wise Ulysses heard, he bade their
20 comrades bind them and carry them, sadly complaining, to the ships.

> "Still onward driven before those baleful winds
> Across the fishy deep for nine whole days,
> On the tenth day we reached the land where dwell
25 The Lotus-eaters, men whose food is flowers.
> We landed on the mainland, and our crews
> Near the fleet galleys took their evening meal.
> And when we all had eaten and had drunk
> I sent explorers forth—two chosen men,
30 A herald was the third—to learn what race
> Of mortals nourished by the fruits of earth
> Possessed the land. They went and found themselves
> Among the Lotus-eaters soon, who used
> No violence against their lives, but gave

pel″ō pō nē'sĭ an   mā'lē a

Into their hands the lotus plant to taste.
Whoever tasted once of that sweet food
Wished not to see his native country more,
Nor give his friends the knowledge of his fate.
And then my messengers desired to dwell
Among the Lotus-eaters, and to feed
Upon the lotus, never to return.
By force I led them weeping to the fleet,
And bound them in the hollow ships beneath
The benches. Then I ordered all the rest
Of my beloved comrades to embark
In haste, lest, tasting of the lotus, they
Should think no more of home. All straightway went
On board, and on the benches took their place,
And smote the hoary ocean with their oars."

Then, the wind having abated, they took to their oars, and
rowed for many days till they came to the country where the
Cyclopes dwell. Now, a mile or so from the shore there was
an island, very fair and fertile, but no man dwells there or tills
the soil, and in the island a harbor where a ship may be safe
from all winds, and at the head of the harbor a stream falling
from the rock, and whispering alders all about it. Into this
the ships passed safely, and were hauled up on the beach, and
the crews slept by them, waiting for the morning. And the next
day they hunted the wild goats, of which there was great store
on the island, and feasted right merrily on what they caught,
with draughts of red wine which they had carried off from the
town of the Ciconians.

But on the morrow, Ulysses, for he was ever fond of adventure, and would know of every land to which he came what manner of men they were that dwelt there, took one of his twelve
ships and bade them row to land. There was a great hill sloping
to the shore, and there rose up here and there a smoke from
the caves where the Cyclopes dwelt apart, holding no converse

with each other, for they were a rude and savage folk, but ruled each his own household, not caring for others. Now, very close to the shore was one of these caves, very huge and deep, with laurels round about the mouth, and in front a fold with walls
5 built of rough stone, and shaded by tall oaks and pines. So Ulysses chose out of the crew the twelve bravest, and bade the rest guard the ship, and went to see what manner of dwelling this was, and who abode there. He had his sword by his side, and on his shoulder a mighty skin of wine, sweet-smelling and
10 strong, with which he might win the heart of some fierce savage, should he chance to meet with such, as indeed his prudent heart forecasted that he might.

So they entered the cave, and judged that it was the dwelling of some rich and skilful shepherd. For within, there were pens
15 for the young of the sheep and of the goats, divided all according to their age, and there were baskets full of cheeses, and full milkpails ranged along the wall. But the Cyclops himself was away in the pastures. Then the companions of Ulysses besought him that he would depart, taking with him, if he would, a store
20 of cheeses and sundry of the lambs and of the kids. But he would not, for he wished to see, after his wont, what manner of host this strange shepherd might be. And truly he saw it to his cost!

It was evening when the Cyclops came home, a mighty giant,
25 twenty feet in height, or more. On his shoulder he bore a vast bundle of pine logs for his fire, and threw them down outside the cave with a great crash, and drove the flocks within, and closed the entrance with a huge rock which twenty wagons and more could not bear. Then he milked the ewes and goats, and half of
30 the milk he curdled for cheese, and half he set ready for himself, when he should sup. Next he kindled a fire with the pine logs, and the flame lighted up all the cave, showing him Ulysses and his comrades.

"Who are ye?" cried Polyphemus, for that was the giant's
35 name. "Are ye traders, or, haply, pirates?"

sī′klŏps   pŏl ĭ fē′mus

Ulysses shuddered at the dreadful voice and shape, but bore him bravely, and answered, "We are no pirates, mighty sir, but Greeks, sailing back from Troy, and subjects of the great King Agamemnon, whose fame is spread from one end of heaven to 5 the other. And we are come to beg hospitality of thee in the name of Zeus, who rewards or punishes hosts and guests according as they be faithful the one to the other, or no."

"Nay," said the giant, "it is but idle talk to tell me of Zeus and the other gods. We Cyclopes take no account of gods, hold-10 ing ourselves to be much better and stronger than they. But come, tell me, where have you left your ship?"

But Ulysses saw his thought when he asked about the ship, how he was minded to break it, and take from them all hope of flight. Therefore he answered him craftily—

15 "Ship have we none, for that which was ours King Poseidon brake, driving it on a jutting rock on this coast, and we whom thou seest are all that are escaped from the waves."

Polyphemus answered nothing, but without more ado caught up two of the men, as a man might catch up some morsel of 20 food when the pangs of hunger had come over him, and killed them, and devoured them, with huge draughts of milk between, leaving not a morsel, not even the very bones. But the others, when they saw the dreadful deed, could only weep and pray to Zeus for help. And when the giant had ended his foul meal, 25 he lay down among his sheep and slept.

Then Ulysses questioned much in his heart whether he should slay the monster as he slept, for he doubted not that his good sword would pierce to the giant's heart, mighty as he was. But, being very wise, he remembered that, should he slay him, he and 30 his comrades would yet perish miserably. For who should move away the great rock that lay against the door of the cave? So they waited till the morning. And the monster woke, and milked his flocks, and afterwards, seizing two men, devoured them for his meal. Then he went to the pastures, but put the great rock on the mouth of the cave, just as a man puts down the lid upon his quiver.

All that day the wise Ulysses was thinking what he might best do to save himself and his companions, and the end of his 5 thinking was this: there was a mighty pole in the cave, green wood of an olive tree, big as a ship's mast, which Polyphemus purposed to use, when the smoke should have dried it, as a walking staff. Of this he cut off a fathom's length, and his comrades sharpened it and hardened it in the fire, and then hid 10 it away. At evening the giant came back, and drove his sheep into the cave, nor left the rams outside, as he had been wont to do before, but shut them in. And having duly done his shepherd's work, he made his cruel feast as before. Then Ulysses came forward with the wine-skin in his hand, and said—

15   "Drink, Cyclops, now that thou hast feasted. Drink, and see what precious things we had in our ship. But no one hereafter will come to thee with such like, if thou dealest with strangers as cruelly as thou hast dealt with us."

Then the Cyclops drank, and was mightily pleased, and said, 20 "Give me again to drink, and tell me thy name, stranger, and I will give thee a gift such as a host should give. In good truth this is a rare drink. We, too, have vines, but they bear not wine like this, which indeed must be such as the gods drink in heaven."

25   Then Ulysses gave him the cup again, and he drank. Thrice he gave it to him, and thrice he drank, not knowing what it was, and how it would work within his brain.

Then Ulysses spake to him. "Thou didst ask my name, Cyclops. Lo! my name is No Man. And now that thou 30 knowest my name, thou shouldst give me thy gift."

And he said, "My gift shall be that I will eat thee last of all thy company."

As he spake he fell back in a drunken sleep. Then Ulysses bade his comrades be of good courage, for the time was come 35 when they should be delivered. And they thrust the stake of olive wood into the fire till it was ready, green as it was, to burst into flame, and with it they put out the monster's eye; for he had but one eye, and that in the midst of his forehead, with the eyebrow below it.

Then the giant leaped up, and tore away the stake, and cried aloud, so that all the Cyclopes who dwelt on the mountain side heard him and came about his cave, asking him, "What aileth thee, Polyphemus, that thou makest this uproar in the peaceful night, driving away sleep? Is any one robbing thee of thy sheep, or seeking to slay thee by craft or force?"

And the giant answered, "No Man slays me by craft."

"Nay, but," they said, "if no man does thee wrong, we cannot help thee. The sickness which great Zeus may send, who can avoid? Pray to our father, Poseidon, for help."

Then they departed; and Ulysses was glad at heart for the good success of his device, when he said that he was No Man.

But the Cyclops rolled away the great stone from the door of the cave, and sat in the midst, stretching out his hands, to feel whether perchance the men within the cave would seek to go out among the sheep.

Long did Ulysses think how he and his comrades should best escape. At last he lighted upon a good device, and much he thanked Zeus for that this once the giant had driven the rams with the other sheep into the cave. For, these being great and strong, he fastened his comrades under the bodies of the beasts, tying them with osier twigs, of which the giant made his bed. One ram he took, and fastened a man beneath it, and two others he set, one on either side. So he did with the six, for but six were left out of the twelve who had ventured with him from the ship. And there was one mighty ram, far larger than all the others, and to this Ulysses clung, grasping the fleece tight with both his hands. So they waited for the morning. And when the morning came, the rams rushed forth to the pasture; but the giant sat in the door and felt the back of each as it went by, nor thought to try what might be underneath. Last of all went the great ram. And the Cyclops knew him as he passed, and said—

"How is this, thou who art the leader of the flock? Thou art not wont thus to lag behind. Thou hast always been the first
5 to run to the pastures and streams in the morning, and the first to come back to the fold when evening fell; and now thou art last of all. Perhaps thou art troubled about thy master's eye, which some wretch—No Man, they call him—has destroyed, having first mastered me with wine. He has not escaped, I
10 ween. I would that thou couldst speak, and tell me where he is lurking. Of a truth I would dash out his brains upon the ground, and avenge me of this No Man."

So speaking, he let him pass out of the cave. But when they were out of reach of the giant, Ulysses loosed his hold of the
15 ram, and then unbound his comrades. And they hastened to their ship, not forgetting to drive before them a good store of the Cyclops' fat sheep. Right glad were those that had abode by the ship to see them. Nor did they lament for those that had died, though they were fain to do so, for Ulysses forbade, fear-
20 ing lest the noise of their weeping should betray them to the giant, where they were. Then they all climbed into the ship, and sitting well in order on the benches, smote the sea with their oars, laying-to right lustily, that they might the sooner get away from the accursed land. And when they had rowed a hundred
25 yards or so, so that a man's voice could yet be heard by one who stood upon the shore, Ulysses stood up in the ship and shouted—

"He was no coward, O Cyclops, whose comrades thou didst so foully slay in thy den. Justly art thou punished, monster, that devourest thy guests in thy dwelling. May the gods make
30 thee suffer yet worse things than these!"

Then the Cyclops, in his wrath, broke off the top of a great hill, a mighty rock, and hurled it where he had heard the voice. Right in front of the ship's bow it fell, and a great wave rose as it sank, and washed the ship back to the shore. But Ulysses
35 seized a long pole with both hands and pushed the ship from

the land, and bade his comrades ply their oars, nodding with his head, for he was too wise to speak, lest the Cyclops should know where they were. Then they rowed with all their might and main.

And when they had gotten twice as far as before, Ulysses made as if he would speak again; but his comrades sought to hinder him, saying, "Nay, my lord, anger not the giant any more. Surely we thought before we were lost, when he threw the great rock and washed our ship back to the shore. And if he hear thee now, he may crush our ship and us, for the man throws a mighty bolt, and throws it far."

But Ulysses would not be persuaded, but stood up and said, "Hear, Cyclops! If any man ask who blinded thee, say that it was the warrior Ulysses, son of Laertes, dwelling in Ithaca."

And the Cyclops answered with a groan, "Of a truth, the old oracles are fulfilled, for long ago a prophet foretold to me that one Ulysses would rob me of my sight. But I looked for a great man and a strong, who should subdue me by force, and now a weakling has done the deed, having cheated me with wine. But come thou hither, Ulysses, and I will be a host indeed to thee. Or, at least, may Poseidon give thee such a voyage to thy home as I would wish thee to have. For know that Poseidon is my sire. May be that he may heal me of my grievous wound."

And Ulysses said, "Would that I could send thee down to the abode of the dead, where thou wouldst be past all healing, even from Poseidon's self."

Then Cyclops lifted up his hands to Poseidon and prayed—
"Hear me, Poseidon, if I am indeed thy son and thou my father. May this Ulysses never reach his home! or, if the Fates have ordered that he should reach it, may he come alone, all his comrades lost, and come to find sore trouble in his house!"

And as he ended he hurled another mighty rock, which almost lighted on the rudder's end, yet missed it as by a hair's breadth. So Ulysses and his comrades escaped, and came to the island of the wild goats, where they found their comrades, who indeed had

lā er'tēz

waited long for them, in sore fear lest they had perished. Then
Ulysses divided amongst his company all the sheep which they
had taken from the Cyclops. And all, with one consent, gave
him for his share the great ram which had carried him out of
5 the cave, and he sacrificed it to Zeus. And all that day they
feasted right merrily on the flesh of sheep and on sweet wine,
and when the night was come, they lay down upon the shore and
slept.

CHAPTER TWO

THE ISLAND OF ÆOLUS—THE LÆSTRYGONIANS—CIRCE

AFTER sailing awhile, they came to the island of Æolus, who
10 is the king of the winds, and who dwelt there with his children,
six sons and six daughters. Right well did Æolus entertain
them, feasting them royally for a whole month, while he heard
from Ulysses the story of all that had been done at Troy. And
when Ulysses prayed him that he would help him on his way
15 homewards, Æolus hearkened to him, and gave him the skin of
an ox, in which he had bound all contrary winds, so that they
should not hinder him. But he let a gentle west wind blow, that
it might carry him and his comrades to their home. For nine
days it blew and now they were near to Ithaca, their country,
20 so that they saw lights burning in it, it being night-time. But
now, by an ill-chance, Ulysses fell asleep, being wholly wearied
out, for he had held the helm for nine days, nor trusted it to
any of his comrades. While he slept, his comrades, who had cast
eyes of envy on the great ox-hide, said one to another—

25   "Strange it is how men love and honor this Ulysses whithersoever he goes. Now he comes back from Troy with much spoil,
but we with empty hands. Let us see what it is that Æolus
hath given, for doubtless in this ox-hide is much silver and
gold."

30   So they loosed the great bag of ox-hide, and lo! all the winds
rushed out, and carried them far away from their country. But

ē'ō lus   lĕs trĭ gō'ni anz   sir'sē

Ulysses, waking with the tumult, doubted much whether he should not throw himself into the sea and so die. But he endured, thinking it better to live. Only he veiled his face and so sat, while the ships drave before the winds, till they came once more to the island of Æolus. Then Ulysses went to the palace of the king, and found him feasting with his wife and children, and sat him down on the threshold. Much did they wonder to see him, saying, "What evil power has hindered thee, that thou didst not reach thy country and home?"

Then he answered, "Blame not me, but the evil counsels of my comrades, and sleep, which mastered me to my hurt. But do ye help me again."

But they said, "Begone; we may not help him whom the gods hate; and hated of them thou surely art."

So Æolus sent him away. Then again they launched their ships and set forth, toiling wearily at the oars, and sad at heart.

Six days they rowed, nor rested at night, and on the seventh they came to Lamos, which was a city of the Læstrygonians, in whose land the night is as the day, so that a man might earn double wage, if only he wanted not sleep—shepherd by day and herdsman by night. There was a fair haven with cliffs about it, and a narrow mouth with great rocks on either side. And within are no waves, but always calm.

Now Ulysses made fast his ship to the rocks, but the others entered the haven. Then he sent two men and a herald with them, and these came upon a smooth road by which wagons brought down wood from the mountain to the city. Here they met a maiden, the daughter of the king of the land, and asked of her who was lord of that country. Whereupon she showed them her father's lofty palace. And they, entering this, saw the maiden's mother, big as a mountain, horrible to behold, who straightway called to her husband. The messengers, indeed, fled to the ships; but he made a great shout, and the Læstrygonians came flocking about him, giants, not men. These broke off great stones from the cliffs, each stone as much as a man could carry,

lä′mos

and cast them at the ships, so that they were broken. And the
men they speared, as if they were fishes, and devoured them.
So it happened to all the ships in the haven. Ulysses only
escaped, for he cut the hawser with his sword, and bade his men
5 ply their oars, which indeed they did right willingly.

After a while they came to the island of Æææ, where Circe
dwelt, who was the daughter of the Sun. Two days and nights
they lay upon the shore in great trouble and sorrow. On the
third, Ulysses took his spear and sword and climbed a hill that
10 there was, for he wished to see to what manner of land they had
come. And having climbed it, he saw smoke rising from the
palace of Circe, where it stood in the midst of a wood. Should
he go straightway to the palace that he saw, or first return to his
comrades on the shore? And this last seemed better; and it
15 chanced that as he went he saw a great stag which was going
down to the river to drink, for indeed the sun was now hot,
and casting his spear at it he pierced it through. Then he
fastened together the feet with green withes and a fathom's
length of rope, and slinging the beast around his neck, so carried
20 it to the ship, leaning on his spear; for indeed it was heavy to
bear, nor could any man have carried it on the shoulder with
one hand. And when he was come to the ship, he cast down his
burden. Now the men were sitting with their faces muffled, so
sad were they. But when he bade them be of good cheer, they
25 looked up and marvelled at the great stag. And all that day
they feasted on deer's flesh and sweet wine, and at night lay
down to sleep on the shore. But when morning was come,
Ulysses called them all together and spake—

"I know not, friends, where we are. Only I know, having
30 seen smoke yesterday from the hill, that there is a dwelling in
this island."

It troubled the men much to hear this, for they thought of
the Cyclops and the Læstrygonians; and they wailed aloud, but
there was no counsel in them. Wherefore Ulysses divided them
35 into two companies, setting Eurylochus over the one and him-

ē ē'a   ū rĭl'o kus

self over the other, and shook lots in a helmet who should go and search out the island, and the lot of Eurylochus leaped out. So he went, and comrades twenty and two with him. And in an open space in the wood they found the palace of Circe. All about were wolves and lions; yet these harmed not the men, but stood up on their hind legs, fawning upon them, as dogs fawn upon their master when he comes from his meal. And the men were afraid. They stood in the porch and heard the voice of Circe as she sang with a lovely voice and plied the loom. Then said Polites, who was dearest of all his comrades to Ulysses—

"Some one within plies a great loom, and sings with a loud voice. Some goddess is she, or woman. Let us make haste and call."

So they called to her, and she came out and beckoned to them that they should follow. So they went, in their folly. And she bade them sit, and mixed for them a mess, red wine, and in it barley-meal and cheese and honey, and mighty drugs withal, of which, if a man drank, he forgot all that he loved. When they had drunk she smote them with her wand. And lo! they had of a sudden the heads and the voices and the bristles of swine, but the heart of a man was in them still. And Circe shut them in sties, and gave them mast and acorns and cornel to eat.

But Eurylochus fled back to the ship. For a while he could not speak, so full was his heart of grief, but at the last he told the tale of what had befallen. Then Ulysses took his silver-studded sword and his bow, and bade Eurylochus guide him by the way that he had gone.

Nor would he hearken when Eurylochus would have hindered him, but said, "Stay here by the ship, eating and drinking, if it be thy will, but I must go, for necessity constrains me."

When he had come to the house, there met him Hermes of the golden wand, in the shape of a fair youth, who said to him—

"Art thou come to rescue thy comrades that are now swine

pō lĭ′tēz

in Circe's house? Nay, but thou shalt never go back thyself.
Yet, stay; I will give thee such a drug as shall give thee power
to resist all her charms. For when she shall have mixed thee
a potion, and smitten thee with her wand, then do thou rush
5 upon her with thy sword, making as if thou wouldst slay her.
And when she shall pray for peace, do thou make her swear by
the great oath that binds the gods that she will not harm thee."

Then Hermes showed Ulysses a certain plant, whose root
was black, but the flower white as milk. Moly, the gods call it,
10 and very hard it is for mortal man to find.

Then Ulysses went into the palace, and all befell as Hermes
had told him. For Circe would have changed him as she had
changed his comrades. Then he rushed at her with his sword,
and made her swear the great oath which binds the gods that
15 she would not harm him.

> "Back through the woody island Hermes went
> Toward high Olympus, while I took my way
> To Circe's halls, yet with a beating heart.
> There, as I stood beneath the portico
20 > Of that bright-haired divinity, I called
> Aloud; the goddess heard my voice and came,
> And threw at once the shining doors apart,
> And prayed me to come in. I followed her,
> Yet grieving still. She led me in and gave
25 > A seat upon a silver-studded throne,
> Beautiful, nobly wrought, and placed beneath
> A footstool, and prepared a mingled draught
> Within a golden chalice, and infused
> A drug with mischievous intent. She gave
30 > The cup; I drank it off; the charm wrought not,
> And then she smote me with her wand and said:—
> 'Go to the sty, and with thy fellows sprawl.'
> She spake; but drawing forth the trusty sword
> Upon my thigh, I rushed at her as if

mō'li

To take her life. She shrieked and, stooping low,
Ran underneath my arm and clasped my knees,
And uttered piteously these winged words:—
'Who art thou? of what race and of what land,
And who thy parents? I am wonder-struck
To see that thou couldst drink that magic juice
And yield not to its power. No living man,
Whoever he might be, that tasted once
Those drugs, or passed them o'er his lips, has yet
Withstood them. In thy breast a spirit dwells
Not to be thus subdued. Art thou not then
Ulysses, master of wise stratagems,
Whose coming hither, on his way from Troy,
In his black galley, oft has been foretold
By Hermes of the golden wand?'"

But afterwards, when they sat at meat together, the goddess perceived that he was silent and ate not. Wherefore she said, "Why dost thou sit, Ulysses, as though thou wert dumb? Fearest thou any craft of mine? Nay, but that may not be, for have I not sworn the great oath that binds the gods?"

And Ulysses said, "Nay, but who could think of meat and drink when such things had befallen his companions?"

Then Circe led the way, holding her wand in her hand, and opened the doors of the sties, and drove out the swine that had been men. Then she rubbed on each another mighty drug, and the bristles fell from their bodies and they became men, only younger and fairer than before. And when they saw Ulysses they clung to him and wept for joy, and Circe herself was moved with pity.

Then she said, "Go, Ulysses, to thy ship, and put away all the goods and gear in the caves that are on the shore, but come again hither thyself, and bring thy comrades with thee."

Then Ulysses went. Right glad were they who had stayed to see him, glad as are the calves who have been penned in the fold-yard when their mothers come back in the evening.

So they went to the dwelling of Circe, who feasted them royally, so that they remained with her for a whole year, well content.

But when the year was spent they said to Ulysses, "It were
5 well to remember thy country, if it is indeed the will of the gods that thou shouldst return thither."

Then Ulysses besought Circe that she would send him on his way homewards, as indeed she had promised to do. And she answered—

10 "I would not have you abide in my house unwillingly. Yet must thou first go another journey, even to the dwellings of the dead, there to speak with the seer Tiresias."

But Ulysses was sore troubled to hear such things, and wept aloud, saying, "Who shall guide us in this journey?—for never
15 yet did ship make such a voyage as this."

Then said Circe, "Seek no guide; only raise the mast of thy ship and spread the white sails, and sit in peace. So shall the north wind bear thee to the place on the ocean shore where are the groves of Persephone, tall poplars and willows. There must
20 thou beach thy ship. And after that thou must go alone."

Then she told him all that he must do if he would hold converse with the dead seer Tiresias, and hear what should befall him. So the next morning he roused his companions, telling them that they should now return. And when they were assem-
25 bled, Ulysses told them how they must take another journey first, even to the dwellings of the dead. This they were much troubled to hear, yet they made ready the ship and departed.

tī rē'si as   per sĕf'o ne

CHAPTER THREE

THE REGIONS OF THE DEAD—SCYLLA—THE OXEN OF THE SUN—
CALYPSO

So they came to the place of which Circe had told them. And when all things had been rightly done, Ulysses saw spirits of the dead; among them came the spirit of Tiresias, holding a sceptre of gold in his hand. And when Ulysses asked him of his return, he said—

"Thy return shall be difficult, because of the anger of Poseidon, whose son thou madest blind. Yet, when thou comest to the island of Thrinacia, where feed the oxen of the Sun, if thou leave these unhurt, thou and thy comrades shall return to Ithaca. But otherwise they shall perish, and thou shalt return, after long time, in a ship not thine own, and shalt find in thy palace, devouring thy goods, men of violence, suitors of thy wife. These shalt thou slay, openly or by craft. So shalt thou die at last in peace."

And having seen many other things, Ulysses went back to his ship, and returned with his companions to the island of Circe. And being arrived there, Circe made them a feast. But while the others slept she told to Ulysses all that should befall him, saying—

"First thou wilt come to the island of the Sirens, who sing so sweetly, that whosoever hears them straightway forgets wife and child and home. In a meadow they sit, singing sweetly, but about them are bones of men. Do thou, then, close with wax the ears of thy companions, and make them bind thee to the mast, so that thou mayest hear the song and yet take no hurt. And do thou bid them, when thou shalt pray to be loosed, not to hearken, but rather to bind thee the more.

"And this peril being past, there lie others in thy path, of which thou must take thy choice. For either thou must pass between the rocks which the gods call the Wanderers—and these

sĭl′a   ka lĭp′so   thrin ā′shia   sī′rens

close upon all that passes between them, even the very doves
in their flight, nor has any ship escaped them—or thou must
go through the strait, where there is a rock on either hand.   In
the one rock dwells Scylla, in a cave so high above the sea that
5 an archer could not reach it with his arrow.   A horrible monster
is she.   Twelve unshapely feet she hath, and six long necks, and
on each a head with three rows of teeth.   In the cave she lies,
but her heads are without, fishing for sea-dogs and dolphins, or
even a great whale, if such should chance to go by.   Think not
10 to escape her, Ulysses, for, of a truth, with each head will she
take one of thy companions.

"But the other rock is lower and more flat, with a wild fig-tree
on the top.   There Charybdis thrice a day draws in the dark
water, and thrice a day sends it forth.   Be not thou near when
15 she draws it in; not even Poseidon's self could save thee.   Choose
rather to pass near Scylla, for it is better to lose six of thy companions than that all should perish."

Then said Ulysses, "Can I not fight with this Scylla, and
so save my companions?"

20   But Circe answered, "Nay, for she is not of mortal race.   And
if thou linger to arm thyself, thou wilt but lose six others of thy
companions.   Pass them with all the speed that may be, and
call on the mother of Scylla, that she may keep her from coming
the second time.   Then wilt thou come to the island of
25 Thrinacia, where feed the oxen of the Sun.   Beware that thy
companions harm them not."

The next day they departed.   Then Ulysses told his companions of the Sirens, and how they should deal with him.   And
after a while, the wind that had blown ceased, and there was a
30 windless calm; so they took down the sails and laid them in the
ship, and put forth the oars to row.   Then Ulysses made great
cakes of wax, kneading them in the hot sun, and put them into
the ears of his companions.   And they bound him upright to the
mast and so rowed on.   Then the Sirens sang—

ka rib′dis.

"O world-renowned Ulysses! thou who art
The glory of the Achaians, turn thy bark
Landward, that thou mayest listen to our lay.
No man has passed us in his galley yet,
Ere he has heard our warbled melodies.
He goes delighted hence a wiser man;
For all that in the spacious realm of Troy
The Greeks and Trojans by the will of Heaven
Endured we know, and all that comes to pass
In all the nations of the fruitful earth."

Then Ulysses prayed that they would loose him, nodding his head, for their ears were stopped; but they plied their oars, and put new bonds upon him. But after the island was passed, the men took the wax from their ears and loosed the bonds from Ulysses.

After this they saw smoke and surf, and heard a mighty roar, and their oars dropped out of their hands for fear; but Ulysses bade them be of good heart, for that by his counsel they had escaped other dangers in past time. And the rowers he bade row as hard as they might. But to the helmsman he said, "Steer the ship outside the smoke and the surf, and steer close to the cliffs, lest the ship shoot off unawares and lose us." But of Scylla he said nothing, fearing lest they should lose heart and cease rowing altogether. Then he armed himself, and stood in the prow waiting till Scylla should appear.

But on the other side Charybdis was sucking in the water with a horrible noise, and with eddies so deep that a man might see the sand at the bottom. But while they looked trembling at this, Scylla caught six of the men from the ship, and Ulysses heard them call him by his name as the monster carried them away. And never, he said in after days, did he see with his eyes so piteous a sight.

But after this they came to the land where fed the oxen of the Sun. And Ulysses said, "Let us pass by this island, for

a kā'yanz

there we shall find the greatest evil that we have yet suffered."
But they would not hearken; only they said that the next day
they would sail again.

Then spake Ulysses, "Ye constrain me, being many to one.
5 Yet promise me this, that ye will not take any of the sheep or
oxen, for if ye do great trouble will come to us."

So they promised. But for a whole month the south wind
blew and ceased not. And their store of meat and drink being
spent, they caught fishes and birds, as they could, being sore
10 pinched with hunger. And at last it chanced that Ulysses, being
weary, fell asleep. And while he slept, his companions, Eurylochus persuading them, took of the oxen of the Sun, and slew
them, for they said that their need was great, and that when
they came to their own land they would build a temple to the
15 Sun to make amends. But the Sun was very wroth with them.
And a great and dreadful thing happened, for the hides crept,
and the meat on the spits bellowed.

"O Father Jove, and all ye blessed gods
Who never die, avenge the wrong I bear
Upon the comrades of Laertes' son,
20   Ulysses, who have foully slain my beeves,
In which I took delight when'er I rose
Into the starry heaven, and when again
I sank from heaven to earth. If for the wrong
25   They make not large amends, I shall go down
To Hades, there to shine among the dead.
The cloud-compelling Jupiter replied:—
'Still shine, O Sun! among the deathless gods
And mortal men, upon the nourishing earth.
30   Soon will I cleave, with a white thunderbolt,
Their galley in the midst of the black sea.'"

Six days they feasted on the oxen, and on the seventh they
set sail. But when they were now out of sight of land, Zeus
brought up a great storm over the sea, and a mighty west wind

hā'dēz

blew, breaking both the forestay and the backstay of the mast, so that it fell. And after this a thunderbolt struck the ship, and all the men that were in it fell overboard and died. But Ulysses lashed the keel to the mast with the backstay, and on these he sat, borne by the winds across the sea.

All night was he borne along, and in the morning he came to Charybdis. And it chanced that Charybdis was then sucking in the water; but Ulysses, springing up, clung to a wild fig-tree that grew from the rock, but could find no rest for his feet, nor yet could climb into the tree. All day long he clung, waiting till the raft should come forth again; and at evening the raft came forth. Then he loosed his hands and fell, so that he sat astride upon the raft.

After this he was borne for nine days upon the sea, till he came to the island Ogygia, where dwelt the goddess Calypso.

In this island Ulysses abode seven years, much against his will, thinking always of his home and his wife and his young son. And when the seven years were ended, Athene, who had ever loved him much, spake to Zeus, complaining much that one so wise had been so long balked of his return.

Then said Zeus that it should not be so any longer, for that Poseidon must give up his wrath against the man, if all the other gods were of one mind.

Then said Athene to Zeus, "Do thou send Hermes, thy messenger, to Calypso, that she let Ulysses depart, and I will go to Ithaca to Telemachus, to bid him go search for his father; for indeed it is but seemly that he should do so, now that he is come to man's estate."

So she went to Ithaca in the guise of a young man, a stranger.

Now there were gathered in the house of Ulysses many princes from the islands, suitors of the Queen Penelope, for they said that Ulysses was dead, and that she should choose another husband. These were gathered together, and were sitting playing draughts and feasting. And Telemachus sat among them,

jij'i a   te lem'a kus

vexed at heart, for they wasted his substance, neither was he master in his house.

Penelope put off making a choice among the suitors by saying, "Hasten not my marriage till I finish this web to be a
5 burial cloth for Laertes." So she spake and for three years she undid at night what she wove during the day.

Athene put might and courage into the heart of Telemachus and urged him to seek news of his father.

Straightway he set out and went first to Pylos where dwelt
10 the old Nestor and then to Sparta, even to the palace of King Menelaus. The king told him that Ulysses was still alive and that the nymph Calypso was keeping him against his will upon the island of Ogygia.

CHAPTER FOUR

ULYSSES ON HIS RAFT

WHILE Telemachus was yet sojourning in Sparta, Zeus sent
15 Hermes to Calypso, to bid her that she should let Ulysses go. So Hermes donned his golden sandals, and took his wand in his hand, and came to the island of Ogygia, and to the cave where Calypso dwelt. A fair place it was. In the cave was burning a fire of sweet-smelling wood, and Calypso sat at her
20 loom and sang with a lovely voice. And round about the cave was a grove of alders and poplars and cypresses, wherein many birds, falcons and owls and sea-crows, were wont to roost; and all about the mouth of the cave was a vine with purple clusters of grapes; and there were four fountains which streamed four
25 ways through meadows of parsley and violet. But Ulysses was not there, for he sat, as was his wont, on the sea-shore, weeping and groaning because he might not see wife and home and country.

And Calypso spied Hermes, and bade him come within, and
30 gave him meat and drink, ambrosia and nectar, which are the

food of the gods. And when he had ended his meal, she asked him of his errand. So he told her that he was come, at the bidding of Zeus, in the matter of Ulysses, for that it was the pleasure of the gods that he should return to his native country, 5 and that she should not hinder him any more. It vexed Calypso much to hear this, for she would fain have kept Ulysses with her always, and she said—

"Ye gods are always jealous when a goddess loves a mortal man. And as for Ulysses, did not I save him when Zeus had 10 smitten his ship with a thunderbolt, and all his comrades had perished? And now let him go—if it pleases Zeus. Only I cannot send him, for I have neither ship nor rowers. Yet will I willingly teach him how he may safely return."

And Hermes said, "Do this thing speedily, lest Zeus be wroth 15 with thee."

So he departed. And Calypso went seeking Ulysses, and found him on the shore of the sea, looking out over the waters, as was his wont, and weeping, for he was weary of his life, so much did he desire to see Ithaca again. She stood by him and 20 said—

"Weary not for thy native country, nor waste thyself with tears. If thou wilt go, I will speed thee on thy way. Take therefore thine axe and cut thee beams, and join them together, and make a deck upon them, and I will give thee bread and water and wine, and clothe thee also, so that thou mayest return safe to thy native country, for the gods will have it so."

"Nay," said Ulysses, "what is this that thou sayest? Shall I pass in a raft over the dreadful sea, over which even ships go not without harm? I will not go against thy will; but thou must swear the great oath of the gods that thou plannest no evil against me."

Then Calypso smiled and said, "These are strange words. By the Styx I swear that I plan no harm against thee, but only such good as I would ask myself, did I need it; for indeed my heart is not of iron, but rather full of compassion."

stïx

The next day, so soon as early Dawn shone forth, the rosy-fingered, Calypso gave him an axe with a handle of olive wood, and an adze, and took him to the end of the island, where there were great trees, long ago sapless and dry, alder and poplar
5 and pine. Of these he felled twenty, and lopped them, and worked them by the line. Then the goddess brought him augers, and he made holes in the logs and joined them with pegs. And he made decks and side-planking also; also a mast and a yard, and a rudder wherewith to turn the raft. And he fenced it about
10 with a bulwark of osier against the waves. The sails, indeed, Calypso wove, and Ulysses fitted them with braces and halyards. And afterwards, with ropes, he moored the raft to the shore.

On the fourth day all was finished, and on the fifth day he departed. And Calypso gave him goodly garments, and a skin of
15 wine, and a skin of water, and rich provender in a wallet of leather. She sent also a fair wind blowing behind, and Ulysses set his sails and proceeded joyfully on his way; nor did he sleep, but watched the sun and the stars, still steering, as indeed Calypso had bidden, to the left. So he sailed for seventeen
20 days, and on the eighteenth he saw the hills of Phæacia and the land, which had the shape of a shield.

But Poseidon spied him as he sailed, and was wroth to see him so near to the end of his troubles. Wherefore he sent all the winds of heaven down upon him. Sore troubled was Ulysses, and
25 said to himself, "It was truth that Calypso spake when she said how that I should suffer many troubles returning to my home. Would that I had died that day when many a spear was cast by the men of Troy over the dead Achilles. Then would the Greeks have buried me; but now shall I perish miserably."

30 And as he spake a great wave struck the raft and tossed him far away, so that he dropped the rudder from his hand.

So for two days and two nights he swam, Athene helping him, for otherwise he had perished. But on the third day there was a calm, and he saw from the top of a great wave, for the waves
35 were yet high, the land, close at hand. Dear as a father to his

fē ä'shi a

son, rising up from grievous sickness, so dear was the land to
Ulysses. But when he came near he heard the waves breaking
along the shore, for there was no harbor there, but only cliffs
and rugged rocks.

And while he doubted what he should do, a great wave bore
him to the shore. Then would he have perished, all his bones
being broken; but Athene put it in his heart to lay hold of a
great rock till the wave had spent itself. And even then had
he died, for the ebb caught him and bore him far out to sea;
but he bethought him that he would swim along, if haply
he might see some landing place. And at last he came to the
mouth of a river, where there were no rocks. Then at last he
won his way to the land. His knees were bent under him and his
hands dropped at his side, and the salt water ran out of his
mouth and nostrils. Breathless was he and speechless; but when
he came to himself, he looked about him to see what manner of
land he had reached.

Then he lay down on the rushes by the bank of the river
and kissed the earth, thinking within himself, "What now shall
I do? for if I sleep here by the river, I fear that the dew and
the frost may slay me; for indeed in the morning-time the wind
from the river blows cold. And if I go up to the wood, to lay me
down to sleep in the thicket, I fear that some evil beast may
devour me."

But it seemed better to go to the wood. So he went. Now
this was close to the river, and he found two bushes, of wild
olive one, and of fruitful olive the other. So thickly grown
together were they, that the winds blew not through them, nor
did the sun pierce them, nor yet the rain. Thereunder crept
Ulysses, and found great stores of leaves, shelter enough for two
or three, even in a great storm. Then, even as a man who dwells
apart from others cherishes his fire, hiding it under the ashes, so
Ulysses cherished his life under the leaves. And Athene sent
down upon his eyelids deep sleep, that might ease him of his
toil.

CHAPTER FIVE

IN THE LAND OF THE PHÆACIANS

Now the king of Phæacia was Alcinous, and he had five sons and one daughter, Nausicaa. To her, where she slept with her two maidens by her, Athene went, taking the shape of Nausicaa's friend, and said —

5 "Why hath thy mother so idle a daughter, Nausicaa? Lo! thy garments lie unwashed, and thy wedding must be near, seeing that many nobles in the land are suitors to thee. Ask then thy father that he give thee the wagon with the mules, for the places where we must wash are far from the city, and I will go with 10 thee."

And when Dawn, the rosy-fingered, shone forth, Nausicaa awoke, marvelling at the dream, and went seeking her parents. Her mother she found busy with her maidens at the loom, and her father she met as he was going to the council with the chiefs 15 of the land. Then she said, "Give me, father, the wagon with the mules, that I may take the garments to the river to wash them. Thou shouldst always have clean robes when thou goest to the council, and there are my five brothers also, who love to have newly washed garments at the dance."

20 But of her own marriage she said nothing. And her father, knowing her thoughts, said, "It is well. The men shall harness the wagon for thee."

So they put the clothing into the wagon. And her mother put also food and wine, and olive oil also, wherewith she and 25 her maidens might anoint themselves after the bath. So they climbed into the wagon and went to the river. And then they washed the clothing, and spread it out to dry on the rocks by the sea. And after they had bathed and anointed themselves, they sat down to eat and drink by the river side; and after the 30 meal they played at ball, singing as they played, and Nausicaa, fair as Artemis when she hunts wild goats and stags, led the

al sin'ō us   naw sik'ā a

song. But when they had nearly ended their play, the princess, throwing the ball to one of her maidens, cast it so wide that it fell into the river. Whereupon they all cried aloud, and Ulysses awoke. And he said to himself, "What is this land to which I have come? Are they that dwell therein fierce or kind to strangers? Just now I seemed to hear the voice of nymphs, or am I near the dwellings of men?"

Then he gazed about him in bewilderment, and rose up and went towards the maidens, who indeed were frightened to see him, for he was wild of aspect, and fled hither and thither. But Nausicaa stood and fled not.

Then she called to her maidens, "What mean ye, to flee when ye see a stranger? No enemy comes hither to harm us, for we are dear to the gods, and also we live in an island of the sea, so that men may not approach to work us wrong; but if one cometh here overborne by trouble, it is well to succour him. Give this man, therefore, food and drink, and wash him in the river, where there is shelter from the wind."

So they brought him down to the river, and gave him a tunic and a cloak to clothe himself withal, and also olive-oil in a flask of gold. Then Nausicaa said to Ulysses—

"Follow thou with the maidens, and I will lead the way in the wagon. For I would not that the people should speak lightly of me, seeing me in company with a stranger. Do thou, then, follow behind, and when we are come to the city, tarry in a poplar grove that thou shalt see, till I shall have come to my father's house. Then follow; and for the house, that any one, even a child, can show thee, for the other Phæacians dwell not in such. And when thou art come within the doors, pass quickly through the hall to where my mother sits. Close to the hearth is her seat, and my father's hard by, where he sits with the wine cup in his hand. Pass him by and lay hold of her knees, and pray her that she give thee safe return to thy country."

At evening they came to the city. Nausicaa drove the wagon to the palace. Ulysses came from the grove, and lest any one should see him, Athene spread a mist about him, and when he had now reached the city, she took the shape of a young maiden carrying a pitcher, and met him.

Then Ulysses asked her, "My child, canst thou tell me where 5 dwells Alcinous? for I am a stranger in this place."

And she answered, "I will show thee, for indeed he dwells nigh to my own father. But be thou silent, for we Phæacians love not strangers over much." Then she led him to the palace. A wondrous place it was, with walls of brass and doors of gold, 10 hanging on posts of silver; and on either side of the door were dogs of gold and silver, the work of Hephæstus, and against the wall, all along from the threshold to the inner chamber, were set seats, on which sat the chiefs of the Phæacians, feasting; and youths wrought in gold stood holding torches in their hands, to 15 give light in the darkness. Fifty women were in the house grinding corn and weaving robes, for the women of the land are no less skilled to weave than are the men to sail the sea. And round about the house were gardens beautiful exceedingly, with orchards of fig, and apple, and pear, and pomegranate, and olive. Drought 20 hurts them not, nor frost, and harvest comes after harvest without ceasing. Also there was a vineyard; and some of the grapes were parching in the sun, and some were being gathered, and some again were but just turning red. And there were beds of all manner of flowers; and in the midst of all were two fountains 25 which never failed.

These things Ulysses regarded for a space, and then passed into the hall. And there the chiefs of Phæacia were drinking their last cup to Hermes. Quickly he passed through them, and put his hands on the knees of Arete and said—and as he spake 30 the mist cleared from about him, and all that were in the hall beheld him—

"I am a suppliant to thee, and to thy husband, and to thy guests. The gods bless thee and them, and grant you to live in peace, and that your children should come peacefully after you. 35 Only, do you send me home to my native country."

a rē′tē

And he sat down in the ashes of the hearth. Then for a space all were silent, but at the last spake one, who was the oldest man in the land—

"King Alcinous, this ill becomes you that this man should sit in the ashes of the hearth. Raise him and bid him sit upon a seat, and let us pour out to Father Zeus, who is the friend of suppliants, and let the keeper of the house give him meat and drink."

And Alcinous did so, bidding his eldest born, Laodamas, rise from his seat. And an attendant poured water on his hands, and the keeper of the house gave him meat and drink. Then, when all had poured out to Father Zeus, King Alcinous said that they would take counsel on the morrow about sending this stranger to his home. And they answered that it should be so, and each went to his home. Only Ulysses was left in the hall, and Alcinous and Arete with him. And Arete saw his cloak and tunic, that she and her maidens had made them, and said—

"Whence art thou, stranger? and who gave thee these garments?"

So Ulysses told her how he had come from the island of Calypso, and what he had suffered, and how Nausicaa had found him on the shore, and had guided him to the city.

But Alcinous blamed the maiden that she had not herself brought him to the house. "For thou wast her suppliant," he said.

"Nay," said Ulysses; "she would have brought me, but I would not, fearing thy wrath." For he would not have the maiden blamed.

Then said Alcinous, "I am not one to be angered for such cause. Gladly would I have such a one as thou art to be my son-in-law, and I would give him house and wealth. But no one would I stay against his will. And as for sending thee to thy home, that is easy; for thou shalt sleep, and they shall take thee meanwhile."

And after this they slept. And the next day the king called

lā ŏd′a mas

the chiefs to an assembly, and told them of his purpose, that he would send this stranger to his home, for that it was their wont to show such kindness to such as needed it. And he bade fifty and two of the younger men to make ready a ship, and that the elders
5 should come to his house, and bring Demodocus, the minstrel, with them, for that he was minded to make a great feast for this stranger before he departed. So the youths made ready the ship. And afterwards there were gathered together a great multitude, so that the palace was filled from the one end to the other. And
10 Alcinous slew for them twelve sheep and eight swine and two oxen. And when they had feasted to the full, the minstrel sang to them of Achilles and Ulysses. But when Ulysses heard the song, he wept, holding his mantle before his face.

This Alcinous perceived, and said to the chiefs, "Now that
15 we have feasted and delighted ourselves with song, let us go forth, that this stranger may see that we are skilful in boxing and wrestling and running."

So they went forth, a herald leading Demodocus by the hand, for the minstrel was blind. Then stood up many Phæacian
20 youths, and the fairest and strongest of them all was Laodamas, eldest son to the king, and after him Euryalus. These strove with one another in feats of racing, wrestling, boxing, throwing the quoit, and in leaping at the bar.

Then Laodamas, Euryalus urging him, said to Ulysses,
25 "Father, wilt thou not try thy skill in some game, and put away the trouble from thy heart?"

But Ulysses answered, "Why askest thou this? I think of my troubles rather than of sport, and sit among you, caring only that I may see again my home."

30 Then said Euryalus, "And in very truth, stranger, thou hast not the look of a wrestler or boxer. Rather would one judge thee to be some trader, who sails over the sea for gain."

"Nay," answered Ulysses, "this is ill said. So true is it that the gods give not all gifts to all men, beauty to one and
35 sweet speech to another. Fair of form art thou, no god could

de mŏd′o kus   ū rī′a lus

better thee; but thou speakest idle words. I am not unskilled in these things, but stood among the first in the old days; but since have I suffered much in battle and shipwreck. Yet will I make trial of my strength, for thy words have angered me."

Whereupon he took a quoit, heavier far than such as the Phæacians were wont to throw, and sent it with a whirl. It hurtled through the air, so that the brave Phæacians crouched to the ground in fear, and fell far beyond all the rest.

Then said Ulysses, "Come now, I will contend in wrestling or boxing, or even in the race, with any man in Phæacia, save Laodamas only, for he is my friend. I can shoot with the bow, and I can cast a spear as far as other men can shoot an arrow. But as for the race, it may be that some one might outrun me, for I have suffered much on the sea."

But they were all silent, till the king stood up and said, "Thou hast spoken well. But we men of Phæacia are not mighty to wrestle or to box; only we are swift of foot, and skilful to sail upon the sea. And we love feasts, and dances, and the harp, and gay clothing, and the bath. In these things no man may surpass us."

Then the king bade Demodocus the minstrel sing again. And when he had done so, the king's two sons, Alius and Laodamas, danced together; and afterwards they played with the ball, throwing it into the air, cloud high, and catching it right skilfully.

And afterwards the king said, "Let us each give this stranger a mantle and a tunic and a talent of gold, and let Euryalus make his peace with words and with a gift."

And they all said that it should be so; also Euryalus gave Ulysses a sword with a hilt of silver and a scabbard of ivory. And after this Ulysses went to the bath, and then they all sat down to the feast. But as he went to the hall, Nausicaa, fair as a goddess, met him and said—

"Hail, stranger; thou wilt remember me in thy native country, for thou owest me thanks for thy life."

And he answered, "Every day in my native country will I remember thee, for indeed, fair maiden, thou didst save my life."

And when they were seated at the feast, Ulysses sent a portion of the chine which the king had caused to be set before
5 him to the minstrel Demodocus, with a message that he should sing to them of the horse of wood and how Ulysses brought it into Troy, full of men of war who should destroy the city.

Then the minstrel sang how that some of the Greeks sailed away, having set fire to their tents, and some hid themselves in
10 the horse with Ulysses, and how the men of Troy sat around, taking counsel what they should do with it, and some judged that they should rip it open, and some that they should throw it from the hill-top, and others again that they should leave it to be a peace-offering to the gods; and how the Greeks issued forth
15 from their lurking-place and spoiled the city.

This was the song the famous minstrel sang and Ulysses wept to hear the tale. Now none of all the company marked him weeping; but Alcinous alone noted it and said to the Phæacians—

20 "Let Demodocus cease his song, for it is no wise pleasing to all. Ever since the minstrel began his tale, yonder stranger has not ceased his weeping. And do thou, stranger, tell us thy name, thy people, and thy home. Declare, too, why this tale of Troy moves thee to tears. Hadst thou a relative or a loving
25 friend who fell before the gates of Troy—for a loving friend is no whit worse than a brother?"

And Ulysses answered him, saying, "Now first will I tell my name. Lo! I am Ulysses, son of Laertes, and I dwelt in clear-scene Ithaca, a rugged isle but a good nurse of noble
30 youths; and for myself I can see naught beside sweeter than a man's own country. But come, let me tell thee, too, of the troubles of my journeying, which Zeus laid on me as I came from Troy."

He told how the wind which drove them from Troy brought
35 them to the land of the Cicones, where he lost six men from each

ship. Then they sailed and would have come to Ithaca all unhurt, but the North Wind swept them from their course and drove them wandering nine whole days until they reached the land of the Lotus-eaters.

Then he told them of the Cyclops and how Poseidon's wrath had followed him; of Aeolus and the bag of winds and of the cruel Læstrygonians who destroyed eleven of his ships with all their company.

He told them, too, of Circe and his descent to Hades; of the song of the Sirens and the dangers of Scylla and Charybdis; how his men had eaten of the cattle of the Sun and how Zeus sent the mighty stroke that destroyed his ship and he alone was saved clinging to a plank; of the nymph Calypso and how he dwelt with her upon her wooded isle.

Al' these things Ulysses told, all that he had done and all that he had suffered down to the time Nausicaa found him on the river shore.

Thus he spoke and dead silence fell on all and they were spell-bound throughout the shadowy halls. Then Alcinous commanded that rich gifts be brought that Ulysses might go forth as befitted so illustrious a guest.

As soon as early Dawn shone forth, the rosy-fingered, the gifts were brought to the ship and then all betook them to the palace of Alcinous for feasting and the mighty king sacrificed before them an ox to Zeus who is lord of all, and the divine Demodocus harped before them. But Ulysses would ever turn his head to the splendor of the sun, as one fain to hasten its setting, so welcome was the sinking of the sunlight to Ulysses. Then he spoke to the Phæacians, masters of the oar, and to Alcinous in chief, saying:

"My lord Alcinous, send me safe upon my way and as for you, fare ye well. For now have I all that my heart desired, an escort and loving gifts. May the gods of heaven give me good fortune with them and may I find my noble wife in my house with my friends unharmed; and may the gods vouchsafe all manner of good to you and may no evil come nigh thy people."

Therewith goodly Ulysses stept over the threshold and departed.

CHAPTER SIX

ULYSSES AND THE SWINEHERD

5 Now Ulysses slept while the ship was sailing to Ithaca. And when it was come to the shore he yet slept. Wherefore the men lifted him out, and put him on the shore with all his goods that the princes of the Phæacians had given him, and so left him. After a while he awoke, and knew not the land, for there was 10 a great mist about him.

But as he walked by the sea, lamenting his fate, Athene met him, having the shape of a young shepherd, fair to look upon, such as are the sons of kings; and Ulysses, when he saw him, was glad, and asked him how men called the country wherein he was.

15 And the shepherd said, "Thou art foolish, or, may be, hast come from very far, not to know this country. Many men know it, both in the east and in the west. Rocky it is, not fit for horses, nor is it very broad; but it is fertile land, and full of wine; nor does it want for rain and a good pasture it is for oxen and goats; 20 and men call it Ithaca. Even in Troy, which is very far off, they say, from this land of Greece, men have heard of Ithaca."

This Ulysses was right glad to hear. Yet he was not minded to say who he was, but rather to feign a tale.

This pleased Athene much, and she changed her shape, becoming like a woman, tall and fair, and said to Ulysses—

"I am Athene, daughter of Zeus, who am ever wont to stand by thee and help thee. And now we will hide these possessions of thine; and thou must be silent, nor tell to any one who thou art, and endure many things, so that thou mayest come 30 to thine own again."

But still Ulysses doubted, and would have the goddess tell

him whether of a truth he had come back to his native land. And she, commending his prudence, scattered the mist that was about him.

Then Ulysses knew the land, and kissed the ground, and prayed to the Nymphs that they would be favourable to him. And after this Athene guiding him, he hid away his possessions in a cave, and put a great stone on the mouth. Then the two took counsel together.

And Athene said, "Think, man of many devices, how thou wilt lay hands on these men, suitors of thy wife, who for three years have sat in thy house devouring thy substance. And she hath answered them craftily, making many promises, but still waiting for thy coming."

Then Ulysses said, "Truly I had perished, even as Agamemnon perished, but for thee. But do thou help me, as of old in Troy, for with thee at my side I would fight with three hundred men."

Then said Athene, "Lo! I will cause that no man shall know thee, for I will wither the fair flesh on thy limbs, and take the bright hair from thy head, and make thine eyes dull. And the suitors shall take no account of thee, neither shall thy wife nor thy son know thee. But go to the swineherd Eumæus, where he dwells by the fountain of Arethusa, for he is faithful to thee and to thy house. And I will hasten to Sparta, to the house of Menelaus, to fetch Telemachus, for he went thither, seeking news of thee."

Then Athene changed him into the shape of a beggar-man. She caused his skin to wither, and his hair to fall off, and his eyes to grow dim, and put on him filthy rags, with a great stag's hide about his shoulders, and in his hand a staff, and a wallet on his shoulder, fastened by a rope.

Then she departed, and Ulysses went to the house of Eumæus, the swineherd. A great courtyard there was, and twelve sties for the sows, and four watchdogs, big as wild beasts, for such did the swineherd breed. He himself was shaping sandals, and of

ū me͞′us   ar e͞ thū′sa

his men three were with the swine in the fields, and one was driving a fat beast to the city, to be meat for the suitors. But when Ulysses came near, the dogs ran upon him, and he dropped his staff and sat down, and yet would have suffered harm, even on his
5 own threshold; but the swineherd ran forth and drove away the dogs, and brought the old man in, and gave him a seat of brushwood, with a great goat-skin over it.

And Ulysses said, "Zeus and the other gods requite thee for this kindness."

10   Then the two talked of matters in Ithaca, and Eumæus told how the suitors of the queen were devouring the substance of Ulysses. Then the beggar asked him of the king, saying that perchance, having travelled far, he might know such an one.

But Eumæus said, "Nay, old man, thus do all wayfarers talk,
15 yet we hear no truth from them. Not a vagabond fellow comes to this island but our queen must see him, and ask him many things, weeping the while. And thou, I doubt not, for a cloak or a tunic, would tell a wondrous tale. But Ulysses, I know, is dead, and either the fowls of the air devour him or the fishes of
20 the sea."

And when the false beggar would have comforted him, saying he knew of a truth that Ulysses would yet return, he hearkened not. Moreover, he prophesied evil for Telemachus also, who had gone to seek news of his father, but would surely be slain
25 by the suitors, who were even now lying in wait for him as he should return. And after this he asked the stranger who he was and whence he had come. Then Ulysses answered him craftily and told a strange tale that he might put to the test the loyalty of the swineherd to his master. After this they talked
30 much, and when the swineherd's men were returned they all feasted together.

After this they slept, but Eumæus tarried without, keeping watch over the swine.

Meanwhile Telemachus returned to Ithaca, having been
35 warned by Athene that the suitors were lying in ambush for

him. The goddess pointed out a different route that he might
have safe return. He went first to the swineherd Eumæus as
Athene had advised him. Here Ulysses made himself known
to his son and together they planned the destruction of the
5 suitors. Lest their plans should fail, he urged Telemachus to
tell no one of his return, not the swineherd, nor Laertes, nor
even Penelope herself.

CHAPTER SEVEN

ULYSSES IN HIS HOME

THE next day Telemachus went to the city. But before he
went he said to Eumæus that he should bring the beggar-man to
10 the city, for that it was better to beg in the city than in the
country. And the beggar also said that he wished this. And
Telemachus, when he was arrived, went to the palace and greeted
the nurse Euryclea and his mother Penelope, who was right
glad to see him, but to whom he told naught of what had hap-
15 pened.

Now in the meanwhile Eumæus and the beggar were coming
to the city. And when they were now near to it, by the fountain
which Ithaca and his brethren had made, where was also an altar
of the Nymphs, the goatherd met them, and spake evil to Eu-
20 mæus, rebuking him that he brought this beggar to the city. And
he came near and smote Ulysses with his foot on the thigh, but
moved him not from the path. And Ulysses thought a while,
should he smite him with his club and slay him, or dash him on
the ground. But it seemed to him better to endure.

25 But Eumæus lifted up his hands and said, "Oh, now may the
Nymphs of the fountain fulfil this hope, that Ulysses may come
back to his home, and tear from thee this finery of thine, wherein
thou comest to the city, leaving thy flock for evil shepherds to
devour!"

30 So they went on to the palace. And at the door of the court

ū ryk lē′a

there lay the dog Argus, whom in the old days Ulysses had reared with his own hand. But ere the dog grew to his full, Ulysses had sailed to Troy. And, while he was strong, men used him in the chase, hunting wild goats and roe-deer and hares. But now he 5 lay neglected in the dust, and no man spake kindly to him. Well he knew his master, and, for that he could not come near to him, wagged his tail and drooped his ears.

And Ulysses, when he saw him, wiped away a tear, and said, "Surely this is strange, Eumæus, that such a dog, being of so 10 fine a breed, should lie here in neglect."

And Eumæus made reply, "He belongeth to a master who died far away. For indeed when Ulysses had him of old, he was the strongest and swiftest of dogs; but now my dear lord has perished far away, and the careless women tend him not. For when the 15 master is away the slaves are careless of their duty. Surely a man, when he is made a slave, loses half the virtue of a man."

And as he spake the dog Argus died. Twenty years had he waited, and he saw his master at the last.

After this the two entered the hall. And Telemachus, when 20 he saw them, took from the basket bread and meat, as much as his hands could hold, and bade carry them to the beggar, and also to tell him that he might go round among the suitors, asking alms. So he went, stretching out his hand, as though he were wont to beg; and some gave, having compassion upon him and marvelling 25 at him, and some asked who he was. But, of all, Antinous was the most shameless. For when Ulysses came to him and told him how he had much riches and power in former days, Antinous mocked him, saying—

"Get thee from my table."

30 Then Ulysses said, "Surely thy soul is evil though thy body is fair; for though thou sittest at another man's feast, yet wilt thou give me nothing."

But Antinous, in great wrath, took the stool on which he sat and cast it at him, smiting his right shoulder. But Ulysses 35 stirred not, but stood as a rock. But in his heart he thought on

ar'gus   an tin'ō us

revenge. So he went and sat down at the door. And being there, he said—

"Hear me, suitors of the queen! There is no wrath if a man be smitten fighting for that which is his own, but Antinous has 5 smitten me because that I am poor. May the curse of the hungry light on him therefore, ere he come to his marriage day."

Also the other suitors blamed him that he had dealt so cruelly with this stranger. Also the queen was wroth when she heard it, as she sat in the upper chamber with her maidens about 10 her.

And that evening, the suitors having departed to their own dwellings, Ulysses and Telemachus took the arms from the hall, as they had also planned to do. And while they did so Telemachus said, "See, my father, this marvellous brightness that is 15 on the pillars and the ceiling. Surely some god is with us."

And Ulysses made reply, "I know it: be silent. And now go to thy chamber and sleep, and leave me here, for I have somewhat to say to thy mother and her maidens."

And when the queen and her maidens came into the hall, for 20 it was their work to cleanse it and make it ready for the morrow, Penelope asked him of his family and his country. And at first he made as though he would not answer, fearing, he said, lest he should trouble her with the story of that which he had suffered. But afterwards, for she urged him, telling him what she herself 25 had suffered, her husband being lost and her suitors troubling her without ceasing, he feigned a tale that should satisfy her. For he told her how he was a man of Crete, a brother of King Idomeneus, and how he had given hospitality to Ulysses, what time he was sailing to Troy with the sons of Atreus.

30 And when the queen, seeking to know whether he spake the truth, asked him of Ulysses what manner of man he was, and with what clothing he was clothed, he answered her rightly, saying, "I remember me that he had a mantle, twofold, woolen, of seapurple, clasped with a brooch of gold, whereon was a dog that held 35 a fawn by the throat; marvellously wrought they were, so hard

ī dŏm′ē nŭs   ā′trŭs

held the one, so strove the other to be free. Also he had a tunic, white and smooth, which the women much admired to see. But whether some one had given him these things I know not, for indeed many gave him gifts, and I also, even a sword and a tunic.
5 Also, he had a herald with him, older than he, dark-skinned, round in the shoulders, with curly hair."

And Penelope, knowing these things to be true, wept aloud, crying that she should see her husband no more. But the beggar comforted her, saying that Ulysses having much wealth with
10 him, had lost his ships and his comrades, yet nevertheless would speedily return.

Then Penelope bade her servants make ready a bed for the stranger of soft mats and blankets, and also that one of them should bathe him. But the mats and blankets he would not have,
15 saying that he would sleep as before, and for the bathing, he would only that some old woman, wise and prudent, should do this. Wherefore the queen bade Euryclea, the keeper of the house, do this thing for him, for that he had been the comrade of her lord, and indeed was marvellously like to him in feet and
20 hands.

And this the old woman was right willing to do, for love for her master. "For never," she said, "of all strangers that had come to the land, had come one so like to him." But when she had prepared the bath for his feet, Ulysses sat by the fire,
25 but as far in the shadow as he might, lest the old woman should see a great scar that was upon his leg, and know him thereby.

Now the scar had chanced in this wise. He had come to see his grandfather Autolycus, who was the most cunning of men, claiming certain gifts which he had promised to him in the old
30 days when, being then newly born, he was set on his grandfather's knees in the halls of Laertes and his grandfather had given him this name. And on the day of his coming there was a great feast, and on the day after a hunting on Mount Parnassus. In this hunting therefore, Ulysses came in the heart of a wood upon
35 a place where lay a great wild boar, and the beast, being stirred

aw tol'ĭ kus   par năs'us

by the noise, rose up, and Ulysses charged him with his spear, but before he could slay the beast it ripped a great wound just above the knee. And afterwards Ulysses slew it, and the young men bound up the wound, singing a charm to stanch the blood.

By this scar, then, the old nurse knew that it was Ulysses himself, and said, "O Ulysses, O my child, to think that I knew thee not!"

And she looked towards the queen, as meaning to tell the thing to her. But Ulysses laid his hand on her throat, "Mother, wouldst thou kill me? I am returned after twenty years; and none must know till I shall be ready to take vengeance."

And the old woman held her peace. And after this Penelope talked with him again, telling him her dreams, how she had seen a flock of geese in her palace, and how that an eagle had slain them, and when she mourned for the geese, lo! a voice that said, "These geese are thy suitors, and the eagle thy husband."

And Ulysses said that the dream was well. And then she said that on the morrow she must make her choice, for that she had promised to bring forth the great bow that was Ulysses', and whosoever should draw it most easily, and shoot an arrow best at a mark, he should be her husband.

And Ulysses made answer to her, "It is well, lady. Put not off this trial of the bow, for before one of them shall draw the string the great Ulysses shall come and duly shoot at the mark that shall be set."

After this Penelope slept, but Ulysses watched.

CHAPTER EIGHT

THE TRIAL OF THE BOW

THE next day many things cheered Ulysses for that which he had to do; for first Athene had told him that she would stand at his side, and next he heard the thunder of Zeus in a clear sky, and last it chanced that a woman who sat at the mill grinding corn, being sore weary of her task, and hating the suitors, said, "Grant, Father Zeus, that this be the last meal which these men shall eat in the house of Ulysses!"

5 And after a while the suitors came and sat down, as was their wont, to the feast. And the servants bare to Ulysses, as Telemachus had bidden, a full share with the others. At this the suitors scoffed, but Telemachus heeded them not, but sat waiting till his father should give the sign.

After this Penelope went to fetch the great bow of Ulysses. 10 From the peg on which it hung she took it with its sheath, and sitting down, she laid it on her knees and wept over it, and after this rose up and went to where the suitors sat feasting in the hall. The bow she brought, and also the quiver full of arrows, and standing by the pillar of the dome, spake thus—

15 "Ye suitors who devour this house, making pretence that ye wish to wed me, lo! here is a proof of your skill. Here is the bow of the great Ulysses. Whoso shall bend it easiest in his hands, and shoot an arrow easily through the holes of the twelve axes that Telemachus shall set up, him will I follow, leaving this 20 house, which I shall remember only in my dreams."

Then she bade Eumæus bear the bow and the arrows to the suitors. And the good swineherd wept to see his master's bow, and the herdsman of the kine wept also, for he was a good man, and loved the house of Ulysses.

25 Then Telemachus planted in due order the axes wherein were the holes, and was minded himself to draw the bow, and indeed would have done the thing, but Ulysses signed to him that he should not. Wherefore he said, "Methinks I am too weak and young; ye that are elder should try the first."

30 Then first, the priest, who alone among the suitors hated their evil ways, made trial of the bow. But he moved it not, but wearied his hands with it, for they were tender, and unwont to toil. And he said, "I cannot bend this bow; let some other try; but it shall be grief and pain to many this day, I trow."

35 And Antinous was wroth to hear such words, and bade Melan-

me lăn'thĭ us

thius bring forth from the stores a roll of fat, that they might
anoint the string and soften it withal. So they softened the
string with fat, but not the more could they bend it, for they tried
all of them in vain, till only Antinous and Eurymachus were left,
5 who indeed were the bravest and the strongest of them all.

Now the swineherd and the herdsman of the kine had gone
forth out of the yard, and Ulysses came behind them and said,
"What would ye do if Ulysses were to come back to his home?
Would ye fight for him, or for the suitors?"

10 And both said that they would fight for him.

And Ulysses said, "It is even I who am come back in the
twentieth year, and ye, I know, are glad at heart that I am come;
nor know I of any one besides. And if ye will help me as brave
men to-day, wives shall ye have, and possessions and houses near
15 to mine own. And ye shall be brothers and comrades to Telemachus. And for a sign, behold this scar, which the wild boar
made when I hunted on Parnassus."

Then they wept for joy and kissed Ulysses, and he also kissed
them. And he said to Eumæus that he should bring the bow to
20 him when the suitors had tried their fortunes therewith; also
that he should bid the women keep within doors, nor stir out if
they should hear the noise of battle. And the herdsman he bade
lock the doors of the hall, and fasten them with a rope.

After this he came back to the hall, and Eurymachus had the
25 bow in his hands, and sought to warm it at the fire. Then he
essayed to draw it, but could not. And he groaned aloud, saying,
"Woe is to me! not for loss of this marriage only, for there are
other women to be wooed in Greece, but that we are so much
weaker than the great Ulysses. This is indeed shame to tell."

30 Then said Antinous, "Not so; to-day is a holy day of the
archer god; therefore we could not draw the bow. But to-morrow
will we try once more, after due sacrifice to Apollo."

And this saying pleased them all; but Ulysses said, "Let
me try this bow, for I would fain know whether I have such
35 strength as I had in former days."

ū rĭm′a kus

At this all the suitors were wroth, and chiefly Antinous, but Penelope said that it should be so, and promised the man great gifts if he could draw this bow.

But Telemachus spoke thus, "Mother, the bow is mine to give
5 or to refuse. And no man shall say me nay, if I will that this stranger make trial of it. But do thou go to thy chamber with thy maidens, and let men take thought for these things."

And this he said, for that he would have her depart from the hall forthwith, knowing what should happen therein. But
10 she marvelled to hear him speak with such authority, and answered not, but departed. And when Eumæus would have carried the bow to Ulysses, the suitors spake roughly to him, but Telemachus constrained him to go. Therefore he took the bow and gave it to his master. Then went he to Euryclea, and bade
15 her shut the door of the women's chambers and keep them within, whatsoever they might hear. Also, the herdsmen shut the doors of the hall, and fastened them with a rope.

Then Ulysses handled the great bow, trying it, whether it had taken any hurt, but the suitors thought scorn of him. Then,
20 when he had found it to be without flaw, just as a minstrel fastens a string upon his harp and strains it to the pitch, so he strung the bow without toil! and holding the string in his right hand, he tried its tone, and the tone was sweet as the voice of a swallow. Then he took an arrow from the quiver, and
25 laid the notch upon the string and drew it, sitting as he was, and the arrow passed through every ring, and stood in the wall beyond. Then he said to Telemachus—

"There is yet a feast to be held before the sun go down."

And he nodded the sign to Telemachus. And forthwith the
30 young man stood by him, armed with spear and helmet and shield.

CHAPTER NINE

ULYSSES RESTORED IN HIS HOME

THEN spake he among the suitors, "This labor has been accomplished. Let me try at yet another mark."

And he aimed his arrow at Antinous. But the man was just raising a cup to his lips, thinking not of death, for who had
5 thought that any man, though mightiest of mortals, would venture on such a deed, being one among many?

And all the suitors, when they saw him fall, leaped from their seats; but when they looked, there was neither spear nor shield upon the wall. And they knew not whether it was by
10 chance or of set purpose that the stranger had smitten him. But Ulysses then declared who he was, saying—

"Dogs, ye thought that I should never come back. Therefore have ye devoured my house, and made suit to my wife while I yet lived, and feared not the gods nor regarded men. Therefore
15 a sudden destruction is come upon you all."

Then, when all the others trembled for fear, Eurymachus said, "If thou be indeed Ulysses of Ithaca, thou hast said well. Foul wrong has been done to thee in the house and in the field. But lo! he, who was the mover of it all, lies here, even Antinous.
20 Nor was it so much this marriage that he sought, as to be king of this land, having destroyed thy house. But we will pay thee back for all that we have devoured, even twenty times as much."

But Ulysses said, "Speak not of paying back. My hands
25 shall not cease from slaying till I have taken vengeance on you all."

And all the while Athene waved her flaming ægis-shield from above, and the suitors fell as birds are scattered and torn by eagles.

30 But Phemius, the minstrel, Ulysses spared, for he had sung

fē'mĭ us

among the suitors in the hall, of compulsion, and not of good will; and also Medon, the herald.

When the slaughtering of the suitors was ended Ulysses bade cleanse the hall with water, and with sulphur. And when this 5 was done he bade that Euryclea, the nurse, should go to Penelope and tell her that her husband was indeed returned.

Euryclea went in all haste to the upper chamber to tell her mistress how her lord had returned. So great was her joy that her feet stumbled one over the other. She stood above the lady's 10 head and said, "Awake, Penelope, dear child, and see with thine own eyes the very thing thou hast desired for all these years. Indeed Ulysses has come back and slain the suitors that devoured his substance."

But Penelope made answer, "Dear nurse, the gods have taken 15 away thy reason, the gods who have it in their power to make foolish the wise and give wisdom to the simple. Why dost thou mock me and rouse me from sweet slumber, the sweetest since the day Ulysses went forth to Troy? Get thee back to thy chamber; thy age alone saves thee from further rebuke."

20 Then the good nurse answered her, "I mock thee not, dear child, but in very deed Ulysses is here and hath come home even as I tell thee. He is the guest who was so dishonored. Telemachus knew, but kept the secret, that with his father he might take vengeance on the haughty wooers."

25 Thus she spake and then was Penelope glad, and leaping from her bed, with tears she spake these winged words, "Come, dear nurse, tell me all the truth. How could he, being but one man, bring death to the crowd of shameless wooers?"

The nurse made answer, "I saw not and I know not how 30 Ulysses slew them, but that it is thy lord himself who has returned I have a manifest token, even the scar of the wound that the boar dealt him with his white tusk. I fain would have told it even to thee, but he laid his hand upon my mouth and in the fullness of his wisdom suffered me not to speak. But

me′don

come with me and I will stake my life upon it; and if I play thee false, do thou slay me by a death most pitiful."

And yet the queen doubted, and said, "Let me go down and see my son, and these men that are slain, and the man who slew
5 them."

So she went, and sat in the twilight by the other wall, and Ulysses sat by a pillar, with eyes cast down, waiting till his wife should speak to him. But she was sore perplexed; for now she seemed to know him, and now she knew him not, being in
10 such evil case, for he had not suffered that the women should put new robes upon him.

And Telemachus said, "Mother, sittest thou apart from my father, and speakest not to him? Surely thy heart is harder than a stone."

15 But Ulysses said, "Let be, Telemachus. Thy mother will know that which is true in good time."

Meanwhile Ulysses went to the bath, and clothed himself in bright apparel, and came back to the hall, and Athene made him fair and young to see. Then he sat down as before, over against
20 his wife, and said—

"Surely, O lady, the gods have made thee harder of heart than all women besides. Would other wife have kept away from her husband, coming back now after twenty years?"

Then Penelope knew him that he was her husband indeed,
25 and ran to him, and threw her arms about him and kissed him, saying, "Forgive me, my lord, if I was slow to know thee; for ever I feared, so many wiles have men, that some one should deceive me, saying that he was my husband. But now I know this, that thou art he and not another."

30 And they wept over each other and kissed each other.

And on the morrow Ulysses went forth to the well-wooded farm land to see his father, the old Laertes. Quickly he came to the well-ordered farm. There was the house, and all about it ran the huts. He found his father alone in the garden
35 digging about a plant. Ulysses questioned him and saw that his

father knew him not. As Laertes spoke of his son, now gone these twenty years, he broke down with grief. Then the heart of Ulysses was moved, and he sprang towards him and fell on his neck and kissed him, saying, "Behold, I here, even I, my father,

5 am the man of whom thou speakest, in the twentieth year am I come to mine own country. But stay thy weeping, for I will tell thee all clearly. I have slain the wooers in our halls and avenged their evil deeds."

Then Laertes answered him, "If thou art indeed Ulysses,

10 mine own child, show me now a manifest token, that I may be assured." Then Ulysses answered him, "Look first on this scar and consider it, that the boar dealt me with his white tusk on Parnassus. But come, and I will even tell thee the trees through all the terraced garden, which thou gavest me once for mine

15 own, and I was begging of thee this and that, being but a little child, and following thee through the garden. Through these very trees we were going, and thou didst tell me the names of each of them. Pear trees thirteen thou gavest me and ten apple trees and figs two-score, and, as we went, thou didst name

20 the fifty rows of vines thou wouldst give me, whereof each one ripened at divers times, with all manner of clusters on their boughs, when the seasons of Zeus wrought mightily on them from on high."

So he spake, and the heart of Laertes melted within him,

25 as he knew the sure tokens that Ulysses showed him. About his dear son he cast his arms and spake, "Father Zeus, verily ye gods yet bare sway on high Olympus, for now my son hath returned and the wooers have paid for their insolent pride."

So did Ulysses come back to his home after twenty years.

HELPS TO STUDY

Historical: The story of Ulysses is told in Homer's Odyssey, one of the oldest of the world's great poems. Like "The Iliad," it was written in the Greek language. There are many translations in both verse and prose. Among the best known verse translations is one by William Cullen Bryant, from which the verse extracts in this story are taken. The poem is called "The Odyssey," from the

Greek name of the hero, Odysseus, who is better known to us by his Latin name, Ulysses. (For sketch of Homer, see Note, p. 173.)

Ulysses was king of Ithaca, a small, rugged isle west of Greece. Agamemnon was a kind of over-lord of all the kings of Greece and the neighboring Greek islands. He called upon all the kings to help win back Helen, wife of his brother, Menelaus, from Paris, son of Priam, king of Troy. Ulysses left his home for Troy when he had been but lately married to Penelope and his son Telemachus was but an infant. When Troy was taken, in the tenth year of the war, and Helen was restored to Menelaus, king of Sparta, Ulysses began his homeward voyage. If he had doubled the cape of Malea in safety he would probably have found Penelope unvexed by wooers and his son, Telemachus, a lad ten years old. But the north wind drove him far out of his course and he encountered the giant, Polyphemus, who called down upon Ulysses the wrath of his father, Poseidon, because Ulysses put out the giant's one eye. To avenge this act, Poseidon drove him wandering for ten long years. "The Odyssey" tells the story of the wanderings and adventures of Ulysses during his homeward journey.

Notes and Questions

Though many places mentioned in this story are mythical, yet many of them may be found, and the journey of Ulysses traced, on a map of the world, as known in Homeric times.

Notice how the gods take sides in this story. Why did Aphrodite favor the Trojans and Here and Athene the Greeks?

Chapter One: What was the story of the Apple of Discord? Why had Ulysses gone to Troy? Review the story of the fall of Troy.

How many ships and men had Ulysses when he left Troy? How did this compare with the number he had with him when he left Ithaca ten years before?

Describe the adventure with the Ciconians.

What effect did the eating of the lotus have upon men?

What characteristics does Ulysses show in the adventure with Polyphemus?

What do you think of Polyphemus when he speaks to the ram?

What was the curse of Poseidon? As you read the story, note how this curse was fulfilled.

Chapter Two: What reason had Æolus for thinking that Ulysses was hated by the gods?

The Læstrygonians were a mythical race of cannibal giants. Some writers locate them on the island of Sicily. How many ships were left after the adventure with the Læstrygonians?

What quality that you admire does Ulysses show in his encounter with Circe?

Chapter Three: What is meant by the expression, "to be between Scylla and Charybdis"?

What were conditions in Ithaca? What do you think of Penelope's device for putting off the suitors?

Chapter Four: Describe in your own words the home of Calypso and compare your description with the text.

What was the food of the gods?

Read passages that show admirable qualities in Calypso.

Describe the raft of Ulysses.

Chapter Five: Phæacia was a mythical land thought by some to be Corcyra.

Describe the method of cleansing clothes in Homeric times.

How did Nausicaa show her royal blood?

Why did Nausicaa advise Ulysses to pass her father by and seek help from Arete?

Describe the home of Alcinous.

In what ways does the king's hospitality show itself? Describe the games.

Chapter Six: Why did Athene wish to have Ulysses return as a stranger?

How did Ulysses greet his home? Notice with what determina-

tion Ulysses throughout the story carries out his purpose to return to his home, in spite of all dangers and the charms of Circe, the Sirens, Calypso, and Nausicaa.

Chapter Seven: Compare Eumaeus and the goatherd as servants of Ulysses.

Did Argus recognize his master? Read the passage that makes you think so.

Who were the sons of Atreus?

How did the stranger gain the queen's confidence?

Chapter Eight: These axes probably had holes or rings back of the blade.

How do you account for the attitude of Telemachus toward his mother?

Chapter Nine: From his speech to Ulysses, what do you think of the character of Eurymachus?

The ægis was a kind of breastplate used also as a shield. It was fringed with serpents.

Why was Penelope so slow to believe the stranger was her husband?

The Odyssey is full of very expressive adjectives. Select some double adjectives that you think especially rich in meaning.

BOOK III

THE STORY OF ÆNEAS

CHAPTER ONE

THE FALL OF TROY

For ten years King Agamemnon and the men of Greece laid siege to Troy. But though sentence had gone forth against the city, yet the day of its fall tarried, because certain of the gods loved it well and defended it, as Phœbus, and Mars, the god of
5 war, and Jupiter himself. Wherefore Minerva put it into the heart of Epeius, Lord of the Isles, that he should make a cunning device wherewith to take the city. Now the device was this: he made a great horse of wood, feigning it to be a peace-offering to Minerva, that the Greeks might have a safe return to their
10 homes. In the body of this there hid themselves certain of the bravest of the chiefs, as Menelaus and Ulysses and Pyrrhus, son of Achilles—but Achilles himself was dead, slain by Paris, Phœbus helping, even as he was about to take the city—and others also, and with them Epeius himself. But the rest of the
15 people made as if they had departed to their homes; only they went not further than Tenedos, which was an island near to the coast.

Great joy was there in Troy when it was noised abroad that the men of Greece had departed. The gates were opened, and
20 the people went forth to see the plain and the camp. And one said to another, as they went, "Here they set the battle in array, and there were the tents of the fierce Achilles, and there lay the ships." And some stood and marvelled at the great peace-offering to Minerva, even the horse of wood.

25 And Thymœtes, who was one of the elders of the city, was the first who advised that it should be brought within the walls

phē′bus   e pī′ŭs   pir′ŭs   ten′e dos   thī mē′tēz

225

and set in the citadel. Now whether he gave this counsel out
of a false heart, or because the gods would have it so, no man
knows. But Capys, and others with him, said that it should
be drowned in water, or burned with fire, or that men should
5 pierce it and see whether there were naught within. And the
people were divided, some crying one thing and some another.

Then came forward the priest Laocoon, and a great company
with him, crying, "What madness is this? Think ye that the
men of Greece are indeed departed, or that there is any profit
10 in their gifts? Surely, there are armed men in this mighty
horse; or haply they have made it that they may look down upon
our walls. Touch it not, for as for these men of Greece, I fear
them, even though they bring gifts in their hands."

And as he spake he cast his great spear at the horse, so that
15 it sounded again. But the gods would not that Troy should be
saved.

Meanwhile certain shepherds came to the city dragging with
them one whose hands were bound behind his back. He pretended to the men of Troy that he had only then burst his
20 bonds and fled from the Greeks, who had chosen him by lot as
a sacrifice to appease the winds that they might have safe return
to Greece.

King Priam had pity upon him and bade them loose his
bonds, saying, "Who art thou and what knowest thou of the
25 horse of wood?" And he said, "Lo, I deny not, I am a Greek,
and my name is Sinon. I call you to witness, ye everlasting fires,
that I break my fealty with the Greeks for just cause. Know
then, King Priam, the horse of wood is a peace-offering to
Minerva, which the Greeks hoped to make large enough that the
30 men of Troy might not receive it into their gates. For once
within the walls of Troy the image will bring woe to the Greeks
and safety to Troy."

These words wrought much on the men of Troy, and as they
pondered on them, lo! the gods sent another marvel to deceive
35 them. For while Laocoon, the priest of Neptune, was slaying

kā′pys   lā ŏk′ō on   sī′non

a bull at the altar of his god, there came two serpents across the sea from Tenedos, whose heads and necks, whereon were thick manes of hair, were high above the waves, and many scaly coils trailed behind in the waters. And when they reached the land they still sped forward. Their eyes were red as blood and blazed with fire, and their forked tongues hissed loud for rage.

Then all the men of Troy grew pale with fear and fled away, but these turned not aside this way or that, seeking Laocoon where he stood. And first they wrapped themselves about his little sons, one serpent about each, and began to devour them. And when the father would have given help to his children, having a sword in his hand, they seized upon himself, and bound him fast with their folds. Twice they compassed him about his body, and twice his neck, lifting their heads far above him. And all the while he strove to tear them away with his hands, his priest's garlands dripping with blood. Nor did he cease to cry horribly aloud, even as a bull bellows when after an ill stroke of the axe it flees from the altar. But when their work was done, the two glided to the citadel of Minerva, and hid themselves beneath the feet and the shield of the goddess.

And men said one to another, "Lo! the priest Laocoon has been judged according to his deeds; for he cast his spear against this holy thing, and now the gods have slain him." Then all cried out together that the horse of wood must be drawn to the citadel.

Whereupon they opened the Scæan gates, and pulled down the wall that was thereby, and put rollers under the feet of the horse, and joined ropes thereto. So, in much joy, they drew it into the city, youths and maidens singing about it the while, and laying their hands to the ropes with great gladness.

And yet there wanted not signs and tokens of evil to come. Four times it halted on the threshold of the gate, and men might have heard a clashing of arms within. Cassandra also opened her mouth, prophesying evil: but no man heeded her, for that was ever the doom upon her, not to be believed speak-

ka săn'dra

ing truth. So the men of Troy drew the horse into the city. And that night they kept a feast to all the gods with great joy, not knowing that the last day of the great city had come.

But when night was now fully come, and the men of Troy 5 lay asleep, lo! from the ship of King Agamemnon there rose up a flame for a signal to the Greeks; and these straightway manned their ships, and made across the sea from Tenedos, there being a great calm, and the moon also giving them light. Sinon likewise opened a secret door that was in the great horse, and the 10 chiefs issued forth therefrom, and opened the gates of the city, slaying those that kept watch.

Meanwhile there came a vision to Æneas, who now, Hector being dead, was the chief hope and stay of the men of Troy. It was Hector's self that he seemed to see, but not such as he had 15 seen him coming back rejoicing with the arms of Achilles, or setting fire to the ships, but even as he lay after Achilles dragged him at his chariot wheels, covered with dust and blood, his feet swollen and pierced with the thongs. To him said Æneas, not knowing what he said, "Why hast thou tarried so 20 long? Much have we suffered waiting for thee! And what grief hath marked thy face? And whence these wounds?"

But to this the spirit answered nothing, but said, groaning the while, "Fly, son of Venus, fly, and save thee from these flames. The enemy is in the walls, and Troy hath utterly per- 25 ished. If any hand could have saved our city, this hand had done so. Thou art now the hope of Troy. Take then her gods, and flee with them for company, seeking the city that thou shalt one day build across the sea."

And now the alarm of battle came nearer and nearer, and 30 Æneas, waking from sleep, climbed upon the roof, and looked upon the city. As a shepherd stands, and sees a fierce flame sweeping before the south wind over the corn-field or a flood rushing down from the mountains, so he stood. And as he looked, the great palace of Deiphobus sank down in the fire and 35 the neighboring houses blazed forth, till the sea hard by shone

de if'ō bus

with the light. Then, scarce knowing what he sought, he girded on his armor, thinking, perchance, that he might yet win some place of vantage, or, at the least, might avenge himself on the enemy, or find honor in his death.

5 But as he passed from out of his house there met him Panthus, the priest of Phœbus that was on the citadel, who cried to him, "O Æneas, the glory is departed from Troy, and the Greeks have the mastery in the city; for armed men are coming forth from the great horse of wood, and thousands also swarm 10 in at the gates, which Sinon hath treacherously opened." And as he spake others came up under the light of the moon, to whom Æneas spake: "If ye are minded, my brethren, to follow me to the death, come on. For how things fare this night ye see. The gods who were the stay of this city have departed 15 from it; nor is aught remaining to which we may bring succour. Yet can we die as brave men in battle. And haply he that counts his life to be lost may yet save it.' Then, even as ravening wolves hasten through the mist seeking for prey, so they went through the city, doing dreadful deeds. And for a 20 while the men of Greece fled before them.

Æneas, hearing a great shouting, hastened to the palace of King Priam, where the battle was fiercer than in any place beside. For some of the Greeks were seeking to climb the walls, laying ladders thereto, whereon they stood, holding forth their 25 shields with their left hands, and with their right grasping the roofs.

Meanwhile others sought to break down the gates of the palace, Pyrrhus, son of Achilles, being foremost among them, clad in shining armor of bronze. And with Pyrrhus was 30 Automedon, who had been armor-bearer to his father Achilles. With a great battle-axe he hewed through the doors, breaking down also the door-posts, though they were plated with bronze, making, as it were, a great window, through which a man might see the palace within, the hall of King Priam and of the kings 35 who had reigned aforetime in Troy.

pan'thus

Then, as a river bursts its bank and overflows the plain, so did the sons of Greece rush into the palace.

But old Priam, when he saw the enemy in his hall, girded on him his armor, which now by reason of old age he had long
5 laid aside, and took a spear in his hand, and would have gone against the adversary, only Queen Hecuba called to him from where she sat. For she and her daughters had fled to the great altar of the household gods, and sat crowded about it like unto doves that are driven by a storm. Now the altar stood in an
10 open court that was in the midst of the palace, with a great bay-tree above it. So when she saw Priam, how he had girded himself with armor as a youth, she cried to him and said, "What hath bewitched thee, that thou girdest thyself with armor? It is not the sword that shall help us this day; no,
15 not though my own Hector were here, but rather the gods and their altars. Come hither to us, for here thou wilt be safe, or at the least wilt die with us."

So she made the old man sit down in the midst. But lo! there came flying through the palace, Polites, his son, wounded
20 to death by the spear of Pyrrhus, and Pyrrhus close behind him. And he, even as he came into the sight of his father and his mother, fell dead upon the ground.

But when King Priam saw it he contained not himself, but cried aloud, "Now may the gods, if there be any justice in
25 heaven, recompense thee for this wickedness, seeing that thou hast not spared to slay the son before his father's eyes. Great Achilles, whom thou falsely callest thy sire, did not thus to Priam, though he was an enemy, but reverenced right and truth, and gave the body of Hector for burial, and sent me
30 back to my city."

And as he spake the old man cast a spear, but aimless and without force, and that pierced not even the boss of the shield. Then said the son of Achilles, "Go thou and tell my father of his unworthy son and all these evils deeds. And that thou mayest
35 tell him, die!" So King Priam, who had ruled mightily over

pō lī'tēz

many peoples and countries in the land of Asia, was slain that night, having first seen Troy burning about him, and his citadel laid even with the ground.

CHAPTER TWO

THE ADVENTURES OF ÆNEAS

ALL these things, indeed, Æneas beheld, but could not bear help,
5 being one against many. But when the deed was done, and the old man lay dead, he bethought him of his father Anchises, and his wife Creusa, and of his little son Ascanius, and how he had left them without defence at home.

But as he turned to seek them, the night being now, by
10 reason of many fires, as clear as the day, he espied Helen sitting in the temple of Vesta, where she had sought sanctuary; for she feared the men of Troy, to whom she had brought ruin and destruction, and not less her own husband, whom she had deceived. Then was his wrath kindled, and he spake to himself,
15 "Shall this evil woman return safe to Sparta? Shall she see again her home and her children, with Trojan women forsooth to be her handmaidens? Shall Troy be burnt and King Priam be slain, and she take no harm? Not so; for though there be no glory to be won from such a deed, yet shall I satisfy my-
20 self, taking vengeance upon her for my kinsmen and my countrymen."

But while he thought these things in his heart, lo! there appeared unto him Venus, his mother, made manifest as he had never seen her before, as fair and as tall as the dwellers
25 in heaven behold her. Then Venus spake thus, "What meaneth all this rage, my son? Hast thou no care for me? Hast thou forgotten thy father Anchises, and thy wife, and thy little son? Of a surety the fire and the sword had consumed them long since but that I cared for them and saved them.
30 It is not Helen; no, nor Paris, that hath laid low this great

an kī′sēz   krē ū′sa   as kā′nǐ us

city of Troy, but the wrath of the gods. See now, for I will take away the mist that covers thine eyes; see how Neptune with his trident is overthrowing the walls and rooting up the the city from its foundations; and how Juno stands with spear
5 and shield in the Scæan gates and calls fresh hosts from the ships; and how Minerva sits on the height with the storm-cloud about her and her Gorgon shield; and how Jupiter himself stirs up the enemy against Troy. Fly, therefore, my son. I will not leave thee till thou shalt reach thy father's house." And as
10 she spake she vanished in the darkness.

Then did Æneas see dreadful forms and gods who were the enemies of Troy, and before his eyes the whole city seemed to sink down into the fire. Even as a mountain oak upon the hills on which the woodmen ply their axes bows its head while
15 all its boughs shake about it, till at last, as blow comes after blow, with a mighty groan it falls crashing down from the height, even so the city seemed to fall. Then did Æneas pass on his way, the goddess leading him, and the flames gave place to him, and the javelins harmed him not.

20 But when he was come to his house he bethought him first of the old man his father; but when he would have carried him to the hills, Anchises would not, being loath to live in some strange country when Troy had perished. "Nay," said he, "fly ye who are strong and in the flower of your days. But as
25 for me, if the gods had willed that I should live, they had saved this dwelling for me. Enough is it, yea, and more than enough, that once I have seen this city taken, and lived. Bid me, then, farewell as though I were dead. Death will I find for myself."

Nor could the old man be moved from his purpose, though
30 his son and his son's wife, and even the child Ascanius, besought him with many tears that he should not make yet heavier the doom that was upon them. Then was Æneas minded to go back to the battle and die. For what hope was left? "Thoughtest thou, my father," he cried, "that I should flee
35 and leave thee behind? What evil word is this that has fallen

gor'gon

from thy lips? If the gods will have it that nought of Troy should be left, and thou be minded that thou and thine should perish with the city, be it so. Comrades, give me my arms, and take me back to the battle. At the least I will die avenged."

5   But as he girded on his arms and would have departed from the house, his wife Creusa caught his feet upon the threshold, staying him, and held out the little Ascanius, saying, "If thou goest to thy death, take wife and child with thee; but if thou hopest aught from arms, guard first the house where thou hast
10 father and wife and child."

And lo! as she spake there befell a mighty marvel, for before the face of father and mother there was seen to shine a light on the head of the boy Ascanius, and to play upon his waving hair and glitter on his temples. And when they feared
15 to see this thing, and would have stifled the flame or quenched it with water, the old man Anchises in great joy raised his eyes to heaven, and cried aloud, "O Father Jupiter, if prayer move thee at all, give thine aid and make this omen sure."

And even as he spake the thunder rolled on his left hand,
20 and a star shot through the skies, leaving a long trail of light behind, and passed over the house-tops till it was hidden in the woods of Ida. Then the old man lifted himself up and did obeisance to the star, and said, "I delay no more: whithersoever ye lead I will follow. Gods of my country, save my
25 house and my grandson. This omen is of you. And now, my son, I refuse not to go."

Then said Æneas, and as he spake the fire came nearer, and the light was clearer to see, and the heat more fierce, "Climb, dear father, on my shoulders; I will bear thee, nor
30 grow weary with the weight. We will be saved or perish together. The little Ascanius shall go with me and my wife follow behind, not over near. And ye, servants of my house, hearken to me; ye mind how that to one who passes out of the city there is a tomb and a temple of Ceres in a lonely place,
35 and an ancient cypress tree hard by. There will we gather

se'rēz

by divers ways. And do thou, my father, take the holy images
in thy hands, for as for me, who have but newly come from
battle, I may not touch them till I have washed me in the running stream."

5   And as he spake he put a cloak of lion's skin upon his
shoulders, and the old man sat thereon. Ascanius also laid
hold of his hand, and Creusa followed behind. So he went in
much dread and trembling. For indeed before sword and spear
of the enemy he had not feared, but now he feared for them
10 that were with him. But when he was come nigh unto the
gates, and the journey was well-nigh finished, there befell a
grievous mischance, for there was heard a sound as of many
feet through the darkness; and the old man cried to him, "Fly,
my son, fly; they are coming. I see the flashing of shields and
15 swords."

But as Æneas hastened to go, Creusa his wife was severed
from him. But whether she wandered from the way or sat
down in weariness, no man may say. Only he saw her no more,
nor knew her to be lost till, all his company being met at the
20 temple of Ceres, she only was found wanting. Very grievous
did the thing seem to him, nor did he cease to cry out in his
wrath against gods and men. Also he bade his comrades have
a care of his father and his son, and of the household gods, and
girded him again with arms, and so passed into the city.

25   And first he went to the wall and to the gate by which he
had come forth, and then to his house, if haply she had returned
thither. And after that he went to the citadel and to the palace
of King Priam. And not the less did he seek his wife through
all the streets of the city, yea, and called her aloud by name.

30   But lo! as he called, the image of her whom he sought
seemed to stand before him, only greater than she had been
while she was yet alive. And the spirit spake, saying, "Why
art thou vainly troubled? These things have not befallen us
against the pleasure of the gods. The ruler of Olympus willeth
35 not that Creusa should bear thee company in thy journey. For

thou hast a long journey to take, and many seas to cross, till thou come to the Hesperian shore, where the Lydian Tiber flows softly through a good land and a fertile. There shalt thou have great prosperity, and take to thyself a wife of royal race.
5 Weep not then for Creusa, whom thou lovest, nor think that I shall be carried away to be a bond-slave to some Grecian woman. Such fate befits not a daughter of Dardanus and daughter-in-law of Venus. The mighty mother of the gods keepeth me in this land to serve her. And now, farewell, and
10 love the young Ascanius, even thy son and mine."

So spake the spirit, and, when Æneas wept and would have spoken, vanished out of his sight. Thrice he would have cast his arms about her neck, and thrice the image mocked him, being thin as air and fleeting as a dream. Then, the night
15 being now spent, he sought his comrades, and found with much joy and wonder that a great company of men and women were gathered together, and were willing, all of them, to follow him whithersoever he went. And now the morning star rose over Mount Ida, and Æneas, seeing that the Greeks held the
20 city, and that there was no longer any hope of succour, went his way to the mountains, taking with him his father. Now for what remains of that year, for it was the time of summer when Troy was taken, Æneas, and they that were gathered to him, builded themselves ships for the voyage, dwelling the while
25 under Mount Ida; and when the summer was well-nigh come again the work was finished, and the old man Anchises commanded that they should tarry no longer. Whereupon they sailed, taking also their gods with them.

There was a certain land named Thrace, loved by Mars
30 beyond all other lands. Here Æneas builded him a city, but this was not decreed by the gods to be their abiding place and so again they launched their ships and set sail.

And first they came to the island of Delos, sacred to the archer-god Phœbus. Here the oracle bade them, "Seek, then, your ancient mother. The land that first bare you shall receive

hes pē'ri an   lĭd'i an

you again and there Æneas and his children's children shall rule from one generation to another."

Then Anchises bethought him that the beginning of their nation was upon a certain island named Crete. Whereupon they
5 offered sacrifices and set sail for Crete. Here they dwelt, but there came a wasting sickness upon the men and a blight upon the harvest so that they scarce knew where to seek for help or whither they should go.

But as Æneas slept there appeared to him the household
10 gods, carried by him from the burning ruins of Troy, and spake to him saying, "It was not Crete that Phœbus decreed to be your home but an ancient land far to the west which men call Italy. Thither sail, there is our home and there the gods would have us dwell."

15 So the men of Troy made ready their ships and departed. And when they could no more see the land, there fell a great storm upon them, driving them for many days far from their course. Many islands did they pass and when now they sailed by Ithaca, they cursed it as they passed because it was the
20 home of the hateful Ulysses.

After many days of wandering they came to a city in Epirus, ruled over by Helenus, son of King Priam, who had for wife Andromache, the widow of brave Hector. Æneas met her in a grove by a river where with many tears she made offerings
25 to the spirit of Hector. Scarce could she believe that it was not a spirit and that it was indeed Æneas of Troy. She told how she had been carried from Troy by Pyrrhus, the haughty son of Achilles.

And while she spoke Helenus came with a great company
30 and bade Æneas and his men welcome. And Æneas saw how all things were ordered and named even as they had been at Troy, only the things at Troy had been great and these were very small. Afterwards King Helenus made a feast to them in his house and they drank together and made merry.

35 But when Æneas saw that the wind favored them, again

e pī′rus   hel′e nus

they set sail. A north wind blew them, not without many hardships, past the dangers of Scylla and Charybdis and the land of the Cyclops. While seeking shelter in a harbor they saw a wretched man as he ran along the shore hailing the ships. His
5 hair was unkempt and his clothes in tatters and pinned together with thorns. He begged that the men of Troy have pity upon him, saying that he had been left behind in the cave when Ulysses and his companions escaped. For many months he had lived upon roots and berries, ever fearing the wrath of the
10 giant should he find him. Though a Greek, they were glad to help one in such sore plight and took him on board.

On the island of Sicily the old Anchises died and was buried with due funeral rites.

When Juno, ever hating the men of Troy, saw them nearing
15 their destination, she came to Æolus, king of the winds, who keeps them under bolt and bar though mightily they roar within the mountain. To him she said, "Loose thy storms against a nation which I hate and which is now sailing over the seas." To whom answered King Æolus, "It is for thee, O Juno, to
20 order what thou wilt." So saying, he drove in with his spear the great doors of their prison and all the winds rushed forth together, rolling great waves upon the shore.

King Neptune heard the tumult where he sat at the bottom of the sea and looked forth and saw how the ships were scat-
25 tered and the men of Troy in sore peril. He bade the winds, "Begone, and tell your king that mine is the dominion over the sea and bid him keep to his rocks."

Then Æneas and his companions, being sore wearied with the storm, made for the nearest shore, even Africa, where they
30 found a haven. Here Æneas came with scarce seven ships out of the twenty with which he had set sail.

All these things did Jupiter behold; and even as he beheld them there came to him Venus, having a sad countenance and her shining eyes dim with tears, and spake: "O great Father,
35 that rulest all things, what have Æneas and the men of Troy

sinned against thee, that the whole world is shut against them?
Didst not thou promise that they should rule over land and
sea? Why, then, art thou turned back from thy purpose? With
this I was wont to comfort myself for the evil fate of Troy, but
5 lo! this same fate follows them still, nor is there any end to
their troubles."

Then her father kissed her once and again, and answered
smiling, "Fear not, my daughter, the fate of thy children
changeth not. Thou shalt see this city for which thou lookest,
10 and shalt receive thy son, the great-hearted Æneas, into the
heavens. Hearken, therefore, and I will tell thee things to
come. Æneas shall war with the nations of Italy, and shall
subdue them, and build a city, and rule therein for three years.
And after the space of thirty years shall the boy Ascanius, who
15 shall hereafter be called Iulus also, change the place of his
throne from Lavinium unto Alba; and for three hundred years
shall there be kings in Alba of the kindred of Hector. Then
shall a priestess bear to Mars twin sons, whom a she-wolf
shall nurse; of whom the one, even Romulus, shall build a city,
20 dedicating it to Mars, and call it Rome, after his own name.
To which city have I given empire without bound or end. And
Juno also shall repent her of her wrath, and join counsel with
me, cherishing the men of Rome, so that they shall bear rule
even over the land of the Greeks."

25   Now it came to pass on the next day that Venus appeared
to Æneas in the form of a Tyrian maiden and told him the
story of the people among whom he and his companions had
come. "The city, hard by," she said, "is peopled by men from
Tyre. Dido is their queen. Her brother Pygmalion was king
30 of Tyre, a wicked man and ever eager to increase his wealth.
For this reason he had secretly put to death the husband of
Dido, that he might come into possession of his great wealth.
After many days, the spirit of her dead husband appeared to
Dido in a dream and, telling her of the manner of his death
35 and showing her his wounds, he bade her flee from Tyre and,

ī ū′lus   la vin′i um   rŏm′ū lus   tir′ĭ an   dī′dō   pig mā′lĭ on that she might do this more easily, he told her of great treasures, gold and silver, hidden in the earth. And Dido made ready for the flight, all those who feared or hated the king joining her. Then did they seize ships that chanced to be ready and, loading them with gold, they fled across the sea. Then came they to this place, asking of the natives as much land as could be covered with a bull's hide. Dido caused the hide to be cut into strips and with it enclosed the spot on which they built their citadel. Yonder walls enclose the city which they are even now building."

Now Jupiter sent Mercury, his messenger, to turn the heart of Dido and her people that they would deal kindly with the strangers.

When Æneas and his companions had come into the city, Dido received them with friendliness and hospitality, saying, "I, too, have wandered far and, having suffered much, have learned to help them that suffer." She prepared a great feast for them and they were entertained with many games.

Æneas was filled with wonder as he passed through the streets and saw the throngs of men, all busily at work, some cutting trees and some rolling great stones for the buildings.

When now he told the queen of all the hardships and sorrow through which they had passed since Troy was burned, she took pity upon them and offered them new homes in Carthage, saying, "Men of Troy and men of Tyre shall have equal privileges in this new city."

And so weary were they of the sea and so good did a home seem to the wanderers that eagerly they lent not only labor but counsel.

The queen said to her sister, Anna, "Never, since the death of my husband, has any man moved my heart as this stranger, so noble of mien and so bold in war. Surely he is one of the sons of the gods."

And gladly would Æneas have spent the rest of his days here but that Jupiter sent his messenger, Mercury, who spake

kar'thāj

to Æneas, "Buildest thou Carthage, forgetting thine own work? Why tarriest thou here? If thou carest not for thyself, yet think of thy son and that the Fates have given to him Italy and Rome."

5 Æneas stood stricken with fear and doubt. He would fain obey the voice but when now his plans were made known to the queen she was loath to have him leave.

And when now naught could prevail upon him to change his purpose, Dido ordered a great funeral pile to be erected near 10 the shore and, as Æneas and his companions sailed forth in their ships, she mounted the pile and, throwing herself upon a sword, was consumed by the flames. Æneas when he saw the flames, had an evil foreboding of what it meant. Years after there was bitter enmity between Carthage and Rome.

15 And so the men of Troy, though weary of the sea, yet endured many hardships more, that the will of the gods might be fulfilled. And lo! after the seventh year from the time Troy was burned, they saw the shores of Italy and landed near Cumae, which was the dwelling place of the Sibyl.

20 Æneas went up to the great cave of the Sibyl, where by the inspiration of Apollo she foretelleth things to come. In company with her and by her aid he made the descent to the realm of shades and there from his father Anchises heard that though he had at last reached the promised land yet there still were 25 sore trials before him. He told him, too, of the glorious future of Rome and called by name the illustrious heroes who would make Rome great.

Latinus was king of this country. He had an only child, a daughter, who was now of an age to be married. Many 30 chiefs came as suitors but none of these found favor for King Latinus minded him of an oracle which said, "There shall come a son-in-law, from beyond the sea, who shall make great thy name from one end of heaven to the other."

And so it came to pass that there was waged a terrible war 35 between the men of Troy and Turnus, a native prince and suitor.

kū'mē   sib'il   tur'nus   la tī'nus

But the gods gave victory to Æneas and he was established in the land with Lavinia for his wife.

Now Juno, when she saw that she was balked in her purpose, prayed for one favor of Jupiter, "Suffer not that the
5 Latins be called after the men of Troy. Let Rome rule the world but let Troy perish forever!"

CHAPTER THREE

THE FOUNDING OF ROME—ROMULUS AND REMUS

ÆNEAS of Troy, coming to the land of Italy, took to wife Lavinia, daughter of King Latinus, and built him a city, which he called Lavinium, after the name of his wife. And, after
10 thirty years, his son Ascanius went forth from Lavinium with many people, and built him a new city, which he called Alba. In this city reigned kings of the house and lineage of Æneas for twelve generations.

Of these kings the eleventh in descent was one Procas, who,
15 having two sons, Numitor and Amulius, left his kingdom, according to the custom, to Numitor, the elder. But Amulius drave out his brother, and reigned in his stead. Nor was he content with this wickedness, but slew all the male children of his brother. And the daughter of his brother, that was named Rhea
20 Silvia, he chose to be a priestess of Vesta, making as though he would do the maiden honor, but his thought was that the name of his brother should perish.

But it came to pass that Rhea bare twin sons, Romulus and Remus, whose father, it was said, was the god Mars. Very
25 wroth was Amulius when he heard this thing; Rhea he made fast in prison, and the children he gave to certain of his servants that they should cast them into the river.

Now it chanced that at this season the Tiber had overflowed his banks, neither could the servants come near to the stream

la vin′i a   prō′cas   nū′mi tor   a mū′lĭ us   rē′a   sil′vi a

of the river; nevertheless they did not doubt that the children would perish, for all that the overflowing of the water was neither deep nor of a swift current. Thinking then that they had duly performed the commandment of the king, they set
5 down the babes in the flood and departed. But after a while the flood abated, and left the basket wherein the children had been laid on dry ground.

And a she-wolf coming down from the hill to drink at the river, for the country in those days was desert and abounding
10 in wild beasts, heard the crying of the children and ran to them. Nor did she devour them, but fed them; nay, so gentle was she that Faustulus, the king's shepherd, chancing to go by, saw that she licked them with her tongue.

Faustulus took the children and gave them to his wife to
15 rear; and these, when they were of age to go by themselves, were not willing to abide with the flocks and herds, but were hunters, wandering through the forests that were in those parts.

And afterward, being now come to full strength, they were not content to slay wild beasts only, but would assail troops of
20 robbers, as these were returning laden with their booty, and would divide the spoils among the shepherds.

Now there was held in those days, on the hill that is now called the Palatine, a yearly festival to the god Pan. This festival King Evander first ordained, having come from Arcadia, in
25 which land, being a land of shepherds, Pan that is the god of shepherds is greatly honored. And when the young men and their company—for they had gathered a great company of shepherds about them, and led them in all matters both of business and of sport—were busy with the festival, there came upon
30 them certain robbers that had made an ambush in the place, being very wroth by reason of the booty which they had lost.

These laid hands on Remus, but Romulus they could not take, so fiercely did he fight against them. Remus, therefore, they delivered up to King Amulius, accusing him of many
35 things and chiefly of this, that he and his companions had in-

faw'stū lus   pal'a tīn   ē van'der   ar kā'di a   rē'mus vaded the land of Numitor, dealing with them in the fashion of an enemy and carrying off much spoil. To Numitor, therefore, did the king deliver Remus, that he might put him to death.

Now Faustulus had believed from the beginning that the children were of the royal house, for he knew that the babes had been cast into the river by the king's command, and the time also of his finding them agreed thereto. Nevertheless he had not judged it expedient to open the matter before due time, but waited till occasion or necessity should arise.

But now, there being such necessity, he opened the matter to Romulus. Numitor also, when he had the young man Remus in his custody, knowing that he and his brother were twins, and that the time agreed, and seeing that they were of a high spirit, bethought him of his grandsons; and, indeed, having asked many questions of Remus, was come nigh to knowing of what race he was.

And now also Romulus was ready to help his brother. To come openly with his whole company he dared not, for he was not a match for the power of King Amulius; but he bade sundry shepherds make their way to the palace, each as best he could, appointing to them a time at which they should meet. And now came Remus also, with a troop of youths gathered together from the household of Numitor.

Then did Romulus and Remus slay King Amulius. In the meanwhile Numitor gathered the youth of Alba to the citadel, crying out that they must make the place safe, for that the enemy was upon them; but when he perceived that the young men had done the deed, forthwith he called an assembly of the citizens, and set forth to them the wickedness which his brother had wrought against him, and how his grandsons had been born and bred and made known to him, and then how the tyrant had been slain, himself having counselled the deed.

When he had so spoken the young men came with their company into the midst of the assembly and saluted him as king; to which thing the whole multitude agreeing with one consent, Numitor was established upon the throne.

After this Romulus and his brother conceived this purpose, that, leaving their grandfather to be king at Alba, they should
5 build for themselves a new city in the place where, having been at the first left to die, they had been brought up by Faustulus, the shepherd. And to this purpose many agreed both of the men of Alba and of the Latins, and also of the shepherds that had followed them from the first, holding it for certain all of
10 them that Alba and Lavinium would be of small account in comparison with this new city which they should build together.

But while the brothers were busy with these things, there sprang up afresh the same evil thing which had before wrought such trouble in their house, even the lust of power. For though
15 the beginnings of the strife between them were peaceful, yet did it end in great wickedness.

The matter fell out in this wise. Seeing that the brothers were twins, and that neither could claim to have the preference to the other in respect of his age, it was agreed between them
20 that the gods that were the guardians of that country should make known by means of augury which of the two they chose to give his name to the new city.

Then Romulus stood on the Palatine hill, and when there had been marked out for him a certain region of the sky,
25 watched therein for a sign; and Remus watched in like manner, standing on the Aventine. And to Remus first came a sign, six vultures; but so soon as the sign had been proclaimed there came another to Romulus, even twelve vultures. Then they that favored Remus clamored that the gods had chosen him for
30 king, because he had first seen the birds; and they that favored Romulus answered that he was to be preferred because he had seen more in number.

This dispute waxed so hot that they fell to fighting; and in the fight it chanced that Remus was slain.

35 But some say that when Romulus had marked out the bor-

ȧv′en tīn

ders of the town which he would build, and had caused them to
build a wall round it, Remus leapt over the wall, scorning it
because it was mean and low; and that Romulus slew him, crying out, "Thus shall every man perish that shall dare to leap
5 over my walls." This much is certain, that Romulus gained the
whole kingdom for himself and called the city after his own
name.

Having first done sacrifice to the gods, Romulus called a
general assembly of the people, that he might give them laws,
10 knowing that without laws no city can endure. And judging
that these would be the better kept by his subjects if he should
himself bear something of the show of royal majesty, he took
certain signs of dignity, and especially twelve men that should
continually attend him, bearing bundles of rods, and in the
15 midst of the rods an axe; these men they called lictors.

Meanwhile the city increased, for the king and his people
enlarged their borders, looking rather to the greatness for which
they hoped than to that which they had. And that this increase
might not be altogether empty walls without men, Romulus set
20 up a sanctuary, to which were gathered a great multitude of men
from the nations round about. All that were discontented and
lovers of novelty came to him. Nor did he take any account of
their condition, whether they were bond or free, but received
them all. Thus was there added to the city great strength.

25 And the king, when he judged that there was strength sufficient, was minded to add to the strength counsel. Wherefore
he chose a hundred men for counsellors. A hundred he chose,
either because he held that number to be sufficient, or because
there were no more that were fit to bear this dignity and be
30 called fathers, for this was the name of these counsellors.

After this the people bethought themselves how they should
get for themselves wives, for there were no women in the place.
Wherefore Romulus sent ambassadors to the nations round
about, praying that they should give their daughters to his peo-
35 ple for wives. "Cities," he said, "have humble beginnings even

as all other things. Nevertheless they that have the gods and their own valor to help become great. Now that the gods are with us, as ye know, be assured also that valor shall not be wanting."

5 But the nations round about would not hearken at all to the ambassadors whom the king had sent to them, thinking scorn of this gathering of robbers and slaves and runaways. Besides they feared for themselves and their children lest this new city might grow to be a source of great danger to them in some
10 future time.

Now when the ambassadors brought back this answer the Romans were greatly wroth, and would take by force that which their neighbors would not give of their free will. And to the end that they might do this more easily, King Romulus ap-
15 pointed certain days whereon he and his people would hold a festival with games to Neptune; and to this festival he called all them that dwelt in the cities round about. But when many were gathered together, for they were fain to see what this new city might be, and were now wholly bent on the spectacle of the
20 games, the young men of the Romans ran in upon them, and carried off all such as were unwedded among the women. To these King Romulus spake kindly, saying, "The fault is not with us but with your fathers, who dealt proudly with us, and would not give you to us in marriage. But now ye shall be held in all
25 honor as our wives, and shall have your portion of all that we possess. Put away therefore your anger, for ye shall find us so much the better husbands than other men, as we must be to you not for husbands only but parents also and native country."

In the meanwhile the parents of them that had been carried
30 off put on sackcloth, and went about through the cities crying out for vengeance upon the Romans. And chiefly they sought for help from Titus Tatius, that was king of the Sabines in those days, and of great power and renown, who came up against Rome with a great army.

35 And first of all they gained the citadel by treachery in this

tī′tus tā′shus   sā′bĭns

manner. One Tarpeius was governor of the citadel, whose
daughter, Tarpeia by name, going forth from the walls to fetch
water for a sacrifice, took money from King Tatius that she
should receive certain of the soldiers within the citadel; but
when they had been so received, the men cast their shields upon
her, slaying her with the weight of them. This they did either
that they might be thought to have taken the place by force, or
that they judged it to be well that no faith should be kept with
traitors.

Some also tell this tale, that the Sabines wore great bracelets
of gold on their left arms, and on their left hands fair rings with
precious stones therein, and that when the maiden covenanted
with them that she should have for a reward that which they
carried in their left hands, they cast their shields upon her.
And others say that she asked for their shields having the purpose to betray them, and for this cause was slain.

Thus the Sabines had possession of the citadel; and the next
day King Romulus set the battle in array on the plain that lay
between the hill of the Capitol and the hill of the Palatine. And
first the Romans were very eager to recover the citadel, a certain
Hostilius being their leader. But when this man, fighting in
the forefront of the battle, was slain, the Romans turned their
backs and fled before the Sabines, even unto the gate of the
Palatine.

Then King Romulus, for he himself had been carried away
by the crowd of them that fled, held up his sword and his spear
to the heavens, and cried aloud, "O Jupiter, here in the Palatine
didst thou first, by the tokens which thou sentest me, lay the
foundations of my city. And lo! the Sabines have taken the
citadel by wicked craft, and have crossed the valley, and are
come up even hither. But if thou sufferest them so far, do thou
at the least defend this place against them, and stay this shame-
ful flight of my people. So will I build a temple for thee in this
place, even a temple of Jupiter the Stayer, that may be a

tar pē′yus   tar pē′ya   hos tĭl′ĭ us

memorial to after generations of how thou didst this day save this city."

And when he had so spoken, even as though he knew that the prayer had been heard, he cried, "Ye men of Rome, Jupiter 5 bids you stand fast in this place and renew the battle."

And when the men of Rome heard these words, it was as if a voice from heaven had spoken to them, and they stood fast, and the king himself went forward and stood among the foremost.

Now the leader of the Sabines was one Curtius. This man, 10 as he drave the Romans before him, cried out to his comrades, "See we have conquered these men, false hosts and feeble foes that they are! Surely now they know that it is one thing to carry off maidens and another to fight with men."

But whilst he boasted himself thus, King Romulus and a 15 company of the youth rushed upon him. Now Curtius was fighting on horseback, and being thus assailed he fled, plunging into a certain pool which lay between the Palatine hill and the Capitol. Thus did he barely escape with his life, and the lake was called thereafter Curtius' pool.

20 And now the Sabines began to give way to the Romans, when suddenly the women for whose sake they fought, having their hair loosened and their garments rent, ran in between them that fought, crying out, "Shed ye not each other's blood ye that are fathers-in-law and sons-in-law to each other. But if 25 ye break this bond that is between you, slay us that are the cause of this trouble. And surely it were better for us to die than to live if we be bereaved of our fathers or of our husbands."

With these words they stirred the hearts both of the chiefs and of the people, so that there was suddenly made a great 30 silence. And afterward the leaders came forth to make a covenant; and these indeed so ordered matters that there was not peace only, but one state where there had been two. For the Sabines came to Rome and dwelt there; and King Romulus and King Tatius reigned together. Only, after a while, certain

ker'shĭ us

men slew King Tatius as he was sacrificing to the gods at Lavinium; and thereafter Romulus only was king as before.

When he had reigned thirty and seven years there befell the thing that shall now be told. On a certain day he called the people together on the field of Mars, and held a review of his army. But while he did this there arose suddenly a great storm with loud thunderings and very thick clouds, so that the king was hidden away from the eyes of all the people. Nor indeed was he ever again seen upon the earth.

And when men were recovered of their fear they were in great trouble, because they had lost their king; though indeed the fathers would have it that he had been carried by a whirlwind into heaven.

Yet after a while they began to worship him as being now a god; and when nevertheless some doubted, and would even whisper among themselves that Romulus had been torn in pieces by the fathers, there came forward a certain Proculus, who spake after this manner: "Ye men of Rome, this day, in the early morning, I saw Romulus, the father of this city, come down from heaven and stand before me. And when great fear came upon me, I prayed that it might be lawful for me to look upon him face to face. Then said he to me, 'Go thy way, tell the men of Rome that it is the will of them that dwell in heaven that Rome should be the chiefest city in the world. Bid them therefore be diligent in war; and let them know for themselves and tell their children after them that there is no power on earth so great that it shall be able to stand against them.' And when he had thus spoken, he departed from me, going up into heaven." All men believed Proculus when he thus spake, and the people ceased from their sorrow when they knew that King Romulus had been taken up into heaven.

And now it was needful that another king should be chosen. No man in those days was more renowned for his righteousness and piety than a certain Numa Pompilius that dwelt in the land of the Sabines. Now it seemed at first to the Senate that the

prŏc′ŭ lus   nū′ma pom pil′ĭ us

Sabines would be too powerful in the state if the king should be chosen from among them, nevertheless because they could not agree upon any other man, at last with one consent they decreed that the kingdom should be offered to him. And Numa
5 was willing to receive it if only the gods consented.

And the consent of the gods was asked in this fashion. Being led by the augur into the citadel, he sat down on a stone with his face looking toward the south, and on his left hand sat the augur, having his head covered and in his hand an augur's staff,
10 which is a wand bent at the end and having no knot. Then looking toward the city and the country round about, he offered prayers to the gods and marked out the region of the sky from the sunrising to the sunsetting; the parts toward the south he called the right, and the parts toward the north he called the
15 left; and he set a boundary before as far as his eye could reach. After this he took his staff in his left hand and laid his right on the head of Numa, praying in these words: "Father Jupiter, if it be thy will that this Numa Pompilius, whose head I hold, should be King of Rome, show us, I pray thee, clear tokens of
20 this thy will within the space which I have marked out." He then named the tokens which he desired, and when they had been shown, Numa was declared to be king.

King Numa, considering that the city was but newly founded, and that by violence and force, conceived that he ought
25 to found it anew, giving it justice and laws and religion; and that he might soften the manners and tempers of the people, he would have them cease a while from war.

To this end he built a temple of Janus, by which it might be signified whether there was peace or war in the state; for, if it
30 were peace, the gates of the temple should be shut, but if it were war, they should be open. Twice only were the gates shut after the days of Numa. This temple then King Numa built, and shut the gates thereof, having first made treaties of peace with the nations round about.

35 Many other things did King Numa set in order for his peo-
jā′nus

ple. First he divided the year into twelve months, each month being according to the course of the moon, and in every twenty-fourth year another month, that the year might so agree with the course of the sun. Also he appointed certain lawful days for business, and other days on which nothing might be done. He made priests also, of whom the chief was the priest of Jupiter, to whom he gave splendid apparel and a chair of ivory. Two other priests he made, one of Mars, and the other of Quirinus, that is to say, of Romulus the god.

And he chose virgins for the service of Vesta, who should keep alive the sacred fire, and twelve priests of Mars to be keepers of the sacred shield. This shield, men said, fell down from heaven, and that it might be kept the more safely, King Numa commanded that they should make eleven other shields like unto it. This shield and its fellows the priests were to carry through the city, having on flowered tunics and breast-plates of brass, and dancing and singing hymns. And many other things as to the worship of the gods, and the interpreting of signs, and the dealing with marvels and portents, King Numa set in order.

And that the people might regard these laws and customs with the more reverence, he gave out that he had not devised them of his own wit, but that he had learnt them from a certain goddess whose name was Egeria, whom he was wont to meet in a grove that was hard by the city.

King Numa died, having reigned forty and three years.

HELPS TO STUDY

Historical and Biographical: Vergil, a Roman poet who lived in the first century B. C., tells the story of Æneas in his great poem, "The Æneid." In this poem Vergil makes the founders of Rome direct descendants of the renowned Trojan hero, Æneas.

Æneas was the son of Anchises and the goddess Venus. He is often represented with burning Troy behind him, bearing upon his shoulders the old Anchises and carrying in one hand the household gods, while with the other he leads his young son Ascanius.

kwi rī'nus   e jē'rĭ a

Notes and Questions

Chapter One: What was the cause of the Trojan war?

Are your sympathies with the Greeks or Trojans in this war? Why?

From the description in this chapter sketch a "picture-map" and locate upon it the relative position of Troy, Tenedos, and the plain and camp of the Greeks.

Tell the story of Sinon. What do you think of him?

What do you think of the fate of Laocoon? Compare this word picture of the priest and his sons with pictures of the famous statue which tells the same story. Which tells the story more forcibly to you?

What reasons did the Trojans have for believing it wise to bring the horse of wood into the city?

Cassandra, daughter of King Priam, was loved by Apollo, who gave her the gift of prophesy. When, however, she rejected his suit, he added this curse to his gift, that she should foretell the doom of Troy but be believed by no one.

Do modern armies destroy cities captured after sieges—as the Greeks did Troy?

How do you account for the fact that a brave warrior like Pyrrhus was willing to strike down the aged and defenseless Priam?

Chapter Two: Creusa was a daughter of King Priam.

What thoughts came to the mind of Æneas when he caught sight of Helen? Do you think you would have felt as he did?

What was the sign that persuaded Anchises to go with Æneas?

Read passages which show that Æneas was a good son to Anchises.

Hesperia is a name given by the ancient poets to the land lying west of Greece, and especially to Italy and Spain.

Dardanus is a name applied to Priam.

The household gods presided over the house and the family. The Romans made images of their household gods.

Tell the story of Creusa.

How long after the fall of Troy did these Trojans begin their wandering and search for a new home?

Tell the story of the companion of Ulysses who was left behind in the cave of the Cyclops.

Are you surprised that these wandering Trojans should be willing to rescue a Greek?

Compare the adventures of Æneas with those of Ulysses.

What part of Jupiter's promise to Venus is most pleasing to her?

Tell the story of Dido and Carthage.

Was the prayer of Juno answered?

Chapter Three: How were Romulus and Remus descended from

Æneas? Which of the brothers was the stronger? What reasons have you for your opinion?

How was Numitor restored to his throne?

Rome was built on seven hills. Three of them are mentioned in this story; the Palatine, the Aventine, and the Capitoline. Tell how the city was founded.

How was the population increased?

Would this new population be difficult to govern?

A sanctuary is a place of refuge and safety for criminals and runaway slaves.

What was the purpose of Romulus in establishing the office of lictor? Was it a wise plan?

Why did the neighbors object to giving their daughters in marriage to these people?

How did they finally gain their wives?

Tell the story of Tarpeia.

How did the war with the Sabines end?

Describe the passing of Romulus.

Why did the Romans like to believe that Romulus passed from earth in the manner told in this story?

Who was Numa? How did he regard war?

Tell about the temple of Janus.

What other good features did Numa establish?

Which was the greater ruler of Rome, Romulus or Numa? Give reasons for your answer.

BOOK IV

THE STORY OF HORATIUS

THE seventh king of Rome was known as Tarquin the Proud.
He was a cruel and wicked man, very different from the earlier
kings. He had gained his power by bloodshed and violence, and
he used it like a tyrant. He repealed the good laws which had
5 been made under the rulers before him, and made others in their
place. The nobles complained that he did everything according
to his own will, and never asked the senate for its advice and
assistance. The people, in their turn, murmured at the constant
wars which he carried on, and the hard tasks at which he set
10 them in time of peace. At last, all Rome was weary of his rule,
and the people of the city only needed some one to direct them
in order to turn against him.

They found their leader in a noble named Brutus, who had
suffered much at the hands of the king. His brother had been
15 put to death by Tarquin; and Brutus, to save himself from a
like fate, had been obliged to give up his property and seem to
be dull and slow of mind, so that the king might find nothing
in him to fear.

But beneath this mask of stupidity the real Brutus was
20 keen and watchful. Once he had been sent as the companion of
the king's sons when they went to consult the great oracle at
Delphi, in Greece. After finishing the business upon which they
had gone, the young men asked the oracle which one of them
should succeed King Tarquin as ruler of Rome. The oracle
25 replied, that he who first kissed his mother upon their return
should rule the city. The princes hastened to draw lots to decide

hō rä'shi us   tar'kwin   brō'tus   del'fī

which one of them should have that privilege, and so gain the throne, but Brutus understood the prophecy better. He pretended to stumble and fall, kissing the ground beneath him as he did so, for he guessed that the oracle had not meant a person, but the great earth, the mother of them all.

In spite of the discontent among the citizens, Tarquin might, perhaps, have been king of Rome until he died, if it had not been for the great wickedness of one of his sons. While the king was away from the city, carrying on war with a neighboring people, this son, Sextus, caused the death of a noble Roman lady named Lucretia. Her husband and her father were overcome with grief and rage, and Brutus, who was with them, threw off his pretended dullness. He seized the bloody dagger that had slain Lucretia, and swore with them that he would never rest until the family of Tarquin had ceased to reign at Rome. Then he hurried to the city and told the story there. The people were filled with anger, and when the king and his sons returned, they found the gates closed against them. Their soldiers had already received Brutus with joy, and, having lost both army and city, the king was obliged to leave the lands of Rome and seek refuge among his friends north of the Tiber.

After they had cast out the Tarquins, the people took an oath that they would never, from that time on, allow any one to become king of Rome. Then one of the first things which they had to do was to find some other form of government to take the place of the old one. For they knew very well that they must have some one in authority over them, or their enemies would be able to overcome their army, and King Tarquin might seize his throne once more.

So the people set up a republic. They agreed that two men, called consuls, should be elected each year; and these consuls, with the senate, should govern Rome in the place of the kings. When the vote was taken for the first consuls, it was found that Brutus was one of the two men who were elected; so the oracle

sex′tus   lu krē′shia

was fulfilled which foretold that he should follow Tarquin as
ruler of the city.

Tarquin the Proud was not content, however, to see his kingdom slip from him so easily; and the Roman people were soon
5 obliged to fight for the right of governing themselves. Their
first trouble came from within the city itself; and this, perhaps,
no one had expected.

There were some of the people of Rome who were not pleased
at the expulsion of the king, and who would have been glad to
10 have him back with them again. These persons were young
men of high family and much wealth, who had been the companions of the young princes, and who had enjoyed rights and
privileges under the rule of Tarquin which were now taken away
from them. They complained bitterly of this, and said that,
15 though the rest of the people had gained by having the Tarquins
go, they had lost by it. So, when the opportunity offered itself,
they began working selfishly to return the king to power.

Their chance came when Tarquin sent men back to Rome to
claim the property which he and his sons had left behind
20 them, when they had been driven away. While these men were
in the city, they made a plot with the dissatisfied young nobles
to place King Tarquin on his throne once more. This was
treason on the part of the young nobles; but they cared more
for their own pleasures than they did for their country. How-
25 ever, the plot was discovered by a slave, and from him the consuls
learned of it. When the plotters had been seized, it was found
that among them were the two sons of the consul, Brutus himself.

It was part of the duty of the consul to act as judge in the
trial of prisoners, and this made the situation doubly terrible for
30 Brutus. But he was a true Roman, and loved his country even
more than he did his own children. He took his seat with the
other consul, and, when the young men were led before the
judges, he joined in condemning them all to death. Then the
prisoners were given into charge of attendants of the consuls,
35 called lictors, who each carried a battle-axe, bound into a bundle

of rods, as a sign that the consuls had the right to punish offenders with flogging and with death itself. They made the erring young nobles suffer the full severity of the law, and the Romans saw, with admiration and pity, that the stern virtue of Brutus did not fail him even when the welfare of his country demanded that his sons be put to death before his eyes.

Tarquin was only made more angry and determined by the failure of this plot. He now decided that if he could not get back his throne by treachery, he would try to do so by open war. He went about from city to city, begging help from the enemies of Rome to bring his people back under his rule once more. No matter how often he was refused, or how often he was defeated in battle when he did succeed in raising a force to lead against the Romans, he was always ready to try again.

At last Tarquin secured the help of Lars Porsena, who ruled over a part of Tuscany, as the district is called which lies north and west of the Tiber.

When the Romans heard this news, they were filled with dismay; and from all sides the country people flocked into the city. Never before had so great a danger threatened the place. The senate and consuls prepared as well as they could to meet the attack, and tried to hope that they might still be able to defeat their enemies.

Just across the river from Rome was a long, high hill. Here the Romans had built a fort as a protection to the city; and to connect this with Rome, a wooden bridge had long ago been placed across the rapid current of the Tiber. If the Romans could hold this height and the bridge below it the city would be safe. But by a quick march and fierce attack Lars Porsena and the Tarquins seized the hill. Then their soldiers pushed on to gain the bridge also, while many of the Romans who guarded it were struck with fear and turned to take refuge in the city.

At this moment a Roman, named Horatius, rushed in among

lärs por′se na   tus′kan i

his countrymen, laying hold of them, and standing in the way of their flight.

"Why do you flee?" he cried. "If you give up the bridge there will soon be more of the enemy in Rome than here. Break
5 down the timbers with fire and sword before you go! I will guard the entrance for you as well as one man may."

At these words the soldiers were seized with shame. Two of their number stepped to Horatius's side to defend the narrow entrance with him, and the others fell to work tearing down the
10 bridge behind them. Until the last beams were ready to fall Horatius and his comrades stood at the end, holding all the army of Lars Porsena in check upon the other side. Though many tried to overcome them, no man proved himself a match for them. Wounded but unflinching, they fought until the bridge
15 began to tremble, and the laboring soldiers warned them to return while there was still a way. At the call Horatius's companions fell back, step by step, but their leader lingered, fighting to the last. Then, just as he had turned to cross, with a mighty crash the bridge fell; and he was left, cut off among his enemies. En-
20 trusting himself to Father Tiber, he plunged into the river, though he was weary and wounded from the fight, and his armor weighed heavily upon him. Many times he seemed sinking in midstream, but each time he rose again. At last, he felt the bottom under his feet, and safely climbed the other shore.

25 The city was saved, and mainly by Horatius. The state was grateful to him for his brave deed, and the senate ordered that he should have as much of the public land as he could plough around in one day. Later, his statue was set up in the forum, but best of all was the gratitude which the people showed him at
30 the time. Then, when food became scarce because of the war with Lars Porsena, the citizens each brought to the house of Horatius little gifts of grain and wine, so that whatever suffering might come upon themselves, there would still be plenty in the house of the man who had saved Rome.

HORATIUS*

Thomas Babington Macaulay

1

Lars Porsena of Clusium
  By the Nine Gods he swore
That the great house of Tarquin
  Should suffer wrong no more.
By the Nine Gods he swore it,
  And named a trysting day,
And bade his messengers ride forth,
East and west and south and north,
  To summon his array.

2

East and west and south and north
  The messengers ride fast,
And tower and town and cottage
  Have heard the trumpet's blast.
Shame on the false Etruscan
  Who lingers in his home,
When Porsena of Clusium
  Is on the march for Rome.

11*

And now hath every city
  Sent up her tale of men;
The foot are fourscore thousand.
  The horse are thousands ten.
Before the gates of Sutrium
  Is met the great array.

* Certain stanzas are omitted as indicated by the stanza numbering but the story of the poem is complete.

A proud man was Lars Porsena
  Upon this trysting day.

13

But by the yellow Tiber
  Was tumult and affright:
From all the spacious champaign
  To Rome men took their flight.
A mile around the city,
  The throng stopped up the ways;
A fearful sight it was to see
  Through two long nights and days.

16

Now, from the rock Tarpeian,
  Could the wan burghers spy
The line of blazing villages
  Red in the midnight sky.
The Fathers of the City,
  They sat all night and day,
For every hour some horseman came
  With tidings of dismay.

17

To eastward and to westward
  Have spread the Tuscan bands;
Nor house, nor fence, nor dovecote
  In Crustumerium stands.
Verbenna down to Ostia
  Hath wasted all the plain;
Astur hath stormed Janiculum,
  And the stout guards are slain.

18

I wis, in all the Senate,
  There was no heart so bold.

But sore it ached, and fast it beat,
   When that ill news was told.
Forthwith up rose the Consul,
   Up rose the Fathers all,
In haste they girded up their gowns,
   And hied them to the wall.

19

They held a council standing
   Before the River-Gate;
Short time was there, ye well may guess,
   For musing or debate.
Out spake the Consul roundly:
   "The bridge must straight go down;
For, since Janiculum is lost,
   Nought else can save the town."

20

Just then a scout came flying,
   All wild with haste and fear:
"To arms! to arms! Sir Consul:
   Lars Porsena is here."
On the low hills to westward
   The Consul fixed his eye,
And saw the swarthy storm of dust,
   Rise fast along the sky.

21

And nearer fast and nearer
   Doth the red whirlwind come;
And louder still and still more loud,
From underneath that rolling cloud,
Is heard the trumpet's war-note proud,
   The trampling, and the hum.

And plainly and more plainly
  Now through the gloom appears,
Far to left and far to right,
In broken gleams of dark-blue light,
The long array of helmets bright,
  The long array of spears.

22

And plainly and more plainly,
  Above that glimmering line,
Now might ye see the banners
  Of twelve fair cities shine;
But the banner of proud Clusium
  Was highest of them all,
The terror of the Umbrian,
  The terror of the Gaul.

26

But the Consul's brow was sad,
  And the Consul's speech was low,
And darkly looked he at the wall,
  And darkly at the foe.
"Their van will be upon us
  Before the bridge goes down;
And if they once may win the bridge,
  What hope to save the town?"

27

Then out spake brave Horatius,
  The Captain of the Gate:
"To every man upon this earth
  Death cometh soon or late.
And how can man die better
  Than facing fearful odds,

For the ashes of his fathers,
   And the temples of his Gods,

29

"Hew down the bridge, Sir Consul,
   With all the speed ye may;
I, with two more to help me,
   Will hold the foe in play.
In yon strait path a thousand
   May well be stopped by three.
Now who will stand on either hand,
   And keep the bridge with me?"

30

Then out spake Spurius Lartius;
   A Ramnian proud was he:
"Lo, I will stand at thy right hand,
   And keep the bridge with thee."
And out spake strong Herminius
   Of Titian blood was he:
"I will abide on thy left side,
   And keep the bridge with thee."

31

"Horatius," quoth the Consul,
   "As thou sayest, so let it be."
And straight against that great array
   Forth went the dauntless Three.
For Romans in Rome's quarrel
   Spared neither land nor gold,
Nor son, nor wife, nor limb, nor life,
   In the brave days of old.

32

Then none was for a party;
　Then all were for the state;
Then the great man helped the poor,
　And the poor man loved the great:
Then lands were fairly portioned;
　Then spoils were fairly sold:
The Romans were like brothers
　In the brave days of old.

34

Now while the Three were tightening
　Their harness on their backs,
The Consul was the foremost man
　To take in hand an axe:
And Fathers mixed with Commons
　Seized hatchet, bar, and crow,
And smote upon the planks above,
　And loosed the props below.

35

Meanwhile the Tuscan army,
　Right glorious to behold,
Came flashing back the noonday light,
Rank behind rank, like surges bright
　Of a broad sea of gold.
Four hundred trumpets sounded
　A peal of warlike glee,
As that great host, with measured tread,
And spears advanced, and ensigns spread,
Rolled slowly towards the bridge's head,
　Where stood the dauntless Three.

36

The Three stood calm and silent,
    And looked upon the foes,
And a great shout of laughter
    From all the vanguard rose;
And forth three chiefs came spurring
    Before that deep array;
To earth they sprang, their swords they drew,
And lifted high their shields, and flew
    To win the narrow way;

37

Aunus from green Tifernum,
    Lord of the Hill of Vines;
And Seius, whose eight hundred slaves
    Sicken in Ilva's mines;
And Picus, long to Clusium
    Vassal in peace and war,
Who led to fight his Umbrian powers
From that grey crag where, girt with towers,
The fortress of Nequinum lowers
    O'er the pale waves of Nar.

38

Stout Lartius hurled down Aunus
    Into the stream beneath:
Herminius struck at Seius,
    And clove him to the teeth:
At Picus brave Horatius
    Darted one fiery thrust;
And the proud Umbrian's gilded arms
    Clashed in the bloody dust.

39

Then Ocnus of Falerii
　　Rushed on the Roman **Three**;
And Lausulus of Urgo,
　　The rover of the sea;
And Aruns of Volsinium,
　　Who slew the great wild boar,
The great wild boar that had his den
Amidst the reeds of Cosa's fen,
And wasted fields, and slaughtered men,
　　Along Albinia's shore.

40

Herminius smote down Aruns:
　　Lartius laid Ocnus low:
Right to the heart of Lausulus
　　Horatius sent a blow.
"Lie there," he cried, "fell pirate!
　　No more, aghast and pale,
From Ostia's walls the crowd shall mark
The track of thy destroying bark.
No more Campania's hinds shall fly
To woods and caverns when they spy
　　Thy thrice accursed sail."

41

But now no sound of laughter
　　Was heard among the foes.
A wild and wrathful clamor
　　From all the vanguard rose.
Six spears' lengths from the entrance
　　Halted that deep array,
And for a space no man came forth
　　To win the narrow way.

42

But hark! the cry is Astur;
   And lo! the ranks divide;
And the great Lord of Luna
   Comes with his stately stride.
Upon his ample shoulders
   Clangs loud the fourfold shield
And in his hand he shakes the brand
   Which none but he can wield.

43

He smiled on those bold Romans
   A smile serene and high;
He eyed the flinching Tuscans,
   And scorn was in his eye.
Quoth he, "The she-wolf's litter
   Stand savagely at bay:
But will ye dare to follow,
   If Astur clears the way?"

44

Then, whirling up his broadsword
   With both hands to the height,
He rushed against Horatius,
   And smote with all his might.
With shield and blade Horatius
   Right deftly turned the blow.
The blow, though turned, came yet too nigh;
It missed his helm, but gashed his thigh:
The Tuscans raised a joyful cry
   To see the red blood flow.

45

He reeled, and on Herminius
　He leaned one breathing-space;
Then, like a wild cat mad with wounds,
　Sprang right at Astur's face.
Through teeth, and skull, and helmet
　So fierce a thrust he sped,
The good sword stood a hand-breadth out
　Behind the Tuscan's head.

46

And the great Lord of Luna
　Fell at that deadly stroke,
As falls on Mount Alvernus
　A thunder-smitten oak.
Far o'er the crashing forest
　The giant arms lie spread;
And the pale augurs, muttering low,
　Gaze on the blasted head.

47

On Astur's throat Horatius
　Right firmly pressed his heel,
And thrice and four times tugged amain,
　Ere he wrenched out the steel.
"And see," he cried, "the welcome,
　Fair guests, that waits you here!
What noble Lucumo comes next
　To taste our Roman cheer?"

48

But at his haughty challenge
　A sullen murmur ran,
Mingled of wrath, and shame, and dread,
　Along that glittering van.

There lacked not men of prowess,
  Nor men of lordly race;
For all Etruria's noblest
  Were round the fatal place.

49

But all Etruria's noblest
  Felt their hearts sink to see
On the earth the bloody corpses,
  In the path the dauntless Three.
And from the ghastly entrance
  Where those bold Romans stood,
All shrank, like boys who unaware,
Ranging the woods to start a hare,
Come to the mouth of the dark lair
Where, growling low, a fierce old bear
  Lies amidst bones and blood.

50

Was none who would be foremost
  To lead such dire attack:
But those behind cried "Forward!"
  And those before cried, "Back!"
And backward now and forward
  Wavers the deep array;
And on the tossing sea of steel,
To and fro the standards reel;
And the victorious trumpet-peal
  Dies fitfully away.

51

Yet one man for one moment
  Stood out before the crowd;
Well known was he to all the Three,
  And they gave him greeting loud.

"Now welcome, welcome, Sextus!
    Now welcome to thy home!
Why dost thou stay, and turn away
    Here lies the road to Rome."

52

Thrice looked he at the city;
    Thrice looked he at the dead;
And thrice came on in fury,
    And thrice turned back in dread;
And white with fear and hatred,
    Scowled at the narrow way
Where, wallowing in a pool of blood,
    The bravest Tuscans lay.

53

But meanwhile axe and lever
    Have manfully been plied;
And now the bridge hangs tottering
    Above the boiling tide.
"Come back, come back, Horatius!"
    Loud cried the Fathers all,
"Back, Lartius! back, Herminius!
    Back, ere the ruin fall!"

54

Back darted Spurius Lartius;
    Herminius darted back:
And, as they passed, beneath their feet
    They felt the timbers crack.
But when they turned their faces,
    And on the farther shore
Saw brave Horatius stand alone,
    They would have crossed once more.

55

But with a crash like thunder
　Fell every loosened beam,
And, like a dam, the mighty wreck
　Lay right athwart the stream;
And a long shout of triumph
　Rose from the walls of Rome,
As to the highest turret-tops
　Was splashed the yellow foam.

56

And like a horse unbroken
　When first he feels the rein,
The furious river struggled hard,
　And tossed his tawny mane,
And burst the curb, and bounded,
　Rejoicing to be free;
And whirling down, in fierce career
Battlement, and plank, and pier,
　Rushed headlong to the sea.

57

Alone stood brave Horatius,
　But constant still in mind;
Thrice thirty thousand foes before,
　And the broad flood behind.
"Down with him!" cried false Sextus,
　With a smile on his pale face.
"Now yield thee," cried Lars Porsena,
　"Now yield thee to our grace."

58

Round turned he, as not deigning
　Those craven ranks to see;

Nought spake he to Lars Porsena,
　　To Sextus nought spake he;
But he saw on Palatinus
　　The white porch of his home;
And he spake to the noble river
　　That rolls by the towers of Rome.

59

"O, Tiber! father Tiber!
　　To whom the Romans pray,
A Roman's life, a Roman's arms,
　　Take thou in charge this day."
So he spake, and speaking sheathed
　　The good sword by his side,
And with his harness on his back,
　　Plunged headlong in the tide.

60

No sound of joy or sorrow
　　Was heard from either bank;
But friends and foes, in dumb surprise,
With parted lips and straining eyes,
　　Stood gazing where he sank;
And when above the surges
　　They saw his crest appear,
All Rome sent forth a rapturous cry,
And even the ranks of Tuscany
　　Could scarce forbear to cheer.

61

But fiercely ran the current,
　　Swollen high by months of rain:
And fast his blood was flowing
　　And he was sore in pain

And heavy with his armor,
   And spent with changing blows:
And oft they thought him sinking,
   But still again he rose.

62

Never, I ween, did swimmer,
   In such an evil case,
Struggle through such a raging flood
   Safe to the landing-place:
But his limbs were borne up bravely
   By the brave heart within;
And our good father Tiber
   Bore bravely up his chin.

63

"Curse on him!" quoth false Sextus;
   "Will not the villain drown?
But for this stay, ere close of day
   We should have sacked the town!"
"Heaven help him!" quoth Lars Porsena,
   "And bring him safe to shore;
For such a gallant feat of arms
   Was never seen before."

64

And now he feels the bottom;
   Now on dry earth he stands;
Now round him throng the Fathers
   To press his gory hands;
And now, with shouts and clapping,
   And noise of weeping loud,
He enters through the River-Gate,
   Borne by the joyous crowd.

65

They gave him of the corn-land,
    That was of public right,
As much as two strong oxen
    Could plough from morn till night;
And they made a molten image,
    And set it up on high,
And there it stands unto this day
    To witness if I lie.

66

It stands in the Comitium,
    Plain for all folk to see;
Horatius in his harness,
    Halting upon one knee:
And underneath is written,
    In letters all of gold,
How valiantly he kept the bridge,
    In the brave days of old.

67

And still his name sounds stirring
    Unto the men of Rome,
As the trumpet-blast that cries to them
    To charge the Volscian home;
And wives still pray to Juno
    For boys with hearts as bold
As his who kept the bridge so well
    In the brave days of old.

68

And in the nights of winter,
    When the cold north winds blow,

And the long howling of the wolves
  Is heard amidst the snow:
When round the lonely cottage
  Roars loud the tempest's din,
And the good logs of Algidus
  Roar louder yet within;

69

When the oldest cask is opened,
  And the largest lamp is lit;
When the chestnuts glow in the embers,
  And the kid turns on the spit;
When young and old in circle
  Around the firebrands close;
When the girls are weaving baskets,
  And the lads are shaping bows;

70

When the goodman mends his armor,
  And trims his helmet's plume;
When the goodwife's shuttle merrily
  Goes flashing through the loom;
With weeping and with laughter
  Still is the story told,
How well Horatius kept the bridge
  In the brave days of old.

HELPS TO STUDY

Biographical and Historical: Thomas Babington Macaulay (1800-1859) was an English historian and essayist. "Horatius" is taken from his collection of poems called "Lays of Ancient Rome."

The story of the overthrow of the last Roman King and of the brave deeds of Horatius in time of war, is told in prose on pages 254-8.

This war between Rome and Etruria furnishes the setting for the poem, which is a fine presentment of courage and patriotism. Etruria of ancient times nearly corresponded, in extent, to modern Tuscany, a province in Italy. Twelve powerful cities in Etruria united and formed "The Confederation of Etruria." Macaulay mentions many of these in the poem, thereby adding vividness to the story. "Lucumo" (lū'cumo) was the title applied to the chief who ruled over each of the "twelve fair cities" and "Lars" was an Etruscan title meaning lord. Porsena (por'sena) was king of the Etruscan town of Clusium (klō'shium), modern Chiusi. The poem shows how the chiefs responded to his call for aid.

Notes and Questions.

On a map of Italy find the province of Tuscany, the Apennines, the Tiber, Rome, Pisa, Sardinia, Elba (ancient Ilva) and Marseilles (ancient Massilia).

Why was Lars Porsena engaged in war with Rome?

Read the stanzas which tell of the gathering of the army. Read those which tell of the effect of this in Rome.

The Janiculum was the highest of the seven hills of Rome. It stretches along the right or west bank of the river. On the east side is the Palatine, the oldest part of the city. Around this, in ancient times, there was a wall with three gates, the one near the bridge being the "River Gate." Draw a sketch of all this and indicate the position of "The Three."

There were three ancient tribes in Rome. The companions of Horatius belonged to two of these, Spu'rius Lar'tius being a Ramnian and Hermin'ius a Titian.

How does the common danger level class distinctions?

What do you think of Horatius when he answers neither Sextus nor Porsena?

Note the difference between Sextus and Lars Porsena.

What were Horatius's rewards? Which do you think gave Horatius greater satisfaction?

In how many different ways is the memory of Horatius and his deed preserved?

Compare the patriotism of Horatius and that of Brutus, told in the prose story preceding the poem.

Words and Phrases for Discussion

"the great house of Tarquin"
"trysting day"
"tale of men"
"I wis"

"the Fathers of the City"
"the rock Tarpeian"
"the pale augurs"
"the she-wolf's litter"

PART III

BIOGRAPHIES

Boston had long been the center of such publishing as was done in colonial times, but with the growth of Philadelphia shortly before the Revolution, newspapers and magazines also began to appear there. About that time, too, Philadelphia became the home of a Boston lad who, almost penniless, came to try his fortunes in the Quaker City and later to honor it as her greatest citizen.

The interesting story of Franklin's life is best learned from his own "Autobiography," a selection from which is given in the following pages. Like several others

BENJAMIN FRANKLIN
1706-1790

of our great American authors, Franklin was an editor. He was also a practical printer; but he achieved such great things in other fields that the world has been accustomed to think of him as Franklin the statesman or the scientist, rather than as Franklin the printer or the editor. Every schoolboy knows of his famous kite experiment, by which he proved that lightning and electricity are one and the same thing. He turned this discovery to practical use in the invention of the lightning-rod. He was the inventor of the "Franklin stove" and many other useful devices, all of which he refused to patent, wishing humanity to have the free and full benefit of them. He drew up the first plan for the union of the colonies. His name appears as a signer of all of those great national documents, the Declaration of Independence, the Treaty of Peace with Great Britain, and the Constitution of the United States.

THE NEW YORK GROUP

Manhattan Island and the picturesque region about it, with its commanding position at the entrance to a great inland waterway, was from the first a prize for which the nations from across

WASHINGTON IRVING
1783-1859

the sea had contended. Such a mingling of diverse people must give rise to interesting experiences, and when someone appears who can put the story of those events into an attractive form, then we begin to have real literature. But we had to wait until this prince among story-tellers had grown to manhood and given his sketches of this region to the world before we could claim at last to have a work of real American literature. Irving is best known as a humorist and a charming storyteller, but he has also written some serious and tender works. His life of Washington was a tribute of loving reverence to the great American after whom he was named. As a boy, Irving was of a rather mischievous turn, a trait which perhaps helped to make him the first "American Humorist." Indeed, it has been said that "before Irving there was no laughter in the land." He is called the Father of American Literature, the Gentle Humorist.

Imagine yourself in New York city the latter part of the last century. If you were walking up Broadway almost any morning, your attention would be attracted to a venerable look-

WILLIAM CULLEN BRYANT
1794-1878

ing man, with heavy, flowing, snow-white hair and beard, whom you would be quite likely to meet swinging along at a vigorous pace. Even though not a New Yorker, you would not need to be told that this man is our first American poet, with whose verses you are already familiar; and you would probably know, too, that he is also editor of the *Evening Post* and that, although now past eighty, he is on his way to his office, walking from his home some two miles away, as he has done daily, rain or shine, for over half a century.

Bryant grew up in the picturesque hill country of western Massachusetts. From infancy he showed remarkable powers of mind. He could read by the time he was two years old, wrote verses at nine, and when scarcely eighteen wrote his most noted poem, "Thanatopsis." In manner, Bryant was kindly and courteous. He had a wonderful memory and it is said he could repeat "by heart" every poem he had written.

THE BOSTON GROUP

During the middle and latter part of the nineteenth century Boston became the center of a remarkable group of scholars and writers, several of whom are represented in the following pages.

RALPH WALDO
EMERSON
1803-1882

The oldest of these, Emerson, was born in the city, not far from Franklin's birthplace. His ancestors had been clergymen for many generations. His father dying when Waldo was but eight years old, his mother "took boarders" and the boy had to do his share towards supporting the family, by running errands, driving the neighbors' cows to pasture across the Commons, and helping his mother with her work. He earned his way through Harvard College by doing janitor service, waiting on tables, acting as errand boy for the president, and by such other "odd jobs" as he could find. In a series of contests he won two prizes for essays, and one of thirty dollars for declamation. This he carried to his mother "to buy a new shawl."

Emerson was tall and slender of stature, with eyes of the "strongest and brightest blue." In manner he was calm and kindly. His "Rules for Reading" are worthy to be considered in this day of many books:

> "Never read a book that is not a year old,
> Never read any but famed books."

The "Old Manse" of Hawthorne's romance was once the home of the Emersons, and it was from the windows of an upper room in it that Emerson's grandmother watched the battle of Concord

Bridge which Emerson has immortalized in his poem.   Emerson has been called the Concord Sage.

Irving found much of his literary materials in the local history of the region in and around New York.   He wrote about nearby places and happenings.   Among those who went still

NATHANIEL HAWTHORNE 1804-1864

further into this new mode of writing was a quiet young man of Salem, Massachusetts—Nathaniel Hawthorne.   His ancestors were among the earliest Puritan settlers.   Nathaniel, when a boy, had been crippled by an accident in playing ball. This led him to a secluded life and the companionship of books. He had a vivid imagination and was fond of inventing stories for the entertainment of his friends.   He graduated from Bowdoin College in the class of 1825.   When he began to think of a career it was quite natural that he should turn to literature, and that in looking about him for material he should follow the example of Irving and choose his materials from those stirring scenes of which he had an intimate, almost personal, knowledge.   "The House of the Seven Gables" is a tale of the house in which he lived many years.   And thus it came that we have in Nathaniel Hawthorne not only our first writer of pure romance, but one who is still our greatest in that field of literature.

Hawthorne's personal appearance was in keeping with his gentle manners.   He had a handsome face, with "the most wonderful eyes in the world," says one admirer.   Another of his friends said: "His voice touched the ear like melody."   He has been called America's Prose Poet; the Romancer without a Peer.

Our next poet in point of time after Bryant, and our most popular poet, was a native of Maine and a graduate of Bowdoin

HENRY WADSWORTH LONGFELLOW 1807-1882

College in the same class with Hawthorne.   Henry Wadsworth Longfellow comes of early New England ancestry, his mother being a daughter of General Wadsworth of the War of the Revolution.   After his graduation from college he spent several years abroad and upon his return to America held rofessorships first in Bowdoin and later in Harvard College. ongfellow is the poet who has spoken most sincerely and sympathetically to the hearts of the common people and to children. This is due to his genuine kindliness. He was a lover of children, and especially of little girls. The style of Longfellow's poetry is notable for its simplicity and grace.

As Emerson came from a family of preachers, so Lowell came from a line of lawyers, his family having been distinguished in that profession in every generation since their coming

JAMES RUSSELL LOWELL 1819-1891

to America. His mother was a fine musician, and it was from her that Lowell inherited his taste for poetry. As a boy he had free access to his father's library, one of the oldest and best private libraries of that time. He had every opportunity of education which wealth and leisure afforded, but at college he says he "read nearly everything except the books prescribed by the faculty." After graduating from Harvard he studied law and opened an office in Boston. But he soon decided that this was not the business for him. He published some poems, edited a magazine, and in 1855 succeeded Longfellow as professor at Harvard, and, like him, spent some years in study abroad. He was one of the founders of the *Atlantic Monthly* and was its first editor.

Lowell was considered one of the greatest scholars in America in his time. He was of a happier disposition than Bryant, and has been called the Poet of June, as Bryant has been called the Poet of Autumn.

Near the town of Haverhill, Massachusetts, not far from Hawthorne's birthplace, is the old homestead where Whittier was born. He had very little opportunity for education beyond

JOHN GREENLEAF WHITTIER 1807-1892

what the district school afforded, except what he was able to give himself. In contrast with Lowell's splendid library, that of Whittier's father contained, as he says, "not a dozen books." His two years' attendance at Haverhill Academy

was paid for by his own work at making ladies' slippers a
twenty-five cents a pair. He began writing verses almost a
soon as he learned to write at all, but his father discourage
this as frivolous, saying it would "never give him bread." H
wrote many idylls of domestic life, such as "Snow-Bound," an
poems of farm life, of which the "Barefoot Boy" is a goo
example. Whittier's ruling traits of character are patriotism
love of freedom, and piety. He was fond of his friends, of chil
dren, of animals, of quiet and peace, and of nature. He i
called the Quaker Poet.

We now come to the merriest, most jovial of the group rep
resented in our selections, the witty professor of anatomy i
Harvard College. He, also, comes of old Puritan stock. Hi

OLIVER WENDELL
HOLMES
1809-1894

grandfather was a surgeon in the Wa
of the Revolution. His father was
Baptist minister for over forty years i
Boston. His mother was descended from the Dutch settlers o
New York. Doctor Holmes, after studying some years abroad
practiced medicine for a time; then for the remainder of hi
long, busy life occupied the chair (the "settee," as he humor
ously called it) of anatomy, first at Dartmouth, then at Harvard
While his work as an author would have been enough to keep
an ordinary man busy, it was rather a diversion for our ener
getic Doctor. He was one of the founders of the *Atlanti*
Monthly and one of the most frequent contributors to it.

In appearance, Doctor Holmes was of small body, fastidiou
in dress, "quick and nervous in his movements," with a "win
ning expression" of countenance. There was always a smil
on his face and a twinkle in his eye. He was the humoris
among American poets and is called the Poet of Mirth.

MY ARRIVAL IN PHILADELPHIA*

BENJAMIN FRANKLIN

I was in my working dress, my best clothes being to come round by sea. I was dirty from my journey; my pockets were stuffed out with shirts and stockings, and I knew no soul nor where to look for lodging. I was fatigued with traveling, rowing, and want of rest, I was very hungry; and my whole stock of cash consisted of a Dutch dollar, and about a shilling in copper. The latter I gave the people of the boat for my passage, who at first refused it, on account of my rowing; but I insisted on their taking it. A man being sometimes more generous when he has but a little money than when he has plenty, perhaps through fear of being thought to have but little.

Then I walked up the street, gazing about till near the market-house I met a boy with bread. I had made many a meal on bread, and, inquiring where he got it, I went immediately to the baker's he directed me to, in Second-street, and asked for biscuit, intending such as we had in Boston; but they, it seems, were not made in Philadelphia. Then I asked for a three-penny loaf, and was told they had none such. So not considering or knowing the difference of money, and the greater cheapness nor the names of his bread, I bade him give me three-penny worth of any sort. He gave me, accordingly, three great puffy rolls. I was surprised at the quantity, but took it, and, having no room in my pockets, walked off with a roll under each arm, and eating the other.

*From Franklin's *Autobiography*.

Thus I went up Market-street as far as Fourth-street, passing by the door of Mr. Read, my future wife's father; when she, standing in the door, saw me, and thought I made, as I certainly did, a most awkward, ridiculous appearance. Then I turned
5 and went down Chestnut-street and part of Walnut-street, eating my roll all the way, and, coming round, found myself again at Market-street wharf, near the boat I came in, to which I went for a draught of the river water; and, being filled with one of my rolls, gave the other two to a woman and her child that came
10 down the river in the boat with us, and were waiting to go farther.

Thus refreshed, I walked again up the street, which by this time had many clean-dressed people in it, who were all walking the same way. I joined them, and thereby was led into the
15 great meeting-house of the Quakers near the market. I sat down among them, and, after looking round awhile and hearing nothing said, being very drowsy through labor and want of rest the preceding night, I fell fast asleep, and continued so till the meeting broke up, when one was kind enough to rouse me. This was,
20 therefore, the first house I was in, or slept in, in Philadelphia.

Walking down again toward the river, and, looking in the faces of people, I met a young Quakerman, whose countenance I liked, and, accosting him, requested he would tell me where a stranger could get lodging. We were then near the sign of the Three
25 Mariners. "Here," says he, "is one place that entertains strangers, but it is not a reputable house; if thee wilt walk with me, I'll show thee a better." He brought me to the Crooked Billet in Water-street. Here I got a dinner; and, while I was eating it, several sly questions were asked me, as it seemed to be sus-
30 pected from my youth and appearance, that I might be some runaway.

After dinner, my sleepiness returned, and being shown to a bed, I lay down without undressing, and slept till six in the evening, was called to supper, went to bed again very early, and slept
35 soundly till next morning. Then I made myself as tidy as I

could, and went to Andrew Bradford the printer's. I found in the shop the old man his father, whom I had seen at New York, and who, traveling on horseback, had got to Philadelphia before me. He introduced me to his son, who received me civilly, gave me a breakfast, but told me he did not at present want a hand, being lately supplied with one; but there was another printer in town, lately set up, one Keimer, who, perhaps, might employ me; if not, I should be welcome to lodge at his house, and he would give me a little work to do now and then till fuller business should offer.

The old gentleman said he would go with me to the new printer; and when we found him, "Neighbor," says Bradford, "I have brought to see you a young man of your business; perhaps you may want such a one." He asked me a few questions, put a composing stick in my hand to see how I worked, and then said he would employ me soon, though he had just then nothing for me to do; and, taking old Bradford, whom he had never seen before, to be one of the town's people that had a good will for him, entered into a conversation on his present undertaking and prospects; while Bradford, not discovering that he was the other printer's father, on Keimer's saying he expected soon to get the greatest part of the business into his own hands, drew him on by artful questions, and starting little doubts, to explain all his views, what interest he relied on, and in what manner he intended to proceed. I, who stood by and heard all, saw immediately that one of them was a crafty old sophister, and the other a mere novice. Bradford left me with Keimer, who was greatly surprised when I told him who the old man was.

Keimer's printing-house, I found, consisted of an old shattered press, and one small, worn-out font of English,[1] which he was then using himself, composing an Elegy on Aquila Rose, before mentioned, an ingenious young man, of excellent character, much

[1] The name given to a certain size of type.

respected in the town, clerk of the Assembly, and a pretty poet. Keimer made verses too, but very indifferently. He could not be said to write them, for his manner was to compose them in the types directly out of his head. So there being no copy, but one
5 pair of cases,[1] and the Elegy likely to require all the letter, no one could help him. I endeavored to put his press (which he had not yet used, and of which he understood nothing) into order fit to be worked with, and, promising to come and print off his Elegy as soon as he should have got it ready, I returned to Brad-
10 ford's, who gave me a little job to do for the present, and there I lodged and dieted. A few days after, Keimer sent for me to print off the Elegy. And now he had got another pair of cases, and a pamphlet to reprint, on which he set me to work.

These two printers I found poorly qualified for their business.
15 Bradford had not been bred to it, and was very illiterate; and Keimer, though something of a scholar, was a mere compositor, knowing nothing of presswork. He had been one of the French prophets, and could act their enthusiastic agitations. At this time he did not profess any particular religion, but something
20 of all on occasion; was very ignorant of the world, and had, as I afterward found, a good deal of the knave in his composition. He did not like my lodging at Bradford's while I worked with him. He had a house, indeed, but without furniture, so he could not lodge me; but he got me a lodging at Mr. Read's,
25 before mentioned, who was the owner of his house; and, my chest and clothes being come by this time, I made rather a more respectable appearance in the eyes of Miss Read than I had done when she first happened to see me eating my roll in the street.

30 I began now to have some acquaintance among the young people of the town, that were lovers of reading, with whom I spent my evenings very pleasantly; and gaining money by my

---

[1] Each compositor uses a separate pair of cases, an "upper case," which contains capital letters, and a "lower case," which contains small letters.

industry and frugality, I lived very agreeably, forgetting Boston as much as I could, and not desiring that any there should know where I resided, except my friend Collins, who was in my secret, and kept it when I wrote to him. At length, an incident happened that sent me back again much sooner than I had intended. I had a brother-in-law, Robert Holmes, master of a sloop that traded between Boston and Delaware. He being at Newcastle, forty miles below Philadelphia, heard there of me, and wrote me a letter mentioning the concern of my friends in Boston at my abrupt departure, assuring me of their good will to me, and that every thing would be accommodated to my mind if I would return, to which he exhorted me very earnestly. I wrote an answer to his letter, thanked him for his advice, but stated my reasons for quitting Boston fully and in such a light as to convince him I was not so wrong as he had apprehended.

Sir William Keith, governor of the province, was then at Newcastle, and Captain Holmes, happening to be in company with him when my letter came to hand, spoke to him of me, and showed him the letter. The governor read it, and seemed surprised when he was told my age. He said I appeared a young man of promising parts, and therefore should be encouraged; the printers at Philadelphia were wretched ones; and, if I would set up there, he made no doubt I should succeed; for his part, he would procure me the public business, and do me every other service in his power. This my brother-in-law afterwards told me in Boston, but I knew as yet nothing of it; when, one day, Keimer and I being at work together near the window, we saw the governor and another gentleman (which proved to be Colonel French, of Newcastle), finely dressed, come directly across the street to our house, and heard them at the door.

Keimer ran down immediately, thinking it a visit to him; but the governor inquired for me, came up, and with a condescension and politeness I had been quite unused to, made me many compliments, desired to be acquainted with me, blamed me kindly for not having made myself known to him when I first came to

the place, and would have me away with him to the tavern, where he was going with Colonel French to taste, as he said, some excellent Madeira. I was not a little surprised, and Keimer stared like a pig poisoned. I went, however, with the governor
5 and Colonel French to a tavern, at the corner of Third-street, and over the Madeira he proposed my setting up my business, laid before me the probabilities of success, and both he and Colonel French assured me I should have their interest and influence in procuring the public business of both governments. On my
10 doubting whether my father would assist me in it, Sir William said he would give me a letter to him, in which he would state the advantages, and he did not doubt of prevailing with him. So it was concluded I should return to Boston in the first vessel, with the governor's letter recommending me to my father. In
15 the mean time the intention was to be kept a secret, and I went on working with Keimer as usual, the governor sending for me now and then to dine with him, a very great honor I thought it, and conversing with me in the most affable, familiar, and friendly manner imaginable.
20 About the end of April, 1724, a little vessel offered for Boston. I took leave of Keimer as going to see my friends. The governor gave me an ample letter, saying many flattering things of me to my father, and strongly recommending the project of my setting up at Philadelphia as a thing that must make my for-
25 tune. We struck on a shoal in going down the bay, and sprung a leak; we had a blustering time at sea, and were obliged to pump almost continually, at which I took my turn. We arrived safe, however, at Boston in about a fortnight.

HELPS TO STUDY

Notes and Questions

What tells you the events related in this story happened many years ago?

What trade had Franklin learned?

To whom did he apply for work?

What interest did Sir William Keith show in him?

Why did he return to Boston?

low long did it take him to reach Boston?

What time does it take now to go from Philadelphia to Boston?

What tells you Franklin was fond of reading?

Tell what you know of the author.

What is the most striking feature of Franklin's style, as shown in this selection?

Words and Phrases for Discussion

"accosting"

"affable"

"crafty"

"sophister"

"ingenious"

"illiterate"

"frugality"

"exhorted"

"apprehended"

"project"

"artful questions"

"enthusiastic agitations"

"promising parts"

"ample letter"

THE BOBOLINK

WASHINGTON IRVING

THE happiest bird of our spring, and one that rivals the European lark, in my estimation, is the Boblincon, or Bobolink, as he is commonly called. He arrives at that choice portion of our year, which, in this latitude, answers to the description of the month of May, so often given by the poets. With us, it begins about the middle of May, and lasts until nearly the middle of June. Earlier than this, winter is apt to return on its traces, and to blight the opening beauties of the year; and later than this, begin the parching, and panting, and dissolving heats of summer. But in this genial interval, nature is in all her freshness and fragrance; "the rains are over and gone, the flowers appear upon the earth, the time of the singing of birds is come, and the voice of the turtle is heard in the land." The trees are now in their fullest foliage and brightest verdure; the woods are gay with the clustered flowers of the laurel; the air is perfumed by the sweet-briar and the wild rose; the meadows are

enameled with clover-blossoms; while the young apple, the peach
and the plum, begin to swell, and the cherry to glow, among th
green leaves.

This is the chosen season of revelry of the Boblink. He come
5 amidst the pomp and fragrance of the season; his life seems al
sensibility and enjoyment, all song and sunshine. He is to b
found in the soft bosoms of the freshest and sweetest meadows
and is most in song when the clover is in blossom. He perche
on the topmost twig of a tree, or on some long flaunting weed
10 and as he rises and sinks with the breeze, pours forth a suc
cession of rich tinkling notes; crowding one upon another, like
the outpouring melody of the skylark, and possessing the same
rapturous character. Sometimes he pitches from the summi
of a tree, begins his song as soon as he gets upon the wing, and
15 flutters tremulously down to the earth, as if overcome with
ecstasy at his own music. Sometimes he is in pursuit of his
mate; always in full song, as if he would win her by his
melody; and always with the same appearance of intoxication
and delight.

20 Of the birds of our groves and meadows, the Boblink was
the envy of my boyhood. He crossed my path in the sweetest
weather, and the sweetest season of the year, when all nature
called to the fields, and the rural feeling throbbed in every bosom;
but when I, luckless urchin! was doomed to be mewed up, during
25 the livelong day, in that purgatory of boyhood, a school-room.
It seemed as if the little varlet mocked at me, as he flew by in
full song, and sought to taunt me with his happier lot. Oh, how
I envied him! No lessons, no tasks, no hateful school; nothing
but holiday, frolic, green fields, and fine weather. Had I been
30 then more versed in poetry, I might have addressed him in the
words of Logan to the cuckoo:

> Sweet bird! thy bower is ever green.
> Thy sky is ever clear;
> Thou hast no sorrow in thy note,
35 > No winter in thy year.

Oh! could I fly, I'd fly with thee;
    We'd make, on joyful wing,
Our annual visit round the globe,
    Companions of the spring!

5   Farther observation and experience have given me a different
idea of this little feathered voluptuary, which I will venture to
impart, for the benefit of my school-boy readers, who may regard
him with the same unqualified envy and admiration which I once
indulged. I have shown him only as I saw him at first, in what
10 I may call the poetical part of his career, when he in a manner
devoted himself to elegant pursuits and enjoyments, and was a
bird of music, and song, and taste, and sensibility, and refinement. While this lasted, he was sacred from injury; the very
school-boy would not fling a stone at him, and the merest rustic
15 would pause to listen to his strain. But mark the difference.
As the year advances, as the clover-blossoms disappear, and the
spring fades into summer, his notes cease to vibrate on the ear.
He gradually gives up his elegant tastes and habits, doffs his
poetical and professional suit of black, assumes a russet or rather
20 dusty garb, and enters into the gross enjoyments of common,
vulgar birds. He becomes a bon-vivant, a mere gourmand; thinking of nothing but good cheer, and gormandizing on the seeds
of the long grasses on which he lately swung, and chaunted so
musically. He begins to think there is nothing like "the joys
25 of the table," if I may be allowed to apply that convivial phrase
to his indulgences. He now grows discontented with plain, every-
day fare, and sets out on a gastronomical tour, in search of foreign luxuries. He is to be found in myriads among the reeds
of the Delaware, banqueting on their seeds; grows corpulent with
30 good feeding, and soon acquires the unlucky renown of the orto-
lan. Wherever he goes, pop! pop! pop! the rusty firelocks of the
country are cracking on every side; he sees his companions
falling by thousands around him; he is the *reed-bird*, the
much-sought-for tit-bit of the Pennsylvanian epicure.

Does he take warning and reform? Not he! He wings his flight still farther south, in search of other luxuries. We hear of him gorging himself in the rice swamps; filling himself with rice almost to bursting; he can hardly fly for corpulency. Last stage
5 of his career, we hear of him spitted by dozens, and served up on the table of the gourmand, the most vaunted of southern dainties, the *rice-bird* of the Carolinas.

Such is the story of the once musical and admired, but finally sensual and persecuted Bobolink. It contains a moral, worthy
10 the attention of all little birds and little boys; warning them to keep to those refined and intellectual pursuits, which raised him to so high a pitch of popularity, during the early part of his career; but to eschew all tendency to that gross and dissipated indulgence, which brought this mistaken little bird to an un-
15 timely end.

Which is all at present, from the well-wisher of little boys and little birds.

HELPS TO STUDY

Notes and Questions

Why does Irving speak of May as a "choice portion" of the year?

By what other names does he speak of this period?

What characteristics has the Bobolink?

What bird is to England what the Bobolink is to America?

In his boyhood how did the author regard the Bobolink?

Learn the beautiful lines Logan wrote to the cuckoo.

Why does Irving speak of the "poetical career" of the Bobolink?

What other career does this bird have?

By what different names is he called?

What lesson does the life of the Bobolink teach?

Words and Phrases for Discussion

"rivals"

"revelry"

"rapturous"

"intoxication"

"varlet"

"rural feeling"

"luckless urchin"

"purgatory of boyhood"

"feathered voluptuary"

"gastronomical"

"foreign luxuries"

"gourmand"

MARCH

WILLIAM CULLEN BRYANT

1

The stormy March is come at last,
 With wind, and cloud, and changing skies;
I hear the rushing of the blast,
 That through the snowy valley flies.

2

Ah, passing few are they who speak,
 Wild stormy month! in praise of thee;
Yet, though thy winds are loud and bleak,
 Thou art a welcome month to me.

3

For thou, to northern lands again
 The glad and glorious sun dost bring,
And thou hast joined the gentle train
 And wear'st the gentle name of Spring.

4

And, in thy reign of blast and storm,
 Smiles many a long, bright, sunny day,
When the changed winds are soft and warm,
 And heaven puts on the blue of May.

5

Then sing aloud the gushing rills
 And the full springs, from frost set free,
That, brightly leaping down the hills,
 Are just set out to meet the sea.

6

The year's departing beauty hides
 Of wintry storms, the sullen threat;
But, in thy sternest frown abides
 A look of kindly promise yet.

7

Thou bring'st the hope of those calm skies,
 And that soft time of sunny showers,
When the wide bloom, on earth that lies,
 Seems of a brighter world than ours.

HELPS TO STUDY

Notes and Questions

What peculiarities of March weather have you observed?

How does the poet regard March? Why? How do you like March?

What "gentle train" has March joined?

Have you ever heard "the gushing rills sing aloud"? When?

Why does the poet say "the full springs are just set out to meet the sea"?

How does "the year's departing beauty hide the threat of wintry storms"?

Whose "sterner frown abides"?

What "kindly promise" is meant?

To what month does the last stanza refer?

How do you like Bryant's description of March?

Which stanza do you like best? Memorize it.

Words and Phrases for Discussion

"changing skies"
"passing few"
"reign of blast"
"full springs"

"changed winds"
"gushing rills"
"sullen threat"
"wide bloom"

THE DEATH OF THE FLOWERS

William Cullen Bryant

1

The melancholy days are come, the saddest of the year,
Of wailing winds, and naked woods, and meadows brown and
　　sear.
Heaped in the hollows of the grove, the withered leaves lie dead;
They rustle to the eddying gust, and to the rabbit's tread.
The robin and the wren are flown, and from the shrubs the jay,
And from the wood-top calls the crow, through all the gloomy
　　day.

2

Where are the flowers, the fair young flowers, that lately sprang
　　and stood
In brighter light and softer airs, a beauteous sisterhood?
Alas! they all are in their graves, the gentle race of flowers
Are lying in their lowly beds, with the fair and good of ours.
The rain is falling where they lie, but the cold November rain,
Calls not, from out the gloomy earth, the lovely ones again.

3

The wind-flower and the violet, they perished long ago,
And the brier-rose and the orchis died amid the summer glow;
But on the hill the golden-rod, and the aster in the wood,
And the yellow sun-flower by the brook in autumn beauty stood,
Till fell the frost from the clear cold heaven, as falls the plague
　　on men,
And the brightness of their smile was gone from upland, glade,
　　and glen.

4

And now, when comes the calm mild day, as still such days will
　　come,
To call the squirrel and the bee from out their winter home;

When the sound of dropping nuts is heard, though all the trees
    are still,
And twinkle in the smoky light the waters of the rill,
The south wind searches for the flowers whose fragrance late
    he bore,
And sighs to find them in the wood and by the stream no more.

. . . .

HELPS TO STUDY

Notes and Questions

To what season does the poet refer in the opening stanza?

Why does he call it "the saddest of the year"?

Does it seem so to you?

What does Bryant say makes the leaves "rustle" at this time of year?

Read the lines that compare summer days with fall days.

What is meant by "a beauteous sisterhood"?

What spring flowers does the poet name? What fall flowers?

What comparison is made in the third stanza?

What signs of spring are mentioned in the last stanza?

Does the poet give a good description of the autumn?

Words and Phrases for Discussion

"melancholy days"
"wailing winds"
"eddying gust"
"rabbit's tread"

"glade"
"glen"
"gentle race of flowers"
"rill"

THE PLANTING OF THE APPLE TREE

William Cullen Bryant

1

Come, let us plant the apple tree!
Cleave the tough greensward with the spade;
Wide let its hollow bed be made;
There gently lay the roots, and there

Sift the dark mold with kindly care,
 And press it o'er them tenderly,
As round the sleeping infant's feet
We softly fold the cradle sheet;
 So plant we the apple tree.

2

 What plant we in this apple tree?
Buds, which the breath of summer days
Shall lengthen into leafy sprays;
Boughs, where the thrush with crimson breast
Shall haunt and sing and hide her nest.
 We plant upon the sunny lea
A shadow for the noontide hour,
A shelter from the summer shower,
 When we plant the apple tree.

3

 What plant we in this apple tree?
Sweets for a hundred flowery springs
To load the May wind's restless wings,
When from the orchard row he pours
Its fragrance through our open doors.
 A world of blossoms for the bee,
Flowers for the sick girl's silent room,
For the glad infant sprigs of bloom
 We plant with the apple tree.

4

 What plant we in this apple tree?
Fruits that shall swell in sunny June,
And redden in the August noon,
And drop when gentle airs come by
That fan the blue September sky,

While children come, with cries of glee,
And seek them where the fragrant grass
Betrays their bed to those who pass,
   At the foot of the apple tree.

5

And when above this apple tree
The winter stars are quivering bright,
And winds go howling through the night,
Girls whose young eyes o'erflow with mirth
Shall peel its fruit by cottage hearth;
   And guests in prouder homes shall see,
Heaped with the grape of Cintra's vine
And golden orange of the line,
   The fruit of the apple tree.

6

The fruitage of this apple tree
Winds and our flag of stripe and star
Shall bear to coasts that lie afar,
Where men shall wonder at the view
And ask in what fair groves they grew;
   And sojourners beyond the sea
Shall think of childhood's careless day
And long, long hours of summer play
   In the shade of the apple tree.

7

And time shall waste this apple tree.
Oh! when its aged branches throw
Thin shadows on the ground below,
Shall fraud and force and iron will

Oppress the weak and helpless still?
What shall the tasks of mercy be
Amid the toils, the strifes, the tears,
Of those who live when length of years
Is wasting this apple tree?

8

"Who planted this old apple tree?"
The children of that distant day
Thus to some aged man shall say;
And, gazing on its mossy stem,
The gray-haired man shall answer them:
"A poet of the land was he,
Born in the rude but good old times;
'Tis said he made some quaint old rhymes
On planting the apple tree."

HELPS TO STUDY

Notes and Questions

Read the stanza that tells how we plant the apple tree.

What comparison in the first stanza?

What does the poet say we plant in the apple tree in the second stanza? In the third stanza? In the fourth?

Why did the poet follow this order?

How does the apple tree relate to the winter season?

With what is "cottage hearth" compared?

What is the meaning of the first three lines of the sixth stanza?

To whom does "A poet of the land" refer?

Do you like this poem? Why?

Read "Apple Blossoms."

Words and Phrases for Discussion

"Cleave the tough greensward"
"A world of blossoms"
"infant sprigs of bloom"
"haunt"

"Cintra"—in Portugal
"line"—equator
"rude but good old time"
"distant day"

THE VILLAGE BLACKSMITH

HENRY WADSWORTH LONGFELLOW

1

Under a spreading chestnut tree
    The village smithy stands;
The smith, a mighty man is he,
    With large and sinewy hands;
And the muscles of his brawny arms
    Are strong as iron bands.

2

His hair is crisp, and black, and long,
    His face is like the tan;
His brow is wet with honest sweat,
    He earns whate'er he can,
And looks the whole world in the face,
    For he owes not any man.

3

Week in, week out, from morn till night,
    You can hear his bellows blow;
You can hear him swing his heavy sledge,
    With measured beat and slow,
Like a sexton ringing the village bell,
    When the evening sun is low.

4

And children coming home from school
    Look in at the open door;
They love to see the flaming forge,
    And hear the bellows roar,
And catch the burning sparks that fly
    Like chaff from a threshing floor.

5

He goes on Sunday to the church,
  And sits among his boys;
He hears the parson pray and preach,
  He hears his daughter's voice,
Singing in the village choir,
  And it makes his heart rejoice.

6

It sounds to him like her mother's voice,
  Singing in Paradise!
He needs must think of her once more,
  How in the grave she lies;
And with his hard, rough hand he wipes
  A tear out of his eyes.

7

Toiling,—rejoicing,—sorrowing,
  Onward through life he goes;
Each morning sees some task begin,
  Each evening sees it close;
Something attempted, something done,
  Has earned a night's repose.

8

Thanks, thanks to thee, my worthy friend,
  For the lesson thou hast taught!
Thus at the flaming forge of life
  Our fortunes must be wrought;
Thus on its sounding anvil shaped
  Each burning deed and thought!

HELPS TO STUDY

Historical: The "village smithy" stood "under a spreading chestnut tree" in Brattle Street, Cambridge, not far from the Longfellow home. In time it gave place to a dwelling-house, and the chestnut tree had to be cut down. On the morning this event took place every one came out to see the wood choppers at work and to see the old tree, immortalized by the poet, tumble over. It was a great event in the village and Longfellow felt very sad.

On his seventy-second birthday, an arm-chair made out of the wood of the old chestnut tree was presented to Longfellow by the children of Cambridge. It was carved with horse chestnuts. One stanza of the poem was inscribed upon it:

> "And children coming home from school
>   Look in at the open door;
> They love to see the flaming forge,
>   And hear the bellows roar,
> And catch the burning sparks that fly
>   Like chaff from a threshing-floor."

A brass plate on the chair bore this inscription:

"To the author of 'The Village Blacksmith,' this chair, made from the wood of the spreading chestnut tree, is presented as an expression of grateful regard and veneration by the children of Cambridge, who, with their friends, join in the best wishes and congratulations on this anniversary, February 27, 1879."

This remembrance was very pleasing to Longfellow, who in reply to the children wrote the poem, "From My Arm-chair."

Notes and Questions

What picture does the first stanza give you?

What does the second stanza add to your picture?

What reason does the poet give for saying, "For he owes not any man"?

In the third stanza what things are compared?

What habits of the blacksmith does this stanza tell you about?

What comparison is used in the fourth stanza?

What "lesson" has the blacksmith taught?

What is compared with "the flaming forge"? With "the sounding anvil"?

What is "the flaming forge of life"?

Notice that when a comparison is direct, the figure of speech is called a *metaphor*, e. g., "the flaming forge of life." But when *like* or *as* is used the comparison is indirect and the figure of speech is called a *simile*, e. g., "like chaff from a threshing floor."

Words and Phrases for Discussion

"spreading"   "flaming"
"brawny"   "repose"
"crisp"   "burning"

For Pronunciation

"chestnut"   "sexton"
"sinewy"   "threshing"
"bellows"   "sorrowing"

THE OLD CLOCK ON THE STAIRS

HENRY WADSWORTH LONGFELLOW

1

Somewhat back from the village street
Stands the old-fashioned country-seat.
Across its antique portico
Tall poplar-trees their shadows throw
And from its station in the hall
An ancient timepiece says to all,—
 "Forever—never!
 Never—forever!"

2

Halfway up the stairs it stands,
And points and beckons with its hands
From its case of massive oak,
Like a monk, who, under his cloak,
Crosses himself, and sighs, alas!
With sorrowful voice to all who pass,—
 "Forever—never!
 Never—forever!"

3

By day its voice is low and light;
But in the silent dead of night,
Distinct as a passing footstep's fall
It echoes along the vacant hall,
Along the ceiling, along the floor,
And seems to say, at each chamber-door,—
    "Forever—never!
    Never—forever!"

4

Through days of sorrow and of mirth,
Through days of death and days of birth,
Through every swift vicissitude
Of changeful time, unchanged it has stood,
And as if, like God, it all things saw,
It calmly repeats those words of awe,—
    "Forever—never!
    Never—forever!"

5

In that mansion used to be
Free-hearted Hospitality;
His great fires up the chimney roared;
The stranger feasted at his board;
But, like the skeleton at the feast,
That warning timepiece never ceased,—
    "Forever—never!
    Never—forever!"

6

There groups of merry children played,
There youths and maidens dreaming strayed.
O precious hours! O golden prime,
And affluence of love and time!

Even as a miser counts his gold,
Those hours the ancient timepiece told,—
    "Forever—never!
    Never—forever!"

7

From that chamber, clothed in white,
The bride came forth on her wedding night:
There, in that silent room below,
The dead lay in his shroud of snow;
And in the hush that followed the prayer,
Was heard the old clock on the stair,—
    "Forever—never!
    Never—forever!"

8

All are scattered now and fled,
Some are married, some are dead;
And when I ask, with throbs of pain,
"Ah! when shall they all meet again?"
As in the days long-since gone by,
The ancient timepiece makes reply,—
    "Forever—never!
    Never—forever!"

9

Never here, forever there,
Where all parting, pain, and care,
And death, and time shall disappear,—
Forever there, but never here!
The horologe of Eternity
Sayeth this incessantly,—
    "Forever—never!
    Never—forever!"

HELPS TO STUDY

Historical: "The Old Clock on the Stairs," that for many years stood in the Longfellow home in Cambridge, is now in the home of Mr. Thomas Appleton, Boston. The Longfellow home, "the most historic building in New England save Faneuil Hall," was Washington's headquarters for nine months following the battle of Bunker Hill. It is a fine example of colonial architecture, "guarded by stately poplars," commanding a good view of the Charles River. Down the street on the opposite side stood "the spreading chestnut tree" and the "village smithy." The house is now occupied by Longfellow's daughter, Alice. It is her custom to invite to it every year a number of the working girls from Boston. She is one of the three daughters of Longfellow composing the "blue-eyed banditti" of his "Children's Hour."

Notes and Questions

What picture do you have after reading the first stanza?

What do "old-fashioned" and "antique" add to your picture?

What picture of the clock do the first two stanzas give you?

Why does Longfellow call this an "ancient" timepiece?

Have you ever seen a clock similar to the one he describes?

In what does he say the clock is like a monk?

Why does the clock's voice seem low by day and loud at night?

What does the poet mean by "dead of night"?

With what does he compare the clock's voice at night?

Is the comparison a good one?

What habit of the clock does Longfellow tell about in the fourth stanza?

Whose fires does he say once roared up the chimney?

To what "previous hours" does he refer in the sixth stanza?

Words and Phrases for Discussion

"vacant"

"beckons"

"massive"

"vicissitude"

"mansion"

"incessantly"

"affluence" =abundance

"horologe" (hor'ō lōj) = a timepiece

"like the skeleton at the feast"

THE BIRDS OF KILLINGWORTH

Henry Wadsworth Longfellow

The Coming of the Birds

1

It was the season, when all through the land
   The merle and mavis build, and building sing
Those lovely lyrics, written by His hand,
   Whom Saxon Cædmon calls the Blithe-heart King;
When on the boughs the purple buds expand,
   The banners of the vanguard of the Spring,
And rivulets, rejoicing, rush and leap,
   And wave their fluttering signals from the steep.

2

The robin and the blue-bird, piping loud,
   Filled all the blossoming orchards with their glee;
The sparrows chirped as if they still were proud
   Their race in Holy Writ should mentioned be;
And hungry crows assembled in a crowd,
   Clamored their piteous prayer incessantly,
Knowing who hears the ravens cry and said:
"Give us, O Lord, this day our daily bread!"

3

Across the Sound the birds of passage sailed,
   Speaking some unknown language strange and sweet
Of tropic isle remote, and passing hailed
   The village with the cheers of all their fleet;
Or quarrelling together, laughed and railed
   Like foreign sailors, landed in the street

Of seaport town, and with outlandish noise
Of oaths and gibberish frightening girls and boys.

4

Thus came the jocund Spring in Killingworth,
  In fabulous days, some hundred years ago;
And thrifty farmers, as they tilled the earth,
  Heard with alarm the cawing of the crow,
That mingled with the universal mirth,
  Cassandra-like, prognosticating woe;
They shook their heads, and doomed with dreadful words
To swift destruction the whole race of birds.

The Town Meeting

5

And a town-meeting was convened straightway
  To set a price upon the guilty heads
Of these marauders, who, in lieu of pay,
  Levied black-mail upon the garden beds
And corn-fields, and beheld without dismay
  The awful scarecrow, with his fluttering shreds;
The skeleton that waited at their feast,
Whereby their sinful pleasure was increased.

6

Then from his house, a temple painted white,
  With fluted columns, and a roof of red,
The Squire came forth, august and splendid sight!
  Slowly descending, with majestic tread,
Three flights of steps, nor looking left nor right,
  Down the long street he walked, as one who said,
"A town that boasts inhabitants like me
Can have no lack of good society!"

7

The Parson, too, appeared, a man austere,
  The instinct of whose nature was to kill;

The wrath of God he preached from year to year,
   And read, with fervor, Edwards on the Will;
His favorite pastime was to slay the deer
   In Summer on some Adirondac hill;
E'en now, while walking down the rural lane,
He lopped the wayside lilies with his cane.

8

From the Academy, whose belfry crowned
   The hill of Science with its vane of brass,
Came the Preceptor, gazing idly round,
   Now at the clouds, and now at the green grass,
And all absorbed in reveries profound
   Of fair Almira in the upper class,
Who was, as in a sonnet he had said,
As pure as water, and as good as bread.

9

And next the Deacon issued from his door,
   In his voluminous neck-cloth, white as snow;
A suit of sable bombazine he wore;
   His form was ponderous, and his step was slow;
There never was so wise a man before;
   He seemed the incarnate "Well, I told you so!"
And to perpetuate his great renown
There was a street named after him in town.

10

These came together in the new town-hall,
   With sundry farmers from the region round.
The Squire presided, dignified and tall,
   His air impressive and his reasoning sound;
Ill fared it with the birds, both great and small;
   Hardly a friend in all that crowd they found,
But enemies enough, who every one
Charged them with all the crimes beneath the sun.

11

When they had ended, from his place apart,
　Rose the Preceptor, to redress the wrong,
And, trembling like a steed before the start,
　Looked round bewildered on the expectant throng;
Then thought of fair Almira, and took heart
　To speak out what was in him, clear and strong,
Alike regardless of their smile or frown,
And quite determined not to be laughed down.

12

"Plato, anticipating the Reviewers,
　From his Republic banished without pity
The Poets; in this little town of yours,
　You put to death, by means of a Committee,
The ballad-singers and the Troubadours,
　The street-musicians of the heavenly city,
The birds who make sweet music for us all
In o' r dark hours, as David did for Saul.

The Song of the Birds

13

"The thrush that carols at the dawn of day
　From the green steeples of the piny wood;
The oriole in the elm; the noisy jay,
　Jargoning like a foreigner at his food;
The blue-bird balanced on some topmost spray,
　Flooding with melody the neighborhood;
Linnet and meadow-lark, and all the throng
That dwell in nests, and have the gift of song.

14

"You slay them all! and wherefore? for the gain
    Of a scant handful more or less of wheat,
Or rye, or barley, or some other grain,
    Scratched up at random by industrious feet,
Searching for worm or weevil after rain!
    Or a few cherries, that are not so sweet
As are the songs these uninvited guests
Sing at their feast with comfortable breasts.

15

"Do you ne'er think what wondrous beings these?
    Do you ne'er think who made them, and who taught
The dialect they speak, where melodies
    Alone are the interpreters of thought?
Whose household words are songs in many keys,
    Sweeter than instrument of man e'er caught!
Whose habitations in the tree-tops even
Are halfway houses on the road to heaven!

16

"Think every morning when the sun peeps through
    The dim leaf-latticed windows of the grove,
How jubilant the happy birds renew
    Their old, melodious madrigals of love!
And when you think of this, remember too
    'Tis always morning somewhere, and above
The awakening continents, from shore to shore,
Somewhere the birds are singing evermore.

The Birds' Service to Man

17

"Think of your woods and orchards without birds!
    Of empty nests that cling to boughs and beams

As in an idiot's brain remembered words
　　Hang empty 'mid the cobwebs of his dreams!
Will bleat of flocks or bellowing of herds
　　Make up for the lost music, when your teams
Drag home the stingy harvest, and no more
The feathered gleaners follow to your door?

18

"What! would you rather see the incessant stir
　　Of insects in the windrows of the hay,
And hear the locust and the grasshopper
　　Their melancholy hurdy-gurdies play?
Is this more pleasant to you than the whir
　　Of meadow-lark, and its sweet roundelay,
Or twitter of little field-fares, as you take
Your nooning in the shade of bush and brake?

19

"You call them thieves and pillagers; but know
　　They are the winged wardens of your farms,
Who from the cornfields drive the insidious foe,
　　And from your harvests keep a hundred harms;
Even the blackest of them all, the crow,
　　Renders good service as your man-at-arms,
Crushing the beetle in his coat of mail,
And crying havoc on the slug and snail.

How Teach Gentleness and Reverence

20

"How can I teach your children gentleness,
　　And mercy to the weak, and reverence,
For Life, which, in its weakness or excess,
　　Is still a gleam of God's omnipotence,
Or Death, which, seeming darkness, is no less
　　The self-same light, although averted hence,

When by your laws, your actions, and your speech,
You contradict the very things I teach?"

21

With this he closed; and through the audience went
  A murmur, like the rustle of dead leaves;
The farmers laughed and nodded, and some bent
  Their yellow heads together like their sheaves;
Men have no faith in fine-spun sentiment
  Who put their trust in bullocks and in beeves.
The birds were doomed; and, as the record shows,
A bounty offered for the heads of crows.

22

There was another audience out of reach,
  Who had no voice nor vote in making laws,
But in the papers read his little speech,
  And crowned his modest temples with applause;
They made him conscious, each one more than each,
  He still was victor, vanquished in their cause.
Sweetest of all the applause he won from thee,
O fair Almira at the Academy!

23

And so the dreadful massacre began;
  O'er fields and orchards, and o'er woodland crests,
The ceaseless fusillade of terror ran.
  Dead fell the birds, with blood-stains on their breasts,
Or wounded crept away from sight of man,
  While the young died of famine in their nests;
A slaughter to be told in groans, not words,
The very St. Bartholomew of Birds!

Consequences of the Destruction of the Birds

24

The Summer came, and all the birds were dead;
  The days were like hot coals; the very ground

Was burned to ashes; in the orchards fed
  Myriads of caterpillars, and around
The cultivated fields and garden beds
  Hosts of devouring insects crawled, and found
No foe to check their march, till they had made
The land a desert without leaf or shade.

25

Devoured by worms, like Herod, was the town,
  Because, like Herod, it had ruthlessly
Slaughtered the Innocents.   From the trees spun **down**
  The canker-worms upon the passers-by,
Upon each woman's bonnet, shawl, and gown,
  Who shook them off with just a little cry;
They were the terror of each favorite walk,
  The endless theme of all the village talk.

26

The farmers grew impatient, but a few
  Confessed their error, and would not complain,
For after all, the best thing one can do
  When it is raining, is to let it rain.
Then they repealed the law, although they knew
  It would not call the dead to life again;
As schoolboys, finding their mistake too late,
Draw a wet sponge across the accusing slate.

27

That year in Killingworth the Autumn came
  Without the light of his majestic look,
The wonder of the falling tongues of flame,
  The illumined pages of his Doom's-Day book.
A few lost leaves blushed crimson with their shame,
  And drowned themselves despairing in the brook,

While the wild wind went moaning everywhere,
Lamenting the dead children of the air !

The Return of the Birds

28

But the next Spring a stranger sight was seen,
    A sight that never yet by bard was sung,
As great a wonder as it would have been
    If some dumb animal had found a tongue !
A wagon, overarched with evergreen,
    Upon whose boughs were wicker cages hung,
All full of singing birds, came down the street,
Filling the air with music wild and sweet.

29

From all the country round these birds were brought,
    By order of the town, with anxious quest,
And, loosened from their wicker prisons, sought
    In woods and fields the places they loved best,
Singing loud canticles, which many thought
    Were satires to the authorities addressed,
While others, listening in green lanes, averred
Such lovely music never had been heard !

30

But blither still and louder carolled they
    Upon the morrow, for they seemed to know
It was the fair Almira's wedding-day,
    And everywhere, around, above, below,
When the Preceptor bore his bride away,
    Their songs burst forth in joyous overflow,
And a new heaven bent over a new earth
Amid the sunny farms of Killingworth.

HELPS TO STUDY

Notes and Questions

What season is described in the poem?

When did the events described occur? What tells you this?

Which of the evidences of spring, here mentioned, have you seen?

What is meant by "the vanguard of the Spring"?

What does the poet say are its "banners"?

What are the "fluttering signals" of the rivulets?

Who does he say wrote "those lovely lyrics" the merle and mavis sing?

Read the prayer the crows utter incessantly.

What tells you the direction from which the "birds of passage" came?

What alarmed the farmers?

For what purpose was a town-meeting called?

What kind of man was the Squire? What lines tell you this?

Read lines that describe the Parson.

Tell about the Preceptor.

Read lines that describe the Deacon.

Who championed the cause of the birds?

Read the stanzas that contain his speech.

What service does he say the birds render to man?

What was the effect of his speech?

What action did the meeting take?

What resulted from the destruction of the birds?

What comparison is made relating to Herod? To schoolboys?

By whom were the birds restored?

How did the Preceptor celebrate the restoration of the birds?

Memorize the last half of stanza sixteen.

Words and Phrases for Discussion

Caedmon—An Anglo-Saxon who wrote a Bible poem called "Caedmon's Paraphrase." He was not a poet and when sometimes at entertainments it was agreed for the sake of mirth that all present should sing in turn, he withdrew and went home. On one such occasion he went to the stable and slept, and in his sleep a vision appeared and said to him, "Caedmon, sing some song to me." He answered, "I cannot sing; for that was the reason I left the entertainment and retired here." The vision said, "However, you shall sing." "What shall I sing?" said Caedmon. "Sing the beginning of created beings," said the vision, whereupon Caedmon began to sing verses to the praise of God. He remembered the poetry which he had composed in his dream and repeated it in the morning to the inmates of the monastery, who concluded the gift of song was a divine gift and had him enter the monastery and devote his time to poetry.

sparrows—Holy Writ—See Matthew X, 29-31.

Cassandra—the daughter of Priam, King of Troy, who was slain in the sacking of Troy. Apollo gave her the gift of prophecy, but afterward became angry at her and decreed that no one should believe her prophecies.—See page 227.

Jonathan Edwards—an American preacher, who wrote a book on the "Freedom of the Will."

"as David did for Saul"—See I Samuel XVI, 14-23.

"A very St. Bartholomew of Birds"—here used to mean a slaughter of birds.

"like Herod"—See Matthew II.

"Who hears the ravens cry"—Luke XII, 24.

Doom's-Day book—A book containing a digest of a census of England under William the Conqueror, so-called because its decision was regarded as final.

"fluttering signals"

"all their fleet"

"jocund Spring"

"fabulous days"

"prognosticating"

"fluted columns"

"majestic tread"

"jargoning"

"melodious madrigals"

"feathered gleaners"

"fine-spun sentiment"

"vanquished"

"winged wardens"

"melancholy hurdy-gurdies"

"ceaseless fusillade"

"his majestic look"

"satires to the authorities addressed"

"a new heaven bent over a new earth"

What things are compared in each of the following figures of speech:

"steeples of the piny wood"

"fusillade of terror"

"tongues of flame"

THE RHODORA

Ralph Waldo Emerson

In May, when sea-winds pierced our solitudes,
I found the fresh Rhodora in the woods,
Spreading its leafless blooms in a damp nook,
To please the desert and the sluggish brook.
The purple petals fallen in the pool
Made the black water with their beauty gay;
Here might the red-bird come his plumes to cool,
And court the flower that cheapens his array.
Rhodora! if the sages ask thee why
This charm is wasted on the earth and sky,
Tell them, dear, that, if eyes were made for seeing,
Then beauty is its own excuse for being;
Why thou wert there, O rival of the rose!
I never thought to ask; I never knew;
But in my simple ignorance suppose
The self-same power that brought me there brought you.

HELPS TO STUDY

Notes and Questions

When did the poet find the rhodora?

What can you tell about Emerson's home which explains his reference to the sea-winds?

Read the line which tells the color of the rhodora.

What comparison is made between the rhodora and the rose?

Read a line which tells that the rhodora grew where few could see it.

What comparison is made between the color of the bird and the color of the flower?

Read the line which tells how the flower came to be in this retired spot.

Words and Phrases for Discussion

"leafless blooms"
"sluggish brook"
"cheapens his array"
"rival of the rose"

"rhodora"—A beautiful shrub with clusters of pale purple flowers preceding the leaves.
"black water"

THE HUMBLEBEE

RALPH WALDO EMERSON

1

Burly dozing humblebee!
Where thou art is clime for me.
Let them sail for Porto Rique,
Far-off heats through seas to seek,
I will follow thee alone,
Thou animated torrid zone!
Zig-zag steerer, desert cheerer,
Let me chase thy waving lines,
Keep me nearer, me thy hearer,
Singing over shrubs and vines.

2

Insect lover of the sun,
Joy of thy dominion!
Sailor of the atmosphere,
Swimmer through the waves of air,
Voyager of light and noon,
Epicurean of June,
Wait I prithee, till I come
Within ear-shot of thy hum,—
All without is martyrdom.

3

When the south wind, in May days,
With a net of shining haze,
Silvers the horizon wall,
And, with softness touching all,
Tints the human countenance
With a color of romance,
And, infusing subtle heats,

Turns the sod to violets,
Thou in sunny solitudes,
Rover of the underwoods,
The green silence dost displace,
With thy mellow breezy bass.

4

Hot midsummer's petted crone,
Sweet to me thy drowsy tone,
Telling of countless sunny hours,
Long days, and solid banks of flowers,
Of gulfs of sweetness without bound
In Indian wildernesses found,
Of Syrian peace, immortal leisure,
Firmest cheer and bird-like pleasure.

5

Aught unsavory or unclean,
Hath my insect never seen,
But violets and bilberry bells,
Maple sap and daffodels,
Grass with green flag half-mast high,
Succory to match the sky,
Columbine with horn of honey,
Scented fern, and agrimony,
Clover, catchfly, adder's-tongue,
And brier-roses dwelt among;
All beside was unknown waste,
All was picture as he passed.

6

Wiser far than human seer,
Yellow-breeched philosopher!
Seeing only what is fair,
Sipping only what is sweet,

Thou dost mock at fate and care,
Leave the chaff and take the wheat.
When the fierce north-western blast
Cools sea and land so far and fast,
Thou already slumberest deep,—
Woe and want thou canst out-sleep,—
Want and woe which torture us,
Thy sleep makes ridiculous.

HELPS TO STUDY

Notes and Questions

What does the poet say others may seek in "Porto Rique"?

Through what "seas" must you sail to reach "Porto Rique"?

What is the torrid zone?

What climate does the bee carry with him?

What names does the poet give the bee in the second stanza?

Read a line from the third stanza which tells the part in music which the bee sings.

Read the lines in the third stanza which tell how the south wind and the sun bring up the violets.

What does the "drowsy tune" of the bee tell to the poet?

Among what flowers does the bee dwell?

What does the bee sip?

What comparison does the poet make between human beings and the bee?

Words and Phrases for Discussion

"thy waving lines"
"sunny solitudes"
"Indian wilderness"
"immortal leisure"
"subtle heats"
"green silence"

"Syrian peace"
"human seer"
"All was picture as he passed"
"Epicurean"—referring to daintiness of appetite

LITTLE DAFFYDOWNDILLY

Nathaniel Hawthorne

DAFFYDOWNDILLY was so called because in his nature he re-
sembled a flower, and loved to do only what was beautiful and
agreeable, and took no delight in labor of any kind. But while
Daffydowndilly was yet a little boy, his mother sent him away
5 from his pleasant home, and put him under the care of a very
strict schoolmaster, who went by the name of Mr. Toil. Those
who knew him best affirmed that this Mr. Toil was a very worthy
character; and that he had done more good, both to children and
grown people, than anybody else in the world. Certainly he had
10 lived long enough to do a great deal of good; for, if all stories
be true, he had dwelt upon earth ever since Adam was driven
from the garden of Eden.

Nevertheless, Mr. Toil had a severe and ugly countenance,
especially for such little boys or big men as were inclined to be
15 idle; his voice, too, was harsh; and all his ways and customs
seemed very disagreeable to our friend Daffydowndilly. The
whole day long, this terrible old schoolmaster sat at his desk
overlooking the scholars, or stalked about the school-room with
a certain awful birch rod in his hand. Now came a rap over the
20 shoulders of a boy whom Mr. Toil had caught at play; now he
punished a whole class who were behindhand with their lessons;
and, in short, unless a lad chose to attend quietly and constantly
to his book, he had no chance of enjoying a quiet moment in the
school-room of Mr. Toil.

25 "This will never do for me," thought Daffydowndilly.

Now, the whole of Daffydowndilly's life had hitherto been
passed with his dear mother, who had a much sweeter face than
old Mr. Toil and who had always been very indulgent to her
little boy. No wonder, therefore, that poor Daffydowndilly
30 found it a woful change, to be sent away from the good lady's

side, and put under the care of this ugly-visaged schoolmaster, who never gave him any apples or cakes, and seemed to think that little boys were created only to get lessons.

"I can't bear it any longer," said Daffydowndilly to himself, when he had been at school about a week. "I'll run away, and try to find my dear mother; and, at any rate, I shall never find anybody half so disagreeable as this old Mr. Toil!"

So, the very next morning, off started poor Daffydowndilly, and began his rambles about the world, with only some bread and cheese for his breakfast, and very little pocket-money to pay his expenses. But he had gone only a short distance when he overtook a man of grave and sedate appearance, who was trudging at a moderate pace along the road.

"Good morning, my fine lad," said the stranger; and his voice seemed hard and severe, but yet had a sort of kindness in it; "whence do you come so early, and whither are you going?"

Little Daffydowndilly was a boy of very ingenuous disposition, and had never been known to tell a lie in all his life. Nor did he tell one now. He hesitated a moment or two, but finally confessed that he had run away from school, on account of his great dislike to Mr. Toil; and that he was resolved to find some place in the world where he should never see or hear of the old schoolmaster again.

"Oh, very well, my little friend!" answered the stranger. "Then we will go together; for I, likewise, have had a good deal to do with Mr. Toil, and should be glad to find some place where he was never heard of."

Our friend Daffydowndilly would have been better pleased with a companion of his own age, with whom he might have gathered flowers along the roadside, or have chased butterflies, or have done many other things to make the journey pleasant. But he had wisdom enough to understand that he should get along through the world much easier by having a man of experience to show him the way. So he accepted the stranger's proposal, and they walked on very sociably together.

They had not gone far, when the road passed by a field where some haymakers were at work, mowing down the tall grass, and spreading it out in the sun to dry. Daffydowndilly was delighted with the sweet smell of the new-mown grass, and thought how 5 much pleasanter it must be to make hay in the sunshine, under the blue sky, and with the birds singing sweetly in the neighboring trees and bushes, than to be shut up in a dismal school-room, learning lessons all day long, and continually scolded by old Mr. Toil. But, in the midst of these thoughts, while he was stopping 10 to peep over the stone wall, he started back and caught hold of his companion's hand.

"Quick, quick!" cried he. "Let us run away, or he will catch us!"

"Who will catch us?" asked the stranger.

15 "Mr. Toil, the old schoolmaster!" answered Daffydowndilly. "Don't you see him amongst the haymakers?"

And Daffydowndilly pointed to an elderly man, who seemed to be the owner of the field, and the employer of the men at work there. He had stripped off his coat and waistcoat, and was busily 20 at work in his shirt-sleeves. The drops of sweat stood upon his brow; but he gave himself not a moment's rest, and kept crying out to the haymakers to make hay while the sun shone. Now, strange to say, the figure and features of this old farmer were precisely the same as those of old Mr. Toil, who, at that very 25 moment, must have been just entering his school-room.

"Don't be afraid," said the stranger. "This is not Mr. Toil the schoolmaster, but a brother of his, who was bred a farmer; and people say he is the most disagreeable man of the two. However, he won't trouble you, unless you become a laborer on the 30 farm."

Little Daffydowndilly believed what his companion said, but was very glad, nevertheless, when they were out of sight of the old farmer, who bore such a singular resemblance to Mr. Toil. The two travelers had gone but little farther, when they came 35 to a spot where some carpenters were erecting a house. Daffy-

downdilly begged his companion to stop a moment; for it was a
very pretty sight to see how neatly the carpenters did their work,
with their broad-axes, and saws, and planes, and hammers, shaping out the doors, and putting in the window-sashes, and nailing
5 on the clapboards; and he could not help thinking that he should
like to take a broad-axe, a saw, a plane, and a hammer, and build
a little house for himself. And then, when he should have a
house of his own, old Mr. Toil would never dare to molest him.

But, just while he was delighting himself with this idea, little
10 Daffydowndilly beheld something that made him catch hold of
his companion's hand, all in a fright.

"Make haste. Quick, quick!" cried he. "There he is again!"

"Who?" asked the stranger, very quietly.

"Old Mr. Toil," said Daffydowndilly, trembling. "There! he
15 that is overseeing the carpenters. 'T is my old schoolmaster, as
sure as I 'm alive!"

The stranger cast his eyes where Daffydowndilly pointed his
finger; and he saw an elderly man, with a carpenter's rule and
compasses in his hand. This person went to and fro about the
20 unfinished house, measuring pieces of timber, and marking out
the work that was to be done, and continually exhorting the
other carpenters to be diligent. And wherever he turned his hard
and wrinkled visage, the men seemed to feel that they had a task-
master over them, and sawed, and hammered, and planed, as if
25 for dear life.

"Oh no! this is not Mr. Toil, the schoolmaster," said the
stranger. "It is another brother of his, who follows the trade of
carpenter."

"I am very glad to hear it," quoth Daffydowndilly; "but if you
30 please, sir, I should like to get out of his way as soon as possible."

Then they went on a little farther, and soon heard the sound
of a drum and fife. Daffydowndilly pricked up his ears at this,
and besought his companion to hurry forward, that they might
35 not miss seeing the soldiers. Accordingly, they made what haste

they could, and soon met a company of soldiers, gayly dressed,
with beautiful feathers in their caps, and bright muskets on their
shoulders. In front marched two drummers and two fifers, beating on their drums and playing on their fifes with might and
5 main, and making such lively music that little Daffydowndilly
would gladly have followed them to the end of the world. And
if he was only a soldier, then, he said to himself, old Mr. Toil
would never venture to look him in the face.

"Quick step! Forward march!" shouted a. gruff voice.

10 Little Daffydowndilly started, in great dismay; for this voice
which had spoken to the soldiers sounded precisely the same as
that which he had heard every day in Mr. Toil's school-room, out
of Mr. Toil's own mouth. And, turning his eyes to the captain
of the company, what should he see but the very image of old
15 Mr. Toil himself, with a smart cap and feather on his head, a
pair of gold epaulets on his shoulders, a laced coat on his back,
a purple sash round his waist, and a long sword, instead of a
birch rod, in his hand. And though he held his head so high,
and strutted like a turkey-cock, still he looked quite as ugly and
20 disagreeable as when he was hearing lessons in the school-room.

"This is certainly old Mr. Toil," said Daffydowndilly, in a
trembling voice. "Let us run away, for fear he should make us
enlist in his company!"

"You are mistaken again, my little ˜friend," replied the
25 stranger, very composedly. "This is not Mr. Toil, the schoolmaster, but a brother of his, who has served in the army all his
life. People say he's a terribly severe fellow; but you and I
need not be afraid of him."

"Well, well," said little Daffydowndilly, "but, if you please,
30 sir, I don't want to see the soldiers any more."

So the child and the stranger resumed their journey; and, by
and by, they came to a house by the roadside, where a number
of people were making merry. Young men and rosy-cheeked
girls, with smiles on their faces, were dancing to the sound of a

fiddle. It was the pleasantest sight that Daffydowndilly had yet met with, and it comforted him for all his disappointments.

"Oh, let us stop here," cried he to his companion; "for Mr. Toil will never dare to show his face where there is a fiddler, and
5 where people are dancing and making merry. We shall be quite safe here!"

But these last words died away upon Daffydowndilly's tongue; for, happening to cast his eyes on the fiddler, whom should he behold again but the likeness of Mr. Toil, holding a fiddle-bow
10 instead of a birch rod, and flourishing it with as much ease and dexterity as if he had been a fiddler all his life! He had somewhat the air of a Frenchman, but still looked exactly like the old schoolmaster; and Daffydowndilly even fancied that he nodded and winked at him, and made signs for him to join in
15 the dance.

"Oh, dear me!" whispered he, turning pale. "It seems as if there was nobody but Mr. Toil in the world. Who could have thought of his playing on a fiddle!"

"This is not your old schoolmaster," observed the stranger,
20 "but another brother of his, who was bred in France, where he learned the profession of a fiddler. He is ashamed of his family, and generally calls himself Monsieur le Plaisir; but his real name is Toil, and those who have known him best think him still more disagreeable than his brothers."

25 "Pray let us go a little farther," said Daffydowndilly. "I don't like the looks of this fiddler at all."

Well, thus the stranger and little Daffydowndilly went wandering along the highway, and in shady lanes, and through pleasant villages; and whithersoever they went, behold! there
30 was the image of old Mr. Toil. He stood like a scarecrow in the cornfields. If they entered a house, he sat in the parlor; if they peeped into the kitchen, he was there. He made himself at home in every cottage, and stole, under one disguise or another, into the most splendid mansions. Everywhere there was
35 sure to be somebody wearing the likeness of Mr. Toil, and who,

as the stranger affirmed, was one of the old schoolmaster's innumerable brethren.

Little Daffydowndilly was almost tired to death, when he perceived some people reclining lazily in a shady place, by the side 5 of the road. The poor child entreated his companion that they might sit down there, and take some repose.

"Old Mr. Toil will never come here," said he; "for he hates to see people taking their ease."

But, even while he spoke, Daffydowndilly's eyes fell upon a 10 person who seemed the laziest, and heaviest, and most torpid of all those lazy and heavy and torpid people who had lain down to sleep in the shade. Who should it be, again, but the very image of Mr. Toil!

"There is a large family of these Toils," remarked the stran- 15 ger. "This is another of the old schoolmaster's brothers, who was bred in Italy, where he acquired very idle habits, and goes by the name of Signor Far Niente. He pretends to lead an easy life, but is really the most miserable fellow in the family."

"Oh, take me back!—take me back!" cried poor little Daffy- 20 downdilly, bursting into tears. "If there is nothing but Toil all the world over, I may just as well go back to the schoolhouse!"

"Yonder it is,—there is the school-house!" said the stranger; for though he and little Daffydowndilly had taken a great many 25 steps, they had traveled in a circle instead of a straight line. "Come; we will go back to school together."

There was something in his companion's voice that little Daffydowndilly now remembered, and it is strange that he had not remembered it sooner. Looking up into his face, behold! 30 there again was the likeness of old Mr. Toil; so that the poor child had been in company with Toil all day, even while he was doing his best to run away from him. Some people, to whom I have told little Daffydowndilly's story, are of opinion that old Mr. Toil was a magician, and possessed the power of multiplying 35 himself into as many shapes as he saw fit.

Be this as it may, little Daffydowndilly had learned a good lesson, and from that time forward was diligent at his task, because he knew that diligence is not a whit more toilsome than sport or idleness. And when he became better acquainted with 5 Mr. Toil, he began to think that his ways were not so very disagreeable, and that the old schoolmaster's smile of approbation made his face almost as pleasant as even that of Daffydowndilly's mother.

HELPS TO STUDY

Notes and Questions

Why was Daffydowndilly so named?

Do you think he disliked school because of work or because of Mr. Toil?

Why do you think so? Read sentences that tell you.

What was his purpose in running away from school?

Who joined him?

On their way they met several groups of workers. What happened in each case?

What conclusion did Daffydowndilly finally make? Read the lines that tell you.

Do you think everyone should do his part of the world's work?

Why should we learn to enjoy work?

Do you think Mr. Toil was a real person?

What was Hawthorne's purpose in writing this story?

Which of all the experiences that Daffydowndilly had in his walk with the stranger surprised him him most?

Has it ever been your own experience that the mere seeking of pleasure has proved tiresome?

Do you know anyone who finds real pleasure in doing work that might prove uninteresting and tedious to you?

Words and Phrases for Discussion

"stalked"

"sedate"

"ugly-visaged"

"ingenuous"

"innumerable"

"magician"

THE FOUNTAIN

JAMES RUSSELL LOWELL

1

Into the sunshine,
  Full of the light,
Leaping and flashing
  From morn till night!

2

Into the moonlight,
  Whiter than snow,
Waving so flower-like
  When the winds blow!

3

Into the starlight,
  Rushing in spray,
Happy at midnight,
  Happy by day!

4

Ever in motion,
  Blithesome and cheery.
Still climbing heavenward,
  Never aweary;—

5

Glad of all weathers,
  Still seeming best,
Upward or downward,
  Motion thy rest;—

6

Full of a nature
   Nothing can tame
Changed every moment,
   Ever the same;—

7

Ceaseless aspiring,
   Ceaseless content,
Darkness or sunshine
   Thy element;—

8

Glorious fountain!
   Let my heart be
Fresh, changeful, constant,
   Upward, like thee!

HELPS TO STUDY

Notes and Questions

What picture does the first stanza give you? The second? The third?

Are the pictures Lowell gives of the fountain good ones?

Which do you like best?

Read the stanza that names the fountain's characteristics.

To what does the poet compare the fountain?

In what qualities would Lowell have his heart like the fountain?

What do you think of this comparison?

Which of these qualities do you like best?

Who is addressed in the last stanza?

Which stanza do you like best?

Words and Phrases for Discussion

"Leaping and flashing"
"Motion they rest"
"Ceaseless aspiring"

"Thy element"
"Blithesome"
"Ever the same"

LONGING

JAMES RUSSELL LOWELL

1

Of all the myriad moods of mind
    That through the soul come thronging,
Which one was e'er so dear, so kind,
    So beautiful as Longing?
The thing we long for, that we are
    For one transcendent moment,
Before the Present poor and bare
    Can make its sneering comment.

2

Still, through our paltry stir and strife,
    Glows down the wished Ideal,
And Longing moulds in clay what Life
    Carves in the marble Real;
To let the new life in, we know,
    Desire must ope the portal;—
Perhaps the longing to be so
    Helps make the soul immortal.

3

Longing is God's fresh heavenward will
    With our poor earthward striving;
We quench it that we may be still
    Content with merely living;
But, would we learn that heart's full scope
    Which we are hourly wronging,
Our lives must climb from hope to hope
    And realize our longing.

4

Ah! let us hope that to our praise
Good God not only reckons
The moments when we tread his ways,
But when the spirit beckons,—
That some slight good is also wrought
Beyond self-satisfaction,
When we are simply good in thought,
Howe'er we fail in action.

HELPS TO STUDY

Notes and Questions

What value to us are our longings?

Read the line that tells how we "let the new life in."

Why must we "realize our longing"?

How does Lowell value being "simply good in thought"?

What is better than being "simply good in thought"?

Why did Lowell value longing so highly?

What longings have you had that made you better?

Words and Phrases for Discussion

"myriad woods"
"earthward striving"

"carves in the marble Real"
"climb from hope to hope"

THE PUMPKIN

John Greenleaf Whittier

1

O, Greenly and fair in the lands of the sun,
The vines of the gourd and the rich melon run,
And the rock and the tree and the cottage enfold,
With broad leaves all greenness and blossoms all gold,
Like that which o'er Nineveh's prophet once grew,
While he waited to know that his warning was true,
And longed for the storm-cloud, and listened in vain
For the rush of the whirlwind and red fire-rain.

2

On the banks of the Xenil the dark Spanish maiden
Comes up with the fruit of the tangled vine laden;
And the Creole of Cuba laughs out to behold
Through orange-leaves shining the broad spheres of gold;
Yet with dearer delight from his home in the North,
On the fields of his harvest the Yankee looks forth,
Where crook-necks are coiling and yellow fruit shines,
And the sun of September melts down on his vines.

3

Ah! on Thanksgiving day, when from East and from West,
From North and from South come the pilgrim and guest,
When the gray-haired New-Englander sees round his board
The old broken links of affection restored,
When the care-wearied man seeks his mother once more,
And the worn matron smiles where the girl smiled before,
What moistens the lip and what brightens the eye?
What calls back the past, like the rich Pumpkin pie?

4

O,—fruit loved of boyhood!—the old days recalling,
When wood-grapes were purpling and brown nuts were falling!
When wild, ugly faces we carved in its skin,
Glaring out through the dark with a candle within!
When we laughed round the corn-heap, with hearts all in tune,
Our chair a broad pumpkin,—our lantern the moon,
Telling tales of the fairy who traveled like steam,
In a pumpkin-shell coach, with two rats for her team!

5

Then thanks for thy present!—none sweeter or better
E'er smoked from an oven or circled a platter!
Fairer hands never wrought at a pastry more fine,
Brighter eyes never watched o'er its baking, than thine!
And the prayer, which my mouth is too full to express,

Swells my heart that thy shadow may never be less,
That the days of thy lot may be lengthened below,
And the fame of thy worth like a pumpkin-vine grow,
And thy life be as sweet, and its last sunset sky
Golden-tinted and fair as thy own Pumpkin pie!

HELPS TO STUDY
Notes and Questions

Which line tells where the gourd and melon vines are found?

Which line tells that the Yankee delights in his pumpkin crop?

What "calls back the past" on Thanksgiving day?

Why does boyhood love the pumpkin?

Read the poet's prayer.

What is compared to the pumpkin pie in the last stanza?

Words and Phrases for Discussion

"links of affection" "care-wearied" "crook-necks"

ALL'S WELL

John Greenleaf Whittier

The clouds, which rise with thunder, slake
    Our thirsty souls with rain;
The blow most dreaded falls to break
    From off our limbs a chain;
And wrongs of man to man but make
    The love of God more plain.
As through the shadowy lens of even
The eye looks farthest into heaven
On gleams of star and depths of blue
The glaring sunshine never knew!

HELPS TO STUDY
Notes and Questions

How do clouds "which rise with thunder" appear?

What feeling do they inspire?

What do these clouds bring?

What is the "shadowy lens of even"?

When does the eye look "farthest into heaven"?

Words and Phrases for Discussion

"wrongs of man to man" "depths of blue"

LEXINGTON

OLIVER WENDELL HOLMES

1

Slowly the mist o'er the meadow was creeping,
  Bright on the dewy buds glistened the sun,
When from his couch, while his children were sleeping,
  Rose the bold rebel and shouldered his gun.
        Waving her golden veil
        Over the silent dale,
Blithe looked the morning on cottage and spire;
        Hushed was his parting sigh,
        While from his noble eye
Flashed the last sparkle of liberty's fire.

2

On the smooth green where the fresh leaf is springing
  Calmly the first-born of glory have met;
Hark! the death-volley around them is ringing!
  Look! with their life-blood the young grass is wet!
        Faint is the feeble breath,
        Murmuring low in death,
"Tell to our sons how their fathers have died;"
        Nerveless the iron hand,
        Raised for its native land,
Lies by the weapon that gleams at its side.

3

Over the hillsides the wild knell is tolling,
  From their far hamlets the yeomanry come;
As through the storm-clouds the thunder-burst rolling,
  Circles the beat of the mustering drum.

Fast on the soldier's path
Darken the waves of wrath,
Long have they gathered and loud shall they fall;
Red glares the musket's flash,
Sharp rings the rifle's crash,
Blazing and clanging from thicket and wall.

4

Gayly the plume of the horseman was dancing,
Never to shadow his cold brow again;
Proudly at morning the war-steed was prancing,
Reeking and panting he droops on the rein;
Pale is the lip of scorn,
Voiceless the trumpet horn,
Torn is the silken-fringed red cross on high;
Many a belted breast
Low on the turf shall rest,
Ere the dark hunters the herd have past by.

5

Snow-girdled crags where the hoarse wind is raving,
Rocks where the weary floods murmur and wail,
Wilds where the fern by the furrow is waving,
Reeled with the echoes that rode on the gale;
Far as the tempest thrills
Over the darkened hills,
Far as the sunshine streams over the plain,
Roused by the tyrant band,
Woke all the mighty land,
Girded for battle, from mountain to main.

6

Green be the graves where her martyrs are lying!
Shroudless and tombless they sunk to their rest,—
While o'er their ashes the starry fold flying
Wraps the proud eagle they roused from his nest.

Borne on her northern pine,
Long o'er the foaming brine
Spread her broad banner to storm and to sun;
Heaven keep her ever free,
Wide as o'er land and sea
Floats the fair emblem her heroes have won.

HELPS TO STUDY

Historical: The battle of Lexington took place April 19th, 1775. It was the beginning of the war for independence. The mother country had imposed unjust and burdensome laws upon the colonists, some of which, notably the tax on tea, was resisted by them. To enforce these laws the British Government had sent troops to Boston under the command of General Gates, who, hearing that the Americans had collected powder, shot, and muskets at Concord, sent a force of soldiers to seize these supplies. Paul Revere was sent to warn the two leaders, Samuel Adams and John Hancock, and to give "his cry of alarm to every Middlesex village and farm."

"It was one by the village clock
When he galloped into Lexington

.   .   .

It was two by the village clock
When he came to the bridge in Concord town."

When the British soldiers, called regulars, reached Lexington, they found some minute-men drawn up on the green by the meeting-house. The British officer ordered them to throw down their arms and disperse, but they stood still. Then he ordered his men to fire and several were killed or wounded. The regulars marched to Concord, where the minute-men were drawn up "by the rude bridge." Here they destroyed some of the stores and then started back to Boston. On the way they were fired upon by farmers and minute-men from behind houses and barns, trees and stone walls. Holmes tries in this poem to give us a picture of the contest at Lexington.

Notes and Questions

Where is Lexington?

When did the Battle of Lexington occur?

What made this a famous battle?

Who is meant by the "bold rebel"?

To what is the beat of the drum compared in the third stanza?

What word in the third stanza refers to the American volunteers?

To whom does the word "soldier" in the same stanza refer?

Find something in the fourth stanza which tells you that the "horseman" was a British soldier.

Read the lines which tell how far the echoes of the battle were heard.

Does the word "echoes" as used here mean the sounds of the battle or the news of the battle?

To what word in the fifth stanza does the word "her" in the last stanza refer?

Who are "her martyrs"?

What is the "starry fold"?

What is the "fair emblem her heroes have won"?

Words and Phrases for Discussion

"first-born of glory"

"foaming brine"

"far hamlets"

"mountain to main"

"silken fringed red cross"—the English flag

"belted breast"—refers to the belt from which the sword hung

"the proud eagle they roused from his nest"—freedom

CONTENTMENT

Oliver Wendell Holmes

"Man wants but little here below."

1

Little I ask; my wants are few;
  I only wish a hut of stone,
(A *very plain* brown stone will do,)
    That I may call my own;—
And close at hand is such a one,
In yonder street that fronts the sun.

2

Plain food is quite enough for me;
  Three courses are as good as ten;—

If Nature can subsist on three,
        Thank Heaven for three.   Amen!
I always thought cold victuals nice;—
My *choice* would be vanilla-ice.

3

I care not much for gold or land;—
    Give me a mortgage here and there,—
Some good bank-stock,—some note of hand,
        Or trifling railroad share;—
I only ask that Fortune send
A *little* more than I shall spend.

4

Honors are silly toys, I know,
    And titles are but empty names;—
I would, *perhaps,* be Plenipo,—
        But only near St. James;—
I'm very sure I should not care
To fill our Gubernator's chair.

5

Jewels are baubles 'tis a sin
    To care for such unfruitful things;—
One good-sized diamond in a pin,—
        Some *not so large,* in rings,—
A ruby, and a pearl, or so,
Will do for me;—I laugh at show.

6

My dame should dress in cheap attire;
    (Good, heavy silks are never dear;)

I own perhaps I *might* desire
  Some shawls of true cashmere,—
Some marrowy crapes of China silk,
Like wrinkled skins on scalded milk.

7

I would not have the horse I drive
  So fast that folks must stop and stare;
An easy gait—two, forty-five—
  Suits me; I do not care;—
Perhaps for just a *single spurt,*
Some seconds less would do no hurt.

8

Of pictures I should like to own
  Titians and Raphaels three or four,—
I love so much their style and tone,—
  One Turner, and no more,—
(A landscape,—foreground golden dirt,
The sunshine painted with a squirt.)

9

Of books but few,—some fifty score
  For daily use, and bound for wear;
The rest upon an upper floor;—
  Some *little* luxury *there*
Of red morocco's gilded gleam,
And vellum rich as country cream.

10

Busts, cameos, gems,—such things as these,
  Which others often show for pride,
I value for their power to please,
  And selfish churls deride;—
One Stradivarius, I confess,
Two Meerschaums, I would fain possess.

11

Wealth's wasteful tricks I will not learn,
    Nor ape the glittering upstart fool;—
Shall not carved tables serve my turn,
    But *all* must be of buhl?
Give grasping pomp its double share,—
I ask but *one* recumbent chair.

12

Thus humble let me live and die,
    Nor long for Midas' golden touch,
If Heaven more generous gifts deny,
    I shall not miss them *much*,—
Too grateful for the blessing lent
Of simple tastes and minds content!

HELPS TO STUDY

Notes and Questions

With what statement does the first stanza open?

How is this statement contradicted in the same stanza?

With what statement does the second stanza open?

What do the words "cold victuals" usually mean?

What seems to be the poet's idea of "cold victuals"?

Find a statement in each stanza which is contradicted by other statements in the same stanza.

What does the poet say of his wants in the first line of the poem?

What have you learned of his wants from the succeeding lines of the poem?

For what does he say that he is grateful?

What are "simple tastes"?

What do you think was his purpose in writing this poem?

Words and Phrases for Discussion

"Plenipo"=Ambassador

"St. James"=The British court

"Gubernator"=governor

"Raphael," "Titian," "Turner"—were great painters

"Stradivarius"=the maker of famous violins

"buhl"=yellow or white metal or tortoise shell inlaid in mosaic patterns in furniture

GLOSSARY

KEY TO THE SOUNDS OF MARKED VOWELS

ā as in ate	ê as in event	ō as in note	ŭ as in cut
ă as in bat	ē as in maker	ŏ as in not	û as in turn
â as in care	ē as in eve	ô as in or	ů as in unite
á as in ask	ĕ as in met	ộ as in obey	ōō as in food
ä as in arm	ī as in kind	ū as in use	ŏŏ as in foot
å as in senate	ĭ as in pin		

a-ban'don (à-băn'dŭn), to give up; to desert.

a-ban'doned (à-băn'dŭnd), extremely wicked; hardened.

a-bate' (à-bāt'), to decrease; to become less.

a-bide' (à-bīd'), to wait for; to remain; to endure.

a-bode' (à-bōd'), residence; dwelling.

ab-rupt' (ăb-rŭpt'), sudden; hasty; steep.

ab-sorbed' (ăb-sôrbd'), fully occupied; engaged wholly; swallowed up.

ac'cess (ăk'sĕs; ăk-sĕs'), the means by which a thing is approached.

ac-com'mo-date (à-kŏm'ô-dāt), to furnish with something desired; to oblige.

ac-com'plish (à-kŏm'plĭsh), to perform; to complete; to effect.

ac-cord' (à-kôrd'), agreement; consent.

ac-cost' (ă-kôst), to approach; to speak first.

ac-cuse' (ă-kūz'), to charge with; to blame.

a-chieve' (à-chēv'), to fulfill; to attain.

a-dept' (à-dĕpt'), one fully skilled in anything.

ad-here' (ăd-hēr'), to stick fast; to hold.

ad-min'is-ter (mĭn'-ĭs-tēr), to manage; to direct.

ad-van'tage (ăd-vàn'tâj), superiority; mastery.

ad-ven'tur-er (ăd-vĕn'-tûr-ẽr), one who engages in new or dangerous undertakings.

ad-ven'tur-ous (ŭs), reckless; daring; venturesome.

ad'ver-sa-ry (ăd'vēr-så-rĭ), enemy; foe.

ad'verse (ăd'vẽrs), opposed; contrary.

ae'gis (ē'jĭs), a breast ornament or protection.

af'fa-ble (ăf'à-b'l), gracious; courteous.

af-firm' (ă-fûrm'), to assert positively; to declare.

af-flict' (ă-flĭkt'), to trouble; to pain; to hurt.

af'flu-ence (ăf'lōō-ĕns), abundance; plenty.

Ag-a-mem'non (ag-a-mĕm'non)

a-ghast (à-gàst), terrified; afraid.

ag'i-ta'tion (ăj'ĭ-tā'shŭn), excitement; commotion.

ag'o-ny (ag'ô-nĭ), extreme pain; anguish.

ag'ri-mo-ny (ăg'rĭ-mô-nĭ), common yellow flowered herbs.

a-kim'bo (à-kĭm'bō), with the hand on the hip.

Al'gi-dus (ăl'jĭ-dŭs), a high mountain near Rome.

al'ien (āl'yĕn), a foreigner; a stranger.

al-lies' (à-līz'), those united by treaty or league.

al'tar (ôl'tẽr), a raised structure on which sacrifices are offered in worship.

al-ter'nate-ly (ăl-tûr'năt), by turns; interchanging regularly.

a-maze'ment (à-māz'), great wonder; surprise.

am-bas'sa-dor (ăm-băs'à-dẽr), an official representative sent by one ruler or country to another.

am'ber (ăm'bẽr), a yellowish resin used for beads.

am-bi'tion (ăm-bĭsh'ŭn), eager desire for power or honor.

am-bro'si-a (ăm-brō'zhĭ-à), the food of the gods.

am'bush (am'boōsh), arrangement of troops for attacking from concealed position.

am'ple (ăm'p'l), large; abundant; sufficient.

a-nat'o-my (a-năt'ô-mĭ), the science which treats of animals and plants.

an'ces-tor (ăn'sĕs-tēr), one from whom a person is descended; a forefather.

an'ces-try (ăn'sĕs-trĭ), those who compose the line of descent; a series of ancestors.

an'cient (ăn'shĕnt), old; aged.

an'gu-lar (ăn'gû-làr), forming an angle; ungraceful; stiff.

an'i-mat'ed (măt'ed), full of life; vigorous; lively.

an-ni'hi-late (à-nī'hĭ-lāt), to destroy; to reduce to nothing.

an-nounce'ment (ă-nouns'), proclamation; publication.

an'nu-al (ăn'û-ăl), returning every year; once in the year.

a-noint' (à-noint'), to apply oil to; to pour oil upon.

an'them (ăn'them), a song or hymn of praise or gladness.

an-tic'i-pate (ăn-tĭs'ĭ-pāt), to do before another; to expect; to foresee.

an-tique' (ăn-tēk'), old; ancient.

an'vil (ăn'vĭl), a block of iron on which metal is shaped.

ape (āp), to mimic; to imitate.

ap-par'el (ă-păr'el), clothing; dress.

ap-par'ent-ly (ă-păr'ĕnt), seemingly; evidently.

ap-pease' (ă-pēz'), to calm, to soothe; to quiet.

ap-plause' (ă-plôz'), commendation; approval shown by clapping.

ap'pre-hend' (ăp're-hĕnd'), to fear; to imagine.

ap'pro-ba'tion (bā'shŭn), approval; commendation.

ap-prove' (ă-prōōv'), to regard as good; to commend.

ar'chi-tec'tur-al (är'kĭ-tĕk'tûr-ăl), conforming to the rules of architecture; of the art of building.

ar-ray' (ă-rā'), order; regular arrangement.

ar-rayed' (ă-rād'), set in order; drawn up.

a-re'na (ă-rē'nà), the space in the center of the amphitheater where the gladiators fought.

art'ful (ärt-fōōl), skillful; tricky; deceitful.

ar'ti-fi'cial (är'tĭ-fĭsh'ăl), produced by human labor; not genuine.

ar-til'ler-y (är-tĭl'ẽr-ĭ), mounted guns; implements of warfare.

ar'ti-san (är'tĭ-zăn), mechanic; artist; workman.

ar-tis'tic (är-tĭs'tĭk), showing taste or skill.

as'cer-tain' (ăs'ẽr-tān'), to make a thing certain; to find out.

as-cribe' (ăs-krīb'), to refer; to assign; to attribute.

as'pi-ra'tion (ăs'pĭ-rā'shŭn), high desire; ambition.

as-pire' (ăs-pīr'), to seek to attain or reach something high or great.

as-sail' (ă-sāl'), to attack with violence.

as-sault' (ă-sôlt'), a violent attack.

as-sort'ment (ă-sort'mĕnt), a collection containing a variety of kinds.

as-tound'ing (ăs-tound'), astonishing; surprising.

as-sume' (ă-sūm'), to take upon one's self; to take for granted.

as-sure' (ă-shōōr'), to pledge; to promise; to persuade.

a-thwart' (ă-thwôrt'), across; sidewise.

at-tire' (ă-tīr'), dress; clothes.

at-trac'tive (ă-trăk'tĭv), having the power of attracting.

au'di-ence (ô'dĭ-ĕns), an assembly of hearers.

au'gur (ô'gŭr), an official prophet or diviner of ancient Rome.

au'gu-ry (ô'gū-rĭ), prediction; omen; sign of the future.

au-gust' (ô-gŭst'), solemn; dignified; stately.

aus-tere' (ôs-tēr'), harsh; stern; severe.

a-vail' (à-vāl'), to make use of; to take advantage of.

av'a-rice (ăv'à-rĭs), greediness; excessive desire for gain.

a-venge' (à-vĕnj'), to inflict punishment upon one who has done an injury.

a-ver' (à-vûr'), to assert; to protest.

a-vert' (à-vûrt'), to turn aside or away.

az'ure (ăzh'ûr), sky blue.

baf'fled (băf''ld), checked; bewildered; defeated.

bal'co-ny (băl'kô-nĭ), a projecting gallery.

bale'ful (bāl'fōōl), destructive; deadly.

bal'lad (băl'ăd), a simple song or short narrative poem.

balm (bäm), anything that heals pain; any fragrant ointment.

ban'ish (băn'ĭsh), to drive out; to compel to depart.

ban'quet (băn'kwĕt), a feast.

bard (bärd), poet.

Bar'me-cide (bär'mē-sĭd), a character in "The Arabian Nights" who made a pretense of serving food to a beggar.

bat'tered (băt'ẽrd), bruised; shattered.

bat'tle-ments (băt''l-mĕnts), low walls or barriers made of solids and open spaces on top of the fortress.

bau'ble (bôb'l), a trifling piece of finery; a cheap plaything.

beck'on (bĕk''n), to motion with the hand or finger.

be-fall' (bê-fôl'), to happen; to come to pass.

be-fit' (bê-fĭt'), to suit; to become.

bel'fry (bĕl'frĭ), a bell tower.

bel'lows (bĕl'ōz), an instrument for blowing fires or filling the pipes of an organ.

be-reft' (bê-rĕft'), deprived of.

be-seech' (bê-sēch'), to ask earnestly; to beg.

be-tray' (bê-trā'), to deliver into the hands of an enemy; to prove false.

bier (bēr), the frame or stand on which a body is borne to the grave.

bil'low-y (bĭl'ô-ĭ), swelling into large waves.

biv'ouac (bĭv'wăk), a night's encampment.

black'mail (blăk'māl), a payment forced by threats; a tribute of money, corn, or cattle.

blast (blàst), a violent gust of wind.

blast'ed (blàs'ted), withered; torn by an explosion.

bleak (blēk), without color; pale; cold; cutting; bitter.

blight (blīt), a disease of plants resulting in withering or decay.

blight'ed, affected with blight; ruined.

bliss (blĭs), gladness; enjoyment.

blithe (blīth), glad; joyous.

blithe'some (sŭm), gay; merry.

blus'ter-ing (blŭs'tēr), noisy; stormy.

boar (bōr), the wild hog.

bol'ster (bōl'stēr), a long cushion generally used under the pillow.

bom'ba-zine (bŏm'bá-zēn), a dress fabric of silk and worsted or cotton and worsted.

bond'age (bŏn'dáj), state of slavery or captivity.

bon'vi'vant' (bôn'vē'vän'), a lover of good living.

boon (bōōn), a prayer or petition.

boo'ty (bōō'tĭ), plunder; that which is obtained by robbery.

boun'te-ous (boun'tẽ-ŭs), liberal; plentiful.

boun'ty (boun'tĭ), liberality; generosity.

bow'er (bou'ẽr), a shelter in a garden; an arbor.

bow'ie knife (bō'ĭ; bōō'ĭ), a knife with a long blade curved to the point.

brag (brăg), to boast.

brand (brănd), a burning piece of wood.

bran'dish (brăn'dĭsh), to shake or wave as a weapon.

brawl (brôl), to quarrel noisily.

breach (brēch), a break; an opening.

bred (brĕd), educated; instructed; trained.

Bre-genz' (Brȧ-gĕnts'), a town in Austria-Hungary.

brid'al (brīd'ăl), marriage.

bril'liant (brĭl'yănt), sparkling; very bright.

brine (brīn), water saturated with salt.

bronze (brŏnz), a substance composed of copper and tin; a reddish brown color.

brooch (brōch; brōōch), an ornamental clasp.

brook (brōōk), to bear; to endure.

bulk'y (bŭl'kĭ), of great size; clumsy.

bul'wark (bōōl'wȧrk), a solid wall raised for defense.

burgh'er (bûr'gẽr), a male citizen having the privilege of voting.

butt (bŭt), a large cask.

cai'tiff (kā'tĭf), a coward; a mean person.

Cam-pa'ni-a (kăm-pā'nĭ-ȧ), a province of central Italy; an open level region.

can'ker-worm (kăn'kẽr), the young of various insects injurious to trees.

can'o-py (kăn'ỏ-pĭ), an overhanging shelter or shade.

can'ti-cle (kăn'tĭ-k'l), a song or hymn.

car'ol (kăr'ŭl), a song of praise.

cas-cade' (kăs-kād'), a fall of water over a precipice.

ca-the'dral (kȧ-thē'drăl), the church which contains the bishop's official chair.

cav'al-ry (kăv'ăl-rĭ), that part of an army which serves on horseback.

cease'less (sēs), without pause or stop.

chafe (chāf), to irritate; to vex.

chaff (chăf), husks of grains.

chal'ice (chăl'ĭs), a drinking cup or goblet.

chal'lenge (chăl'ĕnj), to assert a right; to invite defiantly.

Cham (kăm), or khan (kän; or kăn), lord; prince.

cham-paign' (shăm-pān'), open country; a plain.

chant (chȧnt), to utter with melodious voice; to sing.

charg'er (chär'jẽr), an officer's horse for battle or parade.

char'i-ot (chăr'ĭ-ŏt), a two-wheeled car used by the ancients.

char'i-ot-eer' (ẽr'), one who drives a chariot.

chasm (kăz'm), a deep opening in the earth or rock.

cher'ish (chĕr'ĭsh), to hold dear; to protect.

chief'tain (chēf'tĭn), a chief; leader; captain.

chime (chīm), a set of bells musically tuned.

chine (chīn), a piece of the backbone of an animal with the adjacent parts.

chiv'al-ry (shĭv'ăl-rĭ), distinguished warriors or brave gentlemen; honor, kindness to the weak, generosity to foes.

chops (chŏps), the jaws; the fleshy parts about the mouth.

churl (chûrl), a man without rank; a rough, surly man.

ci-ca'da (sĭ-kā'dȧ), an insect with stout body, wide head, and large wings; locust.

Cin'tra (sẽn-trä), a town in Portugal.

cir-cu'i-tous (sẽr-kū'ĭ-tŭs), roundabout; wandering.

cit'a-del (sĭt'ȧ-dĕl), a fortress; a stronghold.

cit'i-zen (sĭt'ĭ-zĕn), an inhabitant of a city.

civ'ic (sĭv'ĭk), relating to a city or citizen.

clam'or (klăm'ẽr), shouting; outcry.

clar'et (klăr'ĕt), red wine from Bordeaux.

clar'i-on (klăr'ĭ-ŭn), a trumpet.

cleav'ing (klēv), the act of splitting or opening.

cleft (klĕft), a crack; an opening.

clime (klīm), climate; region.

clod (klŏd), a lump of earth.

coat of mail (māl), garment made of metal scales.

code (kōd), a collection of laws; a system of regulations.

com'bat-ant (kŏm'băt-ănt), one who engages in a combat or fight.

com-bine' (kŏm-bīn'), to unite or join.

Co-mi´ti-um (kō-mǐsh´ǐ-ǔm), the place
at the foot of the Capitol in Rome.

com-mend´ (kǒ-mĕnd´), to give praise
or approval.

com´ment (kǒm´mĕnt), a remark or
criticism.

com´men-ta-ry (kǒm´ĕn-tȧ-rǐ), a brief
account of events; a remark.

com-mu´ni-ca´tion (kȧ´shǔn), corre-
spondence; news.

com´pass (kǔm´pȧs), to surround; to
obtain; to accomplish.

com-pas´sion (kǒm-pǎsh´ǔn), sorrow;
pity; sympathy.

com-pel´ (kǒm-pĕl´), to force; to
oblige.

com´plex (kǒm´plĕks), entangled;
twisted.

com´pli-ment (kǒm´plǐ-mĕnt), expression of admiration or praise.

com-posed´ (kǒm-pōzd´), calm; quiet;
self-possessed.

com-pos´i-tor (kǒm-pǒz´ǐ-tēr), one who
sets type.

com-pul´sion (pǔl´shǔn), force; act of
compelling.

com´rade (kǒm´rǎd), companion; associate.

con-ceive´ (kǒn-sēv´), to think; to
suppose.

con-cern´ (kǒn-sûrn´), to interest; to
affect.

con-cer´to (kǒn-chĕr´tō), a musical
composition for two or more instrument.

con-clu´s.ve (kǒn-klōō´sǐv), final; un-
answerable.

con-demn´ (kǒn-dĕm´), to declare guilty; to pronounce sentence against.

con´de-scen´sion (sĕn´shǔn), courtesy;
affability.

con-fess´ (kǒn-fĕs´), to acknowledge
or own a fault.

con´flict (kǒn´flǐkt), strife for the
mastery; a battle.

con´i-cal (kǒn´ǐ-kǎl), cone-shaped;
tapering to a point.

con´scious (kǒn´shǔs), to have knowledge of.

con´se-quence (kǒn´sē-kwĕns), result;
end.

con-serve´ (kǒn-sûrv´), to keep; to
save; to preserve.

con´sta-ble (kǔn´stȧ-b'l), a member
of the county police; an officer of
the peace.

con´ster-na´tion (kǒn´stēr-nā´shǔn),
alarm; horror; fright.

con-strain´ (kǒn-strān´), to compel;
to force.

con-sult´ (kǒn-sǔlt´), to ask advice of
another; to refer to.

con´tem-plate (kǒn´tĕm-plāt), to consider; to think.

con-tend´ (kǒn-tĕnd´), to strive; to
fight.

con´test (kǒn´tĕst), earnest struggle;
battle.

con-tin´u-ous (kǒn-tǐn´ū-ǔs), unbroken; constant.

con´tra-ry (kǒn´trȧ-rǐ), opposite; un-
favorable.

con´trast (kǒn´trȧst), opposition of
qualities or great difference.

con-trive´ (kǒn-trīv´), to plan; to plot.

con-vince´ (kǒn-vǐns´), to satisfy by
proof; to persuade.

con-viv´i-al (kǒn-vǐv´i-ǎl), gay; social;
festive.

cor´nel (kôr´nĕl), a tree or shrub
bearing red or yellow berries.

cor´o-nal (kǒr´ō-nȧl), a crown or cor-
onet.

cor´po-ra´tion (kôr´pō-rā´shǔn), a
group of persons authorized by law
to act as a single person.

cor´pu-len-cy (kôr´pū-lĕn-sǐ), fleshi-
ness; excessive fatness.

cor´pu-lent (kôr´pū-lĕnt), fleshy;
bulky.

corse´let (kôrs´lĕt), armor for the
body.

coun´cil (koun´sǐl), an assembly for
consultation or advice.

coun´sel-lor (koun´sĕ-lēr), an advisor.

cov´e-nant (kǔv´ē-nǎnt), an agreement; a solemn compact.

cow´ard (kou´ērd), a person who lacks
courage.

craft (krȧft), cunning; art; skill.

craft´y (krȧf´tǐ), skillful; sly; deceitful.

cram (krǎm), to crowd; to stuff.

cramp (krǎmp), to confine; to restrain
from free action.

cra´ven (krā´v'n), a coward.

cre´dence (krē´dĕns), belief; credit.

cre´ole (krē´ōl), a person descended
from the French or Spanish settlers
of the Gulf states.

cres´cent (krĕs´ĕnt), the moon in
her first quarter.

crest (krĕst), a tuft on the head of a
bird; the plume on a helmet.

croak´er (krōk´ēr), one who grumbles
or prophesies evil.

crone (krōn), an old woman.

cru´ci-ble (krōō´sǐ-b'l), a melting pot.

Crus tu me´ri um (krǔs tū mē´rǐ ǔm),
an ancient town of the Sabines.

crys´tal (krǐs´tȧl), transparent quartz;
glass of great brilliancy.

cuck´oo (kook´ōō), a European bird
noted for its whistle from which
it is named.

cul´ti-vate (kǔl´tǐ-vȧt), to till; to raise;
to improve by labor or study.

cul´ture (kǔl´tǔr), the training and im-
proving of the moral and intellectual
nature.

cun´ning (kǔn´ǐng), skillful; sly; deceitful.

curb (kûrb), to guide and manage; to
restrain.

cur´dle (kûr´d'l), to thicken; to con-
geal.

cur'rent (kŭr'rĕnt), a stream of water or air.

cus'to-dy (kŭs'tô-dĭ), a keeping or guarding.

cus'tom (kŭs'tŭm), a usage or practice.

cym'bals (sĭm'bălz), a pair of brass plates clashed together to produce a ringing sound.

cy'press (sī'prĕs), an evergreen tree regarded as an emblem of mourning.

dan'dle (dăn'd'l), to move up and down on the knee or in the arms.

daunt'less (dänt; dônt), bold; fearless.

de-bate' (dê-bāt'), discussion; argument.

de-ceit -ful (dê-sēt'fo͞ol), insincere; cheating; full of deceit.

decked (dĕkt), dressed; adorned.

dec'la-ma'tion (dĕk'lȧ-mā'shŭn), loud speaking in public; recitation of speeches.

de-cree' (dê-krē'), an order of decision; law.

deem (dēm), to believe; to regard; to think.

de-fend' (dê-fĕnd'), to protect; to guard.

de-fi'ance (dê-fī'ăns), act of defying; a challenge; opposition.

de-file' (dê-fīl'), a narrow pass between hills or rocks.

de-file' (dê-fīl'), to make impure; to soil.

def'i-nite (dĕf'ĭ-nĭt), having certain limits.

deft'ly (dĕft'), neatly; cleverly; dexterously.

de-fy' (dê fī'), to challenge; to dare.

de-grade' (dê-grād') to lower in rank; to disgrace.

deign (dān), to allow; to grant; to stoop.

de-lib'er-ate (dê-lĭb'ẽr-āt), to consider; to hesitate in deciding.

de-liv'er (dê-lĭv'ẽr), to set free; to save; to rescue.

dell (dĕl), a small valley or ravine.

del'uge (dĕl'ūj), a flood; an overflowing of the land by water.

de-pose' (dê-pōz'), to remove from a throne or high office.

dep're-cate (dĕp'rê-kāt), to pray against some evil; to disapprove.

de-ride' (dê-rīd'), to laugh at; to mock.

de-scend'ant (dê-sĕn'dănt), child, grandchild, greatgrandchild, etc.

des'o-la'tion (lā'shŭn), destruction of inhabitants; ruin.

de-spair' (dê-spâr'), loss of hope; hopelessness.

des'per-ate (dĕs'pẽr-åt), extremely dangerous; rash; furious.

de-spise' (dê-spīz'), to look upon with contempt.

des'ti-na'tion (nā'shŭn), the place set for the end of a journey.

des'tined (dĕs'tĭnd), fixed or determined beforehand.

de-vice' (dê-vīs'), an invention; a scheme; a stratagem.

de-vise' (dê-vīz'), to invent; to plan.

de-vote' (dê-vōt'), to set apart; to give up wholly; to doom.

dex-ter'i-ty (dĕks-tẽr'ĭ-tĭ), readiness and skill; activity; nimbleness.

di'a-dem (dī'ȧ-dĕm), a crown; an ornamental headband.

di'a-lect (dī'ȧ-lĕkt), language; local form of language.

di'et (dī'ĕt), food; allowance of food.

dil'i-gent (dĭl'ĭ-jĕnt), industrious; steady and earnest.

di-min'ish (dĭ-mĭn'ish), to make less; to take away.

di-min'u-tive (dĭ-mĭn'ȗ-tĭv), small; little.

dim'ple (dĭm'p'l), a slight natural depression, usually on cheek or chin.

din (dĭn), loud confused noise; roar.

Di-nar'za de (dê-när'zä dā), the sister of Scheherazade in "The Arabian Nights."

dire (dīr), fearful; dreadful.

dis-cern' (dĭ-zûrn'), to see; to discover; to distinguish.

dis'cord (dĭs'kôrd), disagreement; strife; a harsh noise.

dis-guise' (dĭs-gīz'), a dress put on for concealment or to deceive.

dis'mal (dĭz'măl), gloomy; sorrowful; dark.

dis-may' (dĭs-mā'), to terrify; to alarm; to frighten.

dis'po-si'tion (pô-zĭsh'ŭn), nature; character.

dis-pute' (dĭs-pūt'), to argue against; to discuss.

dis-sem'ble (dĭ-sĕm'b'l), to conceal the real feeling; to pretend something.

dis'si-pat'ed (dĭs'ĭ-pāt'ĕd), wasteful of time or money; intemperate.

dis-solve' (dĭ-zŏlv'), to break up; to melt; to absorb completely.

dis-tin'guish-a-ble (tĭn'gwĭsh-ȧ-b'l), capable of being seen.

dis-tin'guished (gwĭsht), noted; prominent; famous.

dis-tort' (dĭs-tôrt'), to twist out of natural shape.

dit'ty (dĭt'ĭ), a song; a little poem.

di'vers (dī'vẽrz), different; more than one.

di-verse' (dĭ-vûrs'; dī'vẽrs), different; unlike.

di-vin'i-ty (dĭ-vĭn'ĭ'tĭ), a god; a deity.

doc'u-ment (dŏc'ȗ-mĕnt), an official paper.

doff (dŏf), to put off clothing; to remove.

dol'phin (dŏl'fĭn), a water animal about seven feet long, having a large head and fish-like body.

dome (dōm), a roof having a rounded form.

do-mes'tic (dȯ-mĕs'tĭk), relating to home life.

do-min'ion (dȯ-mĭn'yŭn), supreme authority.

doom (dōōm), fate; ruin; destruction.

dou'blet (dŭb'lĕt), a close fitting garment for men; a jacket.

doubt'less (dout'), certainly; without doubt.

dra'ma (drä'mȧ), a play; a composition intended to be performed by actors on a stage.

draught (dráft), the act of drinking; liquid to be swallowed.

drought (drout), dryness; want of rain.

drug (drŭg), any substance used as medicine.

dry'salt'er-y (drī'sȯl-tēr-ĭ), the business of drying or salting meats, pickles, etc.

du'ly (dū'lĭ), properly; orderly.

dun (dŭn), of a dull brown or gray color.

dusk'y (dŭs'kĭ), dark colored; not bright.

dwarf (dwôrf), an animal or plant much below the ordinary size.

dye (dī), stain; color.

ec'sta-sy (ĕk'stȧ-sĭ), overmastering joy; rapture.

ed'dy (ĕd'ĭ), a current of air or water moving circularly; a whirlpool.

ef-fec'tu-al (ĕ-fĕk'tû-ăl), sufficient; adequate.

ef'fer-ves'cent (ĕf'ĕr-vĕs'ĕnt), bubbling and sizzling; lively; gay.

el'e-gy (ĕl'ė-jĭ), a mournful poem.

em-brace' (ĕm-brās') to clasp in the arms with affection.

e-merge' (ė-mûrj'), to rise from; to come into view.

en-am'el (ĕn-ăm'ĕl), to give a smooth glossy surface like that of enamel.

en-chant'ment (ĕn-chȧnt'mĕnt), magic; charm; the state of being controlled by magic.

en-deav'or (ĕn-dĕv'ẽr), to attempt; to strive.

en-dure' (en-dūr'), to remain firm; to suffer patiently.

en'er-get'ic (jĕt'ĭk), forcible; vigorous.

en-gulf' (ĕn-gŭlf'), to swallow up; to absorb.

en-list' (ĕn-lĭst'), to enter on a list; to enroll for military or naval service.

en'mi-ty (ĕn'mĭ-tĭ), hatred; ill-will; malice.

en-no'ble (ė-nō'-b'l), to raise; to make noble.

en-rap'ture (ĕn-răp'tûr), to delight greatly.

en'sign (ĕn'sĭn), a flag; a banner.

en'ter-prise (ĕn'tẽr-prīz), an attempt; an undertaking; eagerness.

en-treat' (trēt), to ask earnestly; to beseech.

e-nu'mer-ate (ė-nū'mēr-āt), to count over; to mention one by one.

ep'au-let (ĕp'ȯ-lĕt), a shoulder ornament worn by military and naval officers.

ep'i-cure (ĕp'ĭ-kūr), one devoted to the luxuries of the table.

ep'i-cu-re'an (rē'ăn), luxurious.

err'ing (ûr), wandering; making mistakes; doing wrong.

er'ror (ĕr'ẽr), belief in what is untrue; a mistake; a sin.

es-chew' (ĕs-chōō'), to avoid; to keep one's self clear of.

es'cort (ĕs'kôrt), protection; care or safeguard on a journey.

es-say' (ĕ-sā'), to attempt; to try.

e-ter'ni-ty (ė-tûr'nĭ-tĭ), immeasurable time; immortality.

e-the're-al (ė-thē'rė-ăl), spirit like; exceedingly light and airy.

e-vap'o-rate (ė-văp'ȯ-rāt), to change from a liquid or solid state into vapor.

ex-act'i-tude (ĕg-zăk'tĭ-tūd), accuracy; correctness.

ex-ag'ger-a'tion (ĕg-zăj'ẽr-ā'shŭn), overstatement; a going beyond the bounds of truth.

ex-ceed'ing (ĕk-sēd'), more than sufficient; extraordinary.

ex-cess' (ĕk-sĕs'), that which exceeds what is usual or proper.

ex-ces'sive (ĕk-sĕs'ĭv), greater than the usual amount.

ex-haust'ed (ĕg-zȯs'tĕd), worn out; tired out.

ex-hort' (ĕg-zôrt'; ĕgz-hôrt'), to advise; to warn.

ex-pand' (ĕks-pănd'), to open wide; to spread out.

ex-pan'sion (shŭn), act or process of expanding; enlargement.

ex-pect'ant (ĕks-pĕk'tănt), expecting; waiting.

ex-pe'di-ent (ĕks-pē'dĭ-ĕnt), practical; wise; advantageous.

ex-pe'ri-ence (ĕks-pē'rĭ-ĕns), the actual living through events.

ex'pi-ra'tion (ĕk'spĭ-rā'shŭn), end; termination.

ex-pul'sion (ĕks-pŭl'shŭn), a driving out; the act of expelling.

ex'qui-site (ĕks'kwĭ-zĭt), choice; delicate; rare.

fab'u-lous (făb'û-lŭs), not real; beyond belief.

fac'ul-ty (făk'ŭl-tĭ), the president, professors, and tutors in a college.

fain (fān), desirous; eager.

faith (fāth), promise; loyalty; belief.

faith'less, false; disloyal; not believing.

fal'con (fô'k'n; fôl'k'n), a hawk trained to pursue and attack wild fowl or game.

Fa-ler'i-i (fȧ-lē'rĭ-ĭ), chief town of Etruria.

fal'low deer (făl'ō), deer of pale yellow color.

fame (fām), reputation; renown; public opinion.

fa-mil'iar (fȧ-mĭl'yȧr), closely acquainted; well known.

fam'ine (făm'ĭn), scarcity of food; starvation.

fa'mous (fā'mŭs), celebrated; renowned.

fan'cy (făn'sĭ), to imagine; to believe, without being certain.

fan-tas'tic (făs'tĭk), imaginary; queer; grotesque.

fas'ci-nate (făs'ĭ-nāt), to charm; to influence irresistibly.

fas-tid'i-ous (făs-tĭd'ĭ-ŭs), difficult to please; critical.

fa'tal (fā'tăl), causing death or destruction; deadly.

fate (fāt), fortune; doom.

fath'om (făth'ŭm), a measure of length containing six feet.

fa-tigue' (fȧ-tēg), weariness; exhaustion.

fawn (fôn), to show delight by crouching, wagging the tail, etc.

fe-ro'cious (fê-rō'shŭs), fierce; cruel; savage.

flat'ter (flăt'ẽr), to praise insincerely or deceitfully.

flaw (flô), a defect; a fault; an imperfection.

fleet (flēt), a group of vessels.

fleet'ed (flēt), passed over quickly.

fleet'ing (flēt), passing swiftly.

flinch (flĭnch), to withdraw from an undertaking; to show signs of yielding.

flin'ty (flĭn'tĭ), resembling flint; very hard.

flour'ish (flŭr'ĭsh), to prosper; to increase and enlarge.

fold (fōld), an inclosure for sheep; a sheep pen.

fol'ly (fŏl'ĭ), foolishness; want of good sense.

for-bear' (fŏr-bâr'), to hold back; to control one's self when provoked.

ford (fōrd), to cross a stream by wading.

fore'cast (fōr'kȧst), a prophecy; an indication of what may be expected.

for'eign (fŏr'ĭn), outside one's own country; belonging to some other country.

forge (fōrj; fôrj), a place where iron is wrought by heating and hammering.

for-lorn' (fŏr-lôrn'), forsaken; helpless; friendless.

for-sooth' (for-sōōth'), in truth; certainly.

for'tress (fôr'trĕs), a place of defense; a fort; a castle.

foul (foul), ill-smelling and ill-looking; dirty; hateful.

found'er (foun'dẽr), one who establishes or lays a foundation.

frag'ile (frăj'ĭl), easily broken; delicate.

fra'grance (frā'grăns), sweetness of smell; perfume.

fra'grant (frā'grănt), sweet-smelling; having a pleasant perfume.

frail (frāl), easily broken; not firm; weak.

fraud (frôd), deceit; trickery; cheat.

fray (frā), contest; fight.

freight'ed (frāt), loaded.

friv'o-lous (frĭv'ō-lŭs), trifling; worthless.

fru-gal'i-ty (frōō-găl'ĭ-tĭ), economy; careful management; sparing use.

fu'sil-lade' (fū'zĭ-lād'), shots in rapid succession.

gait (gāt), manner of walking or running.

gal'lant (găl'ănt), brave; high-spirited.

gal'ley (găl'ĭ), large, low vessel propelled by oars, though generally having a mast carrying an oblong sail.

gar'land (gär'land), a wreath to be worn on the head; woolen head-band worn by priest.

gar'nered (nẽrd), gathered for preservation; stored.

gar'nish (gär'nĭsh), to decorate; to adorn.

gas'tro-nom'i-cal (nŏm'ĭ-kăl), relating to the eating of what is enjoyable.

Gaul (gôl), one of the inhabitants of ancient Gaul, which included France and upper Italy.

gear (gēr), clothing; garments.

gen'er-a'tion (jĕn'ẽr-ā'shŭn), an age; the average life time of man.

ge'ni-al (jē'nĭ-ăl; jēn'yăl), cheerful; kindly.

ge'nie (jē'nĭ), one of the nature spirits or demons of which we read in Arabian and Mohammedan tales.

gen'tian (jĕn'shăn), beautiful blue flower.

gen'u-ine (jĕn'ú-ĭn), real; true; sincere.

ghast'ly (gȧst'lĭ), horrible; shocking; pallid.

gib'ber-ish (gĭb'ẽr-ĭsh), rapid inarticulate talk; unmeaning words.

gid'dy (gĭd'ĭ), dizzy; a sensation of whirling; heedless.

gir'dle (gŭr'd'l), a belt; a sash.

girt (gŭrt), secured by a girdle or belt; encircled.

gla'cier (glā'shẽr; glăs'ĭ-ẽr), a body of ice moving slowly down a mountain slope.

glade (glād), an open passage or cleared space in a wood.

glar'ing (glâr'ĭng), dazzling; brilliant; staring fiercely.

gleam (glēm), a beam; a brightness.

glean'er (glēn), one who picks up what is left by the reapers.

glen (glĕn), a narrow valley.

glib (glĭb), speaking easily and rapidly.

glit′ter (glĭt′er), to sparkle; to shine.

gnash (năsh), to grind the teeth together.

gnat (năt), any of various small insects, especially such as bite.

goal (gōl), the place at which a race or journey is to end.

gorge (gôrj), to eat greedily.

gorge (gôrj), a narrow passage between mountains.

gor′geous (gôr′jŭs), splendid; magnicent.

gor′mand-ize (gôr′măn-dīz), to eat greedily.

gor′y (gôr′ĭ), covered with blood.

gour′mand (gōōr′mănd), a luxurious eater.

grad′u-al-ly (grăd′ū-ăl), by slow or slight changes.

grat′i-tude (grăt′ĭ-tūd), thankfulness; state of being grateful.

green′sward (sword), turf green with grass; grassy surface.

griev′ous (grēv′ŭs), heavy; injurious; severe.

grit (grĭt), unyielding courage.

gross (grōs), not delicate; coarse; vulgar.

guard′i-an (gär′dĭ-ăn), one who guards; one who has the care of another.

guest (gĕst), a visitor entertained without pay.

guil′der (gĭl′dẽr), a coin, German or Dutch, varying in value with the place and time; also called "gulden."

guise (gīz), custom; fashion; mode; appearance.

hab′i-ta′tion (hăb′ĭ-tā′shŭn), dwelling; residence.

hab′i-tude (tūd), habit; usual condition or method of acting.

hal′low (hăl′ō), to make holy.

ha′lo (hā′lō), a circle of light.

halt′ing (hôlt), lame; limping.

ham′let (hăm′lĕt), a cluster of houses in the country.

hap′ly (hăp′lĭ), perhaps; by chance; it may be.

hard′ship (härd′shĭp), hardness; that which is hard to bear.

haugh′ty (hô′tĭ), proud; arrogant.

ha′ven (hā′v′n), a harbor; a port; a bay which affords shelter for vessels.

hav′oc (hăv′ŏk), general destruction; waste.

haw′ser (hô′zẽr), a large rope for securing a ship at a dock.

haze (hāz), mist; fog; dimness.

heark′en (här′k′n), to listen; to hear.

heed′less (hēd), inattentive; careless; unobservant.

her′ald (hĕr′ăld), an officer whose business was to proclaim war or peace and to bear messages.

he′ro (hē′rō), a person of great courage; the principal person in a story.

he-ro′ic (hē-rō′ĭk), brave; daring; noble.

hes′i-tate (hĕz′ĭ-tāt), to stop or pause; to be uncertain; to stammer.

Hes-per′i-des (hĕs-pĕr′ĭ-dēz), the nymphs who guarded the garden in which grew the golden apples which Hercules was sent to find.

hew (hū), to cut by blows with an ax.

hied (hīd), hastened; went in haste.

hilt (hĭlt), the handle of a sword or dagger.

hoar′y (hōr′ĭ), white; white with age.

Hock (hŏk), any white Rhine wine.

ho-ri′zon (hō-rī′zŭn; z′n), the line at which earth and sky seem to meet.

hor′net (hôr′nĕt; nĭt), a large, strong wasp.

hor′o-loge (hŏr′ō-lōj), a watch; a clock; a dial.

hor′rent (hŏr′ĕnt), covered with bristling points.

hos′pi-tal′i-ty (hŏs′pĭ-tăl′ĭ-ti), kind and generous reception and treatment of strangers.

host (hōst), one who receives or entertains a stranger.

hos′tel-ry (hŏs′tĕl-rĭ), an inn; a lodging house.

hos′tile (hŏs′tĭl), warlike; unfriendly; opposed.

hov′er-ing (hŭv′ẽr), moving to and fro near a place threateningly; fluttering.

hud′dled (hŭd′′l), crowded together.

hue (hū), color; tint.

hum′ble (hŭm′b′l), modest; not proud; plain; lowly.

hu-mil′i-ty (hŭmĭl′ĭ-tĭ), modesty; humbleness; lowliness.

hu′mor-ist (hū′mẽr-ĭst), one who shows humor or playfulness in speaking or writing.

hur′dy-gur′dy (hûr′dĭ-gûr′dĭ), any instrument played by turning a handle.

i-de′al (ĭ-de′ăl), a perfect pattern or example; imaginary.

id′i-ot (ĭd′ĭ-ŏt), one who lacks intellectual or reasoning powers.

i′dyll (ī′dĭl), a beautiful description of simple country life.

ig-no′ble (ig-nō′b l), not noble; mean; dishonorable.

ig′no-rant (ĭg′nō-rănt), unlearned; untaught; uninformed.

il-lit′er-ate (ĭ-lĭt′ẽr-āt), ignorant of books; unable to read.

il-lume′ (ĭ-lūm′), to make light or bright.

il-lu′mine (ĭ-lū′mĭn), to light up; to enlighten.

il-lus′tri-ous (ĭl-lŭs′trĭ-ŭs), distinguished; celebrated.

Il′va (ĭl′vȧ), an island west of Etruria; Elba.

im′age (ĭm′ȧj), a representation; an imitation of a person or thing in solid form.

im-ag'i-na-ble (ĭ-măg'ĭ-nȧ-b'l), capable of being imagined.

im-mor'tal (ĭ-môr'tăl), undying; everlasting.

im'mor-tal'i-ty (ĭm'ôr-tăl'ĭ-ti), unending life; everlastingness.

im-mor'tal-ize (ĭ-môr'tăl-īz), to cause to live forever.

im-pen'e-tra ble (ĭm-pĕn'ĕ-trȧ b'l), incapable of being pierced; not to be entered.

im-pe'ri-al (ĭm-pē'rĭ-ăl), belonging to an empire or emperor.

im-pe'ri-ous (ĭm-pē'rĭ-ŭs), commanding; overbearing; haughty.

im'pi-ous (ĭm'pĭ-ŭs), not pious; lacking in reverence or respect.

im-preg'na-ble (ĭm-prĕg'nȧ-b'l), not to be taken by assault; unconquerable.

im-pres'sion (ĭm-prĕsh'ŭn), influence or effect on feeling or intellect.

im-pru'dent (ĭm-prōō'dĕnt), not cautious; rash.

in'ad-vert'ent-ly (ĭn-ăd-vûrt'ĕnt-lĭ), heedlessly; thoughtlessly.

in-car'nate (ĭn-kär'nȧt), taking bodily form; embodied in human form.

in-ces'sant-ly (ĭn-sĕs'ănt-lĭ), continually; unceasingly.

in'ci-dent (ĭn'sĭ-dĕnt), an event; circumstances.

in'cli-na'tion (ĭn'klĭ-nā'shŭn), liking; affection.

in-clined' (ĭn-klīnd'), having a liking for; slanting; sloping.

in'com-mode' (ĭn'kŏ-mōd'), to give trouble; to disturb.

in-dic'a-tive (ĭn-dĭk'ȧ-tĭv), pointing out, giving evidence.

in-dom'i-ta-ble (ĭn-dŏm'ĭ-tȧ-b'l), not to be subdued; unconquerable.

in-dulge' (ĭn-dŭlj'), to give away to; not to oppose or restrain.

in-dul'gence (dŭl'jĕns), act of indulging, humoring; gratification.

in'fan-cy (ĭn'făn-sĭ), early childhood; babyhood.

in'flu-ence (ĭn'flōō-ĕns), the power of producing effect without apparent force.

in-fuse' (ĭn-fūz'), to pour in; to inspire.

in-gen'ious (ĭn-jĕn'yŭs), having inventive skill.

in-gen'u-ous (ĭn-jĕn'ū-ŭs), frank; sincere; noble.

in-her'-it (ĭn-hĕr'ĭt), to receive from an ancestor.

in-her'it-ance (ĭn-hĕr'ĭ-tăns), possession received from an ancestor.

in'no-cent (ĭn'ō-sĕnt), free from sin or evil; blameless.

in-nu'mer-a-ble (ĭ-nū'mẽr-ȧ-b'l; ĭn-nu'), too many to be counted.

in-sid'i-ous (ĭn-sĭd'ĭ-ŭs), watching for an opportunity to entrap or ensnare.

in'so-lent (ĭn'sŏ-lĕnt), very disrespectful; haughty; insulting.

in'spi-ra'tion (ĭn'spĭ-rā-'shŭn), divine influence; influence which exalts or enlivens.

in'stan-ta'ne-ous (ĭn'stăn-tā'nē-ŭs), done or occurring in an instant.

in-sult' (ĭn-sŭlt'), to treat with contempt; to offend purposely.

in'tel-lec'tu-al (ĭn'tĕ-lĕk'tû-ăl), having the power of understanding, mental.

in-tense' (ĭn-tĕns'), an extreme degree.

in'ter-mis'sion (mĭsh'ŭn), interruption; pause.

in'ter-pose' (pōz), to put between; to hinder.

in-ter'pret (ĭn-tûr'prĕt), to tell the meaning of; to translate.

in-ter'pret-er (prĕt-ẽr), one who explains or translates.

in'ti-mate (ĭn'tĭ-mȧt), close in acquaintance; familiar.

in-tol'er-a-ble (ĭn-tŏl'ẽr-ȧ-b'l), not capable of being endured, unbearable.

in-tox'i-ca'tion (ĭn-tŏk'sĭ-kā'shŭn), a high excitement of mind; drunkenness.

in-trac'ta-ble (ĭn-trăk'tȧ-b'l), not easily managed; stubborn; unteachable.

in-vade' (ĭn-vād'), to enter with unfriendly intentions.

in-vad'er (ĭn-vād'ẽr), an intruder; one who enters to attack or plunder.

in-vis i-ble (ĭn-vĭz'ĭ-b'l), incapable of being seen.

i-ron'i-cal-ly (ĭ-rŏn'ĭ-kăl), a manner of speaking which uses words with an opposite meaning to that intended.

jad'ed (jād'ed), wearied; exhausted.

Ja-ni'cu-lum (jȧ-nĭ'cū-lŭm), one of the hills of Rome.

jar'gon (jär'gŏn), confused, unintelligible language.

jaun'ty (jän'tĭ; jôn'), smart; sprightly.

jave'lin (jăv'lĭn; jăv'ĕ-lĭn), a light spear, to be thrown or cast.

jay (jā), a bird belonging to the crow family.

jeal'ous (jĕl'ŭs), fearful or suspicious of favor shown to another.

jet (jĕt), a black mineral of the nature of coal.

joc'und (jŏk'ŭnd), merry; cheerful; joyful.

jo'vi-al (jō'vĭ-ăl), gay; jolly; merry.

ju'bi-lant (jōō'bĭ-lănt), triumphant; rejoicing.

jut'ting (jŭt'), projecting out.

keel (kēl), the timber or timbers extending from stem to stern along the bottom of a vessel.

keen (kēn), sharp; cutting; eager.

kin'dred (kĭn'drĕd), those belonging to the same family or race.

kine (kīn), cows.

kins'folk (kĭnz'fōk), relatives; kindred.

kith (kĭth), relations; family connections.

knead (nēd), to work and press into a mass with the hands.

knell (nĕl), the sound of a bell when tolled.

lad'en (lād'n), loaded; burdened.

lam'en-ta'tion (lăm'ĕn-tā'shŭn), audible expression of sorrow; a lament.

lan'guish (lăn'gwĭsh), to lose strength; to become feeble; to droop.

lay (lā), a song; a ballad; a short narrative poem.

leg'end (lĕj'ĕnd; lē'jĕnd), a story coming down from the past.

lei'sure (lē'zhŭr; lĕzh'ûr), time free from work; ease.

li-ba'tion (lī-bā'shŭn), wine or other liquid poured upon the ground in honor of a god.

liege'man (lēj), a devoted follower; one who gives service and loyalty to a superior.

lime (līm), a small greenish yellow fruit of acid taste.

lin'e-age (lĭn'ē-åj), family; race.

lit'ter (lĭt'ēr), a bed so arranged that a person may be carried upon it.

loath (lōth), unwilling; reluctant.

loathe (lōth), to dislike greatly; to detest.

lo'cal (lō'kăl), relating to a particular place.

lo'cust (lō'kŭst), certain species of grasshopper which travel in vast swarms.

loft'y (lŏf'tĭ), high; tall; haughty.

loom (lōōm), a frame or machine for interweaving threads into a fabric.

lore (lōr), knowledge; learning; knowledge based upon tradition.

loy'al-ty (loi'ăl-tĭ), faithfulness; devotion; fidelity.

lu'rid (lū'rĭd), pale yellow; reddish brown; ghastly.

lust (lŭst), wrong desire.

lus'ti-ly (lĭ), with strength; vigorously.

lux-u'ri-ant (lŭks-ū'rĭ-ănt), exceedingly fertile; very abundant.

lux'u-ry (lŭk'shōō-rĭ), anything which pleases the senses and is costly.

lyre (līr), a stringed instrument used by the ancient Greeks.

Ma-dei'ra (må-dē'ra), wine made on the island of Madeira.

mad'ri-gal (măd'rĭ-găl), a song without accompaniment.

mag'ic (măj'ĭk), the art which pretends to produce effects by assistance of spirits.

ma-gi'cian (må-jĭsh'ŭn), one skilled in magic.

mag'is-trate (măj'ĭs-trāte), a public civil officer having executive powers.

mag'ni-fied (măg'nĭ-fīd), made greater; enlarged.

ma-jes'tic (må-jĕs'tĭk), splendid; stately; royal.

mal'a-dy (măl'å-dĭ), any disease of the human body.

mal'e-dic'-tion (măl'ē-dĭk'shŭn), a curse; a proclaiming of evil against some one.

ma-li'cious (må-lĭsh'ŭs), evil minded; spiteful.

man-at-arms, a soldier.

man'i-fest (măn'ĭ-fĕst), open; clear; plain.

manned (mănd), supplied with men; furnished with sufficient force.

man'sion (măn'shŭn), a large house.

man'tle (man't'l), a cloak; something that covers.

ma-raud'er (må-rôd'ēr), a plunderer; one who goes about seeking plunder.

mar'shal (mär'shăl), to arrange in order.

mar'tyr (mär'tēr), one who gives up his life for the sake of principle.

mar'tyr-dom (dŭm), the suffering of death for the sake of religion or principle.

mar'vel (mär'vĕl), to wonder; to be astonished.

mar'vel-ous (ŭs), astonishing; wonderful.

mas'sive (mås'ĭv), heavy; weighty; bulky.

ma'tron (mā'trŭn), a wife or widow; a housekeeper.

ma-ture' (må-tūr'), full grown; ripe.

ma'vis (mā'vĭs), the European song-thrush.

med'i-ta-tive-ly (mĕd'ĭ-tå-tĭv), thoughtfully.

meer'schaum (mēr'shôm; shŭm), a tobacco pipe made of a fine white clay-like mineral.

mel'an-chol-y (mĕl'ăn-kŏl-ĭ), mournfulness; sorrow.

merle (mûrl), the European blackbird.

me-tal'lic (mē-tăl'ĭk), of the nature or appearance of metal.

me-thought' (thôt), it seemed to me.

mewed (mūd), shut up; confined.

mien (mēn), manner; bearing.

mil'i-ta-ry (mĭl'ĭ tå-rĭ), belonging to soldiers or war.

min'a-ret (mĭn'å-rĕt), a slender, lofty tower on a mosque.

min'gle (mĭn'g'l), to mix; to associate; to combine.

min'gling (glĭng), combining; mixing.

min'i-a-ture (mĭn'ĭ-å-tûr) a small copy; a representation on a much reduced scale.

min'strel (mĭn'strĕl), one who sang verses to the accompaniment of a harp; a poet.

mis-chance' (mĭs-chåns'), ill luck; misfortune.

mis'chie-vous (mĭs'chĭ-vŭs), full of mischief; injurious.

mis-giv'ing (mĭs-gĭv'), fear; distrust; doubt.

mis-hap' (hăp'), misfortune; accident.

mock'er-y (mŏk'ĕr-ĭ), ridicule; contemptuous merriment.

mode (mōd), manner of doing; method.

mod'el (mŏd'ĕl), pattern; example.

mod'er-ate (mŏd'ĕr-āt), to become less violent; not extreme or violent.

mod'est (mŏd'ĕst), not bold, forward, or boastful.

moil (moil), hard work; drudgery.

mold (mōld), form; shape; the cavity in which anything is shaped.

mole (mōl), a small animal living almost entirely underground.

mo-lest' (mô-lĕst'), to trouble; to disturb.

mol'ten (mol't'n), melted.

mo'men-ta-ry (mō'mĕn-tâ-rĭ), continuing only a moment.

mo-men'tous (mō-mĕn'tŭs), very important.

mon'arch (mŏn'ȧrk), a supreme ruler.

mo-not'o-nous (mô-nŏt'ô-nŭs), without change or variety.

mon'ster (mŏn'stĕr), a huge animal; an unnaturally wicked person.

mon'strous (mŏn'strŭs), huge; gigantic; dreadful.

mor'al (mŏr'ăl), the meaning of a fable or story.

mor'als (mŏr'ălz), conduct with respect to right or wrong.

mor'tal (mŏr'tăl), human; subject to death.

mort'gage (mŏr'gȧj), a sale of property to become of no effect upon payment or performance of certain conditions.

mould (mōld), soil; earth suited to the growth of plants.

mourn'ful (mōrn'fŏŏl), full of sorrow or grief.

muf'fle (mŭf''l), to wrap with something that deadens the sound.

mul'ti-tude (mŭl'tĭ-tūd), a great number of persons; a crowd.

mus'ing (mūz'ing), thinking; meditating.

mus'ter (mŭs'tĕr), to assemble; to collect.

myr'i-ad (mĭr'ĭ-ăd), an immense number.

Myr'mi-dons (mûr'mĭ-dŏns), a fierce tribe who followed their king, Achilles, to the Trojan war.

myth (mĭth), a story relating to the actions of the gods or the forces of nature.

naught (nôt), nothing; nought.

ne-ces'si-ty (nê-sĕs'ĭ-tĭ), need; state of being necessary.

nec'tar (nĕk'tȧr), the drink of the gods; any delicious beverage.

nerv'ous (nûr'vŭs), easily excited; strong; vigorous.

New'mar'ket (nū'mär'kĕt; nū'mär'-kĕt), a town in England where horse races are held.

newt (nūt), a small salamander—a vertebrate animal somewhat resembling a lizzard, but having a soft moist skin.

nick'name (nĭk'nām), a name given familiarly in place of the proper name.

nim'ble (nĭm'b'l), light and quick in motion.

Nin'e-veh (nĭn'ê-vĕ), an ancient city of Assyria.

nour'ish (nŭr'ĭsh), to feed; to sustain.

nov'el-ty (nŏv'ĕl-tĭ), newness; freshness; something new.

nov'ice (nŏv'ĭs), one new in any business or calling.

nun'cheon (nŭn'chŭn; shŭn), a light refreshment; a luncheon.

nymphs (nĭmfs), beautiful maidens who were supposed to dwell in trees, in water, and in mountains.

oath (ōth), a solemn appeal to God in witness of the truth.

o-bei'sance (ô-bā'sȧns, ô-bē'), a bending of the body; a bow.

o-bese' (ô-bēs'), very stout or fleshy.

ob-nox'ious (ŏb-nŏk'shŭs) offensive, objectionable.

ob-scure' (ŏb-skūr'), not clear; dim.

ob'ser-va'tion (ŏb'zĕr-vā'shŭn), act of seeing; a remark.

oc-ca'sion-al (ô-kā'zhŭn-ăl), occurring now and then.

o'dor (ō'dĕr), any smell; scent; perfume.

o'men (ō'mĕn), a sign or event supposed to foretell the future.

o-mit' (ô-mĭt'), to leave out.

om-nip'o-tence (ŏm-nĭp'ô-tĕns), Almighty power.

o'pi-ate (ō'pĭ-ȧt), a medicine which induces sleep.

op-press' (ŏ-prĕs'), to weigh down; to burden.

op-pres'sion (ŏ-prĕsh'ŭn), cruelty; severity, tyranny.

or'a-cle. (ŏr'ȧ-k'l), knowledge revealed by a god, or the place where it is given.

orb (ôrb), a globe; a sphere.

or'ches-tra (ôr'kĕs-trȧ), a band of performers on various instruments.

or'chis (ôr'kĭs), any plant of a family common in Europe and the United States and having the flowers arranged in the form of a spike or ear.

or'di-na-ry (ôr'dĭ-nȧ-rĭ), common; usual.

or'i-gin (ŏr'ĭ-jĭn), the beginning; the source.

o-rig'i-nal (ô-rĭj'ĭ-năl), first; not copied; inventive.

or'to-lan (ôr'tô-lăn), a bird about six inches long, considered a great delicacy for the table.

o'sier (ō'zhẽr), twigs of the willow tree.

Os'ti-a (ŏs'tĭ-à), a seaport at the mouth of the Tiber.

o'ver-whelm' (hwĕlm), to cover over completely; to crush.

Ov'id (ŏv'ĭd), a Roman poet.

pac'i-fy (păs'ĭ-fī), to calm; to quiet.

Pa-la-tin'us (pȧ-lă-tĭn'ŭs), one of the hills of Rome.

pal'try (pôl'trĭ), contemptible; worthless.

pam'phlet (păm'flĕt), a book of a few sheets, not bound.

pan'ic (păn'ĭk), extreme and sudden fear.

pan'nier (păn'yẽr; ĭ-ẽr), a wicker basket carried on the back of a horse or the back of a person.

par'a-dise (păr'ȧ-dīs), the abode of the soul after death; a place of bliss.

par'al-lel (păr'ă-lĕl), equally distant in all parts.

par'a-lyze (păr'ȧ-līz), to destroy the energy of.

parch (pärch), to scorch; to roast over the fire.

pas'sion-ate (păsh'ŭn-āt), angry; easily made angry.

pas'time' (pȧs'tīm'), amusement; entertainment.

pat'ri-mo-ny (păt'rĭ-mō-nĭ), property inherited from one's father.

pa'tri-ot (pā'trĭ-ŏt), one who loves his country.

pa'tri-ot-ism (ĭz'm), love of country.

peas'ant (pĕz'ănt), a countryman.

pe-cul'iar (pê-kūl'yȧr), special; unusual; strange.

peer (pēr), an equal; a nobleman.

pen'e-trate (pĕn'ê-trāt), to enter into; to pierce.

per-ceive' (pẽr-sēv'), to see; to observe; to notice.

per-chance' (pẽr-chȧns'), perhaps; possibly.

per'il (pĕr'ĭl), danger; risk.

per'il-ous (pĕr'ĭ-lŭs), dangerous; daring.

per-pet'u-al (pẽr-pĕt'ů-ăl), unceasing; endless.

per-pet'u-ate (pẽr-pĕt'ů-āt), to cause to endure.

per-plexed' (pẽr-plĕkst'), doubtful; puzzled.

per'se-cute (pûr'sê'kūt), to punish or put to death for belief.

per'son-al (pûr'sŭn-ăl), relating to a particular person; direct from one person to another.

per-son'i-fy (pẽr-sŏn'ĭ-fī), to treat or represent as a person.

per'ti-na'cious (pûr'tĭ-nā'shŭs), unyielding; stubborn.

pet'u-lant (pĕt'ů-lănt), irritable; fretful; cross.

pha'lanx (fā'lănks), a body of heavily armed foot soldiers formed in ranks and files close and deep.

phan'tom (făn'tŭm), delusion; deceit.

phi-los'o-pher (fĭ-lŏs'ô-fẽr), one who meets all changes in life with calmness.

pick'er-el (pĭk'ẽr-ĕl), a freshwater fish; a pike.

pic'tur-esque' (pĭk'tûr-ĕsk'), forming a picture, possessing charm.

pie'bald (pī'bôld'), of different colors, especially black and white.

pied (pīd), with large blotches of two or more colors.

pi'e-ty (pī'ê-tĭ), religion; reverence and devotion.

pil'grim (pĭl-grĭm), one who journeys far; a wanderer.

pil'lage (pĭl'ȧj), to rob; to plunder.

pin'ing (pīn), longing; wasting away.

pin'na-cle (pĭn'ȧ-k'l), a spire; a lofty peak.

pi'rate (pī'rȧt), a robber on the high seas.

pit'e-ous-ly (pĭt'ê-ŭs), sadly; pitifully.

plague (plāg), an infectious disease; anything which troubles.

plan'et (plăn'ĕt), a body which revolves about the sun.

Pla'to (plā-tō), a great Greek philosopher.

plat'ter (plăt'), a large plate or dish for serving meat.

Plau'tus (plô'tŭs), a Roman dramatist.

plight (plīt), condition; state.

plot'ter (plŏt'ẽr), one who plans or schemes.

pluck (plŭk), courage; spirit; resolution.

plun'der (plŭn'dẽr), to take by force; to rob.

ply (plī), to use; to handle; to work at steadily.

po-et'i-cal (pô-ĕt'ĭ-kăl), resembling poetry; having to do with poetry.

pol'i-ti'cian (pŏl'ĭ-tĭsh'ăn), one engaged in politics.

pome-gran'ate (pŏm-grăn'ȧt; pŏm'; pŭm'), a tropical fruit resembling an orange in size and color.

pomp (pŏmp), display; splendor; grandeur.

pon'der (pŏn'dẽr), to consider carefully.

pon'der-ous (ŭs), heavy, massive.

pop'u-lar'i-ty (pŏp'ů-lăr'ĭ-tĭ), the state of being approved by, or in favor with people in general.

por'poise (pôr'pŭs), one of a class of water animals having a large head, fish-like body and the tail ending in a broad fin; length from five to eight feet.

por'tal (pôr'tăl), a door; a gate.

por'tent (pôr'tĕnt; pŏr'), a sign which foretells something.

por'ti-co (pôr'tĭ-kō), a covered entrance to a building.

por'tion (pōr'shŭn), to divide; to distribute.

pos'i-tive-ly (pŏz'ĭ-tĭv), certainly; without doubt.

po'tion (pō'shŭn), a dose of a liquid.

pot'tage (pŏt'âj), a dish of vegetables or vegetables and meat.

prac'ti-cal (prăk'tĭ-kăl), useful; capable of being turned to account.

pre-cep'tor (prĕ-sĕp'tẽr), a teacher; an instructor.

prec'i-pice (prĕs'ĭ'pĭs), a very steep place; a cliff.

pre-cise'ly (prĕ-sīs'), in an exact manner.

pref'er-ence (prĕf'ẽr-ĕns), the act of caring more for one thing than another.

pre-scribe' (prĕ-skrīb'), to direct; to appoint.

pres'ence (prĕz'ĕns), act or state of being present; personal appearance.

pre-side' (prĕ-zīd'), to occupy the place of authority.

pre-tense', **pre-tence'** (prĕ-tĕns'), showing or offering what is false or unreal.

pre-vail' (prĕ-vāl'), to overcome; to gain the victory.

prime (prīm), first in rank; chief; having vigor.

pris-mat'ic (prĭz-măt'ĭk), resembling the colors formed by the passing of light through a prism; the colors of the rainbow.

prob'a-bil'i-ty (prŏb'à-bĭl'ĭ-tĭ), that which appears probable or likely.

pro-cure' (prô-kūr'), to get; to obtain.

pro-fess' (prô-fĕs'), to make open declaration; to pretend.

pro-fes'sion (fĕsh'ŭn), open declaration; occupation; employment.

pro-fes'sion-al (ăl), relating to a profession; engaging in any calling for gain.

pro'file (prō'fĭl; fēl), a human head seen or represented in a side view.

pro-found' (prô-found'), extending far below the surface; deep.

prog-nos'ti-cate (prŏg-nŏs'tĭ-kăt), to foretell; to prophesy; to predict.

pro-ject' (prô-jĕkt'), to extend forward; to jut.

proj'ect (prŏj'ĕkt), a plan; a purpose; a scheme.

pro-long' (prô-lông'), to extend in time; to lengthen.

proph'e-sy (prŏf'ĕ-sī), to foretell; to predict.

proph'et (prŏf'ĕt), one inspired by God to announce future events.

pro-pos'al (prô-pōz'al), an offer; that which is proposed.

pro-pri'e-tor (prô-prī'ĕ-tẽr), an owner.

prose (prōz), the ordinary language of men; not verse.

pros'pect (prŏs'pĕkt) that which is seen; a view.

pros'per-ous (prŏs'pẽr-ŭs), successful; fortunate.

pros'trate (prŏs'trāte), lying with the body extended.

prov'en-der (prŏv'ĕn-dẽr), dry food for domestic animals; hay, straw, oats, etc.

prow'ess (prou'ĕs), distinguished bravery.

pru'dent (proō'dĕnt), careful; cautious; economical.

psal'ter-y (sŏl'tẽr-ĭ), an ancient stringed instrument resembling a zither.

punch'eon (pŭn'chŭn), a large cask.

pur'ga-to-ry (pŭr'gà-tô-rĭ), a place of purification after death.

pur-suit' (pŭr-sūt'), the act of following to overtake; a chase.

quaint (kwānt), curious and fanciful.

quake (kwāk), to shake; to tremble.

quench (kwĕnch), to extinguish; to suppress.

quest (kwĕst), search; attempt to find.

quiv'er (kwĭv'ẽr), a case for carrying arrows.

quiv'er (kwĭv'ẽr), to tremble; to shiver.

quoit (kwoit; koit), a heavy flat piece of iron to be pitched in play.

ra'di-ant (rā-dĭ-ănt), bright; beaming.

raid'er (rād'ẽr), one who makes a sudden and rapid attack upon the enemy's territory.

rail (rāl), to utter reproaches.

ral'ly-ing (răl'ĭ), gathering together; reuniting; reviving.

ran'dom (răn'dŭm), acting without settled purpose; left to chance.

rank (rănk), degree of dignity; relative position in any scale of comparison.

ran'som (răn'sŭm), payment for release from captivity.

rap'tur-ous (răp'tŭr-ŭs), expressing or showing great joy.

ras'cal-ly (răs'kăl-ĭ), dishonest; mean.

rav'en-ing (răv''n-ĭng), greedily devouring; eagerness for plunder.

re-al'i-ty (rĕ'ăl'ĭ-tĭ), that which is real.

re'al-ize (rē'ăl-īz), to make real; to cause to seem real.

realm (rĕlm), a kingdom; region.

reb'el (rĕb'ĕl), one who resists or is disobedient to authority.

re-buke' (rĕ-bŭk'), a sharp reproof; a reprimand.

re-call' (rĕ-kôl), to call back.

reck'on (rĕk''n), to count; to calculate.

re-claim (rĕ-klām'), to recover; to reform.

rec'om-mend' (rĕk'ŏ-mĕnd'), to commend to the favorable notice of another.

re-cruit' (rĕ-krōōt'), a newly enlisted soldier or sailor.

re-cum'bent (rĕ-kŭm'bĕnt), leaning; lying.

re-dress' (rĕ-drĕs'), to set right; to make amends for.

reek (rēk), to smoke; to smell; to steam.

reel (rēl), a lively dance.

re-fine'-ment (rĕ-fīn'mĕnt), elegance or fineness in manners or feeling.

re-'form (rĕ-fôrm'), to amend or correct one's character or habits.

re-frac'to-ry (rĕ-frăk'tŏ-rĭ), stubborn; unmanageable.

ref'uge (rĕf'ūj), shelter or protection from danger.

re-fus'al (rĕ-fūz'ăl), act of refusing or denying something asked.

re'gal (rē'găl), royal; splendid; kingly.

re-gard' (rĕ-gärd'), to look closely at.

re-gard' (rĕ-gärd'), respect; affection.

re-ly' (rĕ-lī'), to trust; to have confidence.

rem'nant (rĕm'nănt), that which remains; a small portion.

re-mote' (rĕ-mōt'), distant; far away.

ren'der (rĕn'dẽr), to return; to pay back.

re-new' (rĕ-nū'), to make new; to restore to freshness.

re-nown' (rĕ-noun'), condition of being widely and honorably known.

re-peal' (rĕ-pēl'), to recall or revoke a sentence or a law.

re-pose' (rĕ-pōz'), rest; quiet.

re-proach' (rĕ-prōch'), to charge with a fault; to blame.

re-pub'lic-an (rĕ-pŭb'lĭ-kăn), one who favors a government which recognizes no distinction of classes.

rep'u-ta-ble (rĕp'ū-tà-b'l), respectable; honorable.

res'cue (rĕs'kū), to free; to deliver; to release.

re-sem'blance (rĕ-zĕm'blăns), likeness; similarity.

re-sume' (rĕ-zūm'), to enter upon or begin again.

re-treat' (rĕ-trēt'), to retire; to withdraw.

rev'el (rĕv'ĕl), to make merry in a noisy manner.

rev'el-ry (rĕv'ĕl-rĭ), boisterous merry making.

rev'er-ence (rĕv'ẽr-ĕns), great respect and affection.

rev'er-ies (rĕv'ẽr-ĭz), thoughts; day dreams.

re-view'er (rĕ-vū'ẽr), one who examines books critically and publishes his opinion of them.

re-volve' (rĕ-vŏlv'), to move in a curved path round a center; to turn; to roll.

Rhen'ish (rĕn'ĭsh), on or near the river Rhine.

rib'ald (rĭb'ăld), low; coarse; offensive.

ri-dic'u-lous (rĭ-dĭk'ū-lŭs), comical; absurd.

rife (rīf), existing generally; prevalent.

right'eous-ness (rī'chŭs), uprightness; goodness.

rite (rīt), form; observance.

ri'val (rī'văl), one who strives to excel another.

riv'en (rĭv'n), torn asunder; split.

ro-mance' (rŏ-măns'), a story, not of real life but full of interest.

rook (rōōk), a European bird, about the size of the American crow.

roun'de-lay (roun'dĕ-lā), a song in which a strain is often repeated.

rout (rout), to put to flight; to defeat.

roy'al (roi'ăl), kingly; magnificent.

rud'dy (rŭd'ĭ), of a red color; reddish.

rug'ged (rŭg'ĕd), not smooth, rough; irregular.

Rule of Three (rōōl), the rule for finding the fourth term of a proportion when three are given.

ru'mi-na'tion (rōō'mĭ-nā'shŭn), deliberate meditation.

ru'mor (rōō'mer), a story passed around without any authority for its truth.

ru'ral (rōō'răl), belonging to or living in the country; rustic.

rus'set (rŭs'ĕt), reddish brown color.

rus'tic (rŭs'tĭk), an inhabitant of the country.

ruth'less (rōōth'), cruel; pitiless.

sa'ble (sā'b'l), an animal about eighteen inches long valued for its fur.

sa'ble (sā'b'l), of the color of sable's fur; dark; black.

sack (săk), to plunder after capture.

sa'cred (sā'krĕd), made holy; set apart to religious use.

sage (sāj), a wise man; a philosopher.

sa-lute' (sà-lūt'), to greet; to address with expressions of kind wishes.

sanc'tu-a-ry (sănk'tū-à-rĭ), the most sacred part of any religious building; a place of refuge.

san'dal (săn'dăl), a protection for the foot, covering the lower surface only.

sap (săp), to weaken; to unsettle.

sat'ire (săt'īr), sarcasm; ridicule; severity of remark.

sat'yr (săt'ẽr; sā'tẽr), a being represented as part man and part horse.

saun'ter (sän'ter; sôn'), to walk or wander about idly.

scab'bard (skăb'àrd), a case in which the blade of a sword is enclosed.

scar (skär), a mark in the skin or flesh made by a wound.

scep'ter (sĕp'tẽr), a staff borne by a king as an emblem of authority.

Sche-he'ra-za'de (shĕ-hā'rȧ-zä'dĕ), the Queen who is supposed to tell the stories in the "Arabian Nights."

scheme (skēm), a plan; a plot.

sci'ence (sī'ĕns), knowledge of facts or principles.

scim'i-tar (sĭm'ĭ-tẽr), a sword with a curved blade.

scoff (skŏf), to ridicule; to mock.

scope (skōp), extent of view; free course; liberty.

scorn (skôrn), extreme contempt; mockery.

scor'pi-on (skôr'pĭ-ŭn), an animal, sometimes four to eight inches long, having a poisonous sting at the tip of the tail.

sear (sēr), dried up; withered.

sea'wor'thy (sē'wûr'thĭ), fit for a sea voyage.

se-clud'ed (sė-klōōd'ĕd), apart from others; solitary.

se-date' (sė-dāte'), quiet; serious; calm.

seem'ly (sēm'lĭ), suitable; proper; fitting.

se'er (sēr; sē'ẽr), a person who sees the future; a prophet.

sen'ate (sĕn'ȧt), an assembly with the highest legislative power.

sen'si-bil'i-ty (sĕn'sĭ-bĭl'-ĭtĭ), feeling; quick sympathy.

sen'su-al (sĕn'shōō-ăl), caring too much for the pleasures of the appetite.

sen'ti-ment (sĕn'tĭ-mĕnt), feeling; emotion.

sep'ul-cher (sĕp'ŭl-kẽr), a tomb, a burial vault.

se-rene' (sė-rēn'), bright; clear; calm.

serf (sûrf), a slave.

se'ri-ous (sē'rĭ-ŭs), grave; earnest.

set'ting in (sĕt'ĭng), beginning.

sev'er (sĕ'vẽr), to separate; to cut off from.

se-vere' (sė-vēr'), strict; harsh; stern.

sex'ton (sĕks'tŭn), one who takes care of a church building.

shaft (shȧft), the stem of an arrow or handle of a spear; anything darted or thrown.

shag'gy (shăg'ĭ), rough with long hair or wool.

shame'less (shām), without sense of shame; impudent.

shat'tered (shăt'ẽrd), broken into pieces.

sheath (shēth), a case for a sword or knife.

shift (shĭft), to change; to exchange.

shoal (shōl), a place where the sea is shallow; a sandbar.

shreds (shrĕds), strips; fragments.

shrine (shrīn), a place supposed to be made holy by a deity.

shut'tle (shŭt''l), an instrument for passing the thread in weaving.

sim'i-lar (sĭm'ĭ-lȧr), somewhat alike; having a general likeness.

sim-plic'i-ty (sĭm-plĭs'ĭ-tĭ), plainness; freedom from luxury or ornament.

sin-cere' (sĭn-sēr'), true; real; honest.

sin'ew-y (sĭn'û-ĭ), strong; firm; tough.

sin'gu-lar (sĭn'gů-lȧr), strange; unusual.

sin'is-ter (sĭn'ĭs-tẽr), evil; wrong; disastrous.

sire (sīr), father; a title of respect used in addressing a sovereign.

skill'ful, skil'ful (skĭl'fōōl), showing skill; knowing and ready.

slake (slāk), to quench; to cool.

slan'der (slăn'dẽr), a false, injurious story.

slash (slăsh), to cut by sweeping strokes.

slaugh'ter (slô'tẽr), to kill violently or in large numbers.

sloth'ful (slôth'), lazy; indolent.

slug'gish (slŭg'ĭsh), dull; slow; idle.

smit'ten (smĭt'n), struck.

sneer (snēr), to show contempt by expression of face; to speak with contempt.

so'cia-bly (so'shȧ-b lĭ), in a friendly, familiar manner.

so'journ (sō'jûrn; sȯ-jûrn'), to live in a place as a temporary resident.

so'journer (sō'jûrn-ẽr; sȯ-jûrn'ẽr) one who dwells as a stranger in a place.

sol'emn (sŏl'ĕm), serious; grave.

sol'i-ta-ry (sŏl'ĭ-tȧ-rĭ), alone; having no companion.

sol'i-tude (sŏl'ĭ-tūd), loneliness; a lonely place.

son'net (sŏn'ĕt; ĭt), a verse of fourteen lines.

sooth'ing (sōō'th), comforting; quieting.

soph'ist-er (sŏf'ĭst-ẽr), one who deceives or practices trickery in reasoning or argument.

sov'er-eign (sŏv'ẽr-ĭn; sŭv'), a person who is supreme over others; a king.

spa'cious (spā'shŭs), of great extent; roomy.

span'gled (spăn'g'ld), set or sprinkled with sparkling objects.

speed'i-ly (spēd'ĭ-lĭ), with great haste.

spell (spĕl), a word, or words, supposed to have magic power.

spell'bound (spĕl'), held by a charm; under the power of a charm.

sphere (sfēr), a globe; a globe representing the earth or heavens.

spir'y (spīr'ĭ), tall and slender; like a spire.

spite (spīt), ill will; the wish to annoy or irritate because of dislike.

spit'ted (spĭt'ĕd), put upon a pointed rod for roasting over a fire.

spoil (spoil), plunder taken in war.

sprat (sprăt), a small European herring.

spurt (spûrt), increased exertion for a short time; a sudden gushing.

stake (stāk), a pointed piece of wood.

stalk (stôk), to walk with proud, haughty bearing.

stal'wart (stôl'wẽrt; stŏl), strong; brave;

state (stāt), grandeur; elaborate style.

state'ly (stāt), majestic; grand.

stat'ure (stăt'ûr), the natural height of the human body.

stern (stũrn), severe; hard; harsh.

stim'u-late (stĭm'û-lāte), to excite; to rouse.

stir'ring (stûr'ing), rousing; exciting.

sti'ver (stī'vẽr), a Dutch coin worth about two cents.

strait (strāt), difficulty; need.

strand (strănd), shore; beach.

strat'a-gem (străt'ȧ-jĕm), a trick for deceiving the enemy.

strick'en (strĭk''n), wounded; worn out.

strife (strīfe), struggle; quarrel; contest.

strong'hold' (hōld'), a fort; a place of security.

strut (strŭt), to walk with great affectation of dignity and importance.

stub'ble (stŭb''l), the stumps of grain left in the ground after reaping.

stud (stŭd), a projection; a knob.

sub-due' (sŭb-dū'), to conquer; to overcome.

sub'ject (sŭb'jĕkt), one under the authority or influence of another.

sub-ject' (sŭb-jĕkt'), to subdue; to bring under control.

sub-lime' (sŭb-līm'), noble; majestic.

sub-mis'sive (mĭs'ĭv), obedient; yielding.

sub-sist' (sŭb-sĭst'), to live; to be supplied with food and clothing.

sub'ter-ra'ne-ous (rā'nĕ-ŭs), underground.

sub'tle (sŭt''l), thin; skillful; cunning.

suc'cor (sŭk'ẽr), help; assistance.

suc'co-ry (sŭk'ō-rĭ), a common European and American plant with bright blue flowers; chicory.

suf'fo-ca'tion (sŭf'ō-kā'shŭn), smothering; stifling.

su'i-cide (sū'ĭ-sīd), the act of taking one's own life.

suit'or (sūt'ẽr), one who entreats or petitions.

sulk (sŭlk), to be obstinate and cross; unwilling to associate with others.

sul'len (sŭl'ĕn), silent because of ill humor.

sul'phur-ous (sŭl'fŭr-ŭs; sŭl-fū'rŭs), containing or resembling sulphur.

sul'tan (sŭl-tăn), the ruler of the Turks.

sum'mit (sŭm'ĭt), the top; the highest point.

sum'mon (sŭm'ŭn), to call; to send for.

sun'dry (drĭ), several; various.

sup'pli-ant (sŭp'lĭ-ănt), one who asks or entreats humbly.

sup'po-si'tion (sŭp'ō-zĭsh'ŭn), that which is supposed.

surge (sûrj), a large wave or billow.

sur'geon (sûr'jŭn), one whose profession is to cure disease or injury by operations.

sur-pass' (sŭr-pȧs'), to go beyond; to excel.

sur-pass'ing (sŭr-pȧs'), exceeding others.

sur-viv'or (sŭr-vīv'ẽr), one who lives longer than another.

sward (swôrd), glassy surface of land.

swarth'y (swôr thĭ), of dark complexion.

sway (swā), to rule; to govern; to cause to swing.

symp'tom (sĭmp'tŭm), a sign; a mark; an indication.

ta'bor (tā'bẽr), a small drum.

tal'is-man (tăl'ĭs-măn), something supposed to act as a charm and keep away evil.

ta'per-ing (tā'pẽr-ing), growing gradually smaller toward one end.

Tar-pe'ian (tär-pē'yăn), relating to the rock near the Capitol at Rome, from which criminals were hurled.

tar'ry (tăr'ĭ), to delay; to wait for.

Tar'tar-y (tär'tär-ĭ), a region of eastern Europe and Asia.

tat'ters (tăt'ẽrs), rags.

taunt (tänt; tônt), to mock; to reproach with insulting words.

te'di-ous (tē'dĭ-ăs; tēd'yăs), tiresome; slow.

tend'en-cy (tĕn'dĕn-sĭ), course toward any place or object; inclination.

Ter'ence (tĕr'ĕns), a Roman writer of comedies.

ter'race (tĕr'ȧs), a raised level space; a bank of turf.

ter-res'tri-al (tĕ-rĕs'trĭ-ăl), belonging to the earth.

tex'ture (tĕks'tûr), that which is woven.

threat (thrĕt), the expression of an intention to inflict punishment or evil.

threat'en (thrĕt''n), to utter threats.

thrice (thrīs), three times.

thrift'y (thrĭf'tĭ), careful; saving.

throb (thrŏb), a beat or pulsation of the heart.

throng (thrŏng), a crowd.

ti'dings (tī'dĭngs), news; intelligence.

time'piece' (tīm'pēs'), clock; watch.

tin'sel (tĭn'sĕl), a shining metallic material of little value, used to produce a sparkling appearance.

tithe (tī'th), a tenth part.

toil'some (toil'sŭm), wearisome.

to'ken (tō'k'n), a sign; a signal.

toll (tōl), to cause a bell to sound slowly with uniform strokes.

tor'rent (tŏr'ĕnt), a violent stream.

tor'toise (tôr tŭs; tĭs), a turtle.

tor'ture (tôr'tûr), to inflict severe pain.

to'tal (tō'tăl), the whole.

tra-di'tion (trā-dĭsh'ŭn), information given by father to son through many generations.

train'-oil (trān'oil), oil from the whale.

trait (trāt), a distinguishing feature or characteristic.

tran-scend'ent (sĕn'dĕnt), superior; supreme.

trans-par'ent (trăns-pâr'ĕnt), clear; that which can be clearly seen through.

trav'erse (trăv'ĕrs), to move across or over.

treach'er-ous (trĕch'ĕr-ŭs), untrustworthy; false; faithless.

treach'er-y (trĕch'ĕr-ĭ), treason; betrayal of faith.

trea'son (trē'z'n), betrayal of faith or trust.

trea'ty (trē'tĭ), an agreement between two or more states or rulers.

tre-men'dous (trē-mĕn'dŭs), very great; awe inspiring.

trem'u-lous (trĕm'ū-lŭs), shaking; trembling through fear.

trench (trĕnch), a ditch.

tre-panned' (trē-pănned'), cut through a solid piece.

trib'ute (trĭb'ūt), annual sum paid by one nation to another as sign of submission.

tri'fling (trī'flĭng), of small value.

trin'ket (trĭn'kĕt), a small ornament.

tri'umph (trī'ŭmf), a state of joy over success or victory won.

troop (trōop), a company of mounted soldiers; a company of people.

troop'er (trōop'ẽr), a mounted soldier; a cavalry man.

trop'ic (trŏp'ĭk), either of the two small circles at a latitude 23½° from the equator.

trou'ba-dour (trōo'bà-dōor), a name given to a class of poets from the 11th to the 13th centuries.

trow (trō), to think or suppose.

truce (trōos), a brief rest agreed upon by the commanders of opposing forces.

trudge (trŭj), to walk wearily.

tryst-ing (trĭst; trīst), an appointment.

tu'mult (tū'mŭlt), violent commotion and great noise; uproar.

tu'nic (tū'nĭk), a loose fitting garment reaching to the knees.

tur'ban (tûr'băn), a cap with a sash wound around it, worn by men in the East.

turn'spit' (tŭrn'spĭt'), one who turns the rod used to hold meat while roasting over a fire.

tur'ret (tŭr'ĕt), a little tower.

tyr'an-ny (tĭr'à-nĭ), severe, oppressive or unlawful authority.

ty'rant (tī'rănt), a severe or cruel ruler; a ruler unrestrained by law.

Tyr'ol (tĭr'ŏl), an Alpine province in West Austria.

un'a-wares' (ŭn'à-wârz'), unexpectedly; without preparation.

un-bro'ken (brō'k'n), unsubdued.

un'du-late (ŭn'dù-lāt) to move in waves; to wave.

un-flinch'ing (ŭn-flĭnch'ĭng), unyielding; not shrinking from pain.

u'ni-ver'sal (ū'nĭ-vûr'săl), general; unlimited.

un-kempt' (ŭn-kĕmpt'), not combed; rough.

un-qual'i-fied (ŭn-kwŏl'ĭ-fīd), not limited or restricted; not fit.

un-sa'vor-y (ŭn-sā'vĕr-ĭ), unpleasant to taste or smell.

un-sul'lied (sŭl'ĭd), unsoiled; unstained.

un-time'ly (tīm'lĭ), happening at an unusual or improper time.

un-wont' (ŭn-wŭnt'), unaccustomed; unused.

up-roar'i-ous (rōr'ĭ-ŭs), making great noise and tumult.

ur'chin (ûr'chĭn), a mischievous boy.

u-ten'sil (ù-tĕn'sĭl), a vessel used in a kitchen.

vag'a-bond (văg'à-bŏnd), one who wanders from place to place.

vain (vān), ineffectual; without force; worthless.

val'iant (văl'yănt), courageous; brave.

val'or (văl'ẽr), heroism; courage.

vam'pire-bat' (văm'pīr), a bat supposed to suck the blood of animals.

vane (vān), a piece of metal or wood so arranged as to be moved by the wind and show the way it blows.

van'guard (văn'gärd), the troops who march in front of an army.

van'ish (văn'ĭsh), to disappear; to go out of sight.

van'quish (văn'kwĭsh), to conquer; to overcome.

van'tage (văn'tâj), favorable situation.

va'por (vā'pẽr), smoke; fog; steam, etc.

var'let (văr'lĕt), a servant; a scoundrel; a rascal.

vas'sal (văs'ăl), a subject; servant; slave.

vast (văst), of great extent; mighty.

vat (văt), a large tub.

vault'ed (vôlt), built as a vault; arched.

vaunt (vänt; vônt), to boast; to brag.

vel'lum (vĕl'ŭm), a fine parchment, usually calf-skin, for writing upon, or binding books.

ve-loc'i-ty (vē-lŏs'ĭ-tĭ), quickness of motion; speed.

ven'er-a-ble (vĕn'ẽr-à-b'l), deserving of honor and respect.

ven'ture (vĕn'tûr), an undertaking of chance or danger.

ver'dure (vûr'dûr), greenness of vegetation.

ver'i-ly (vĕr'ĭ-lĭ), certainly; beyond doubt.

ver'min (vûr'mĭn), animals or insects of small size, common and difficult to control; flies, rats, mice, etc.

ver'sa-til'i-ty (vûr'sā-tĭl'ĭ-ti), the power to do many things easily.

versed (vûrst), acquainted or familiar from study or experience.

ves'pers (vĕs'pẽrz), a church service held in the late afternoon or evening.

ves'ture (vĕs'tûr), dress; clothing.

vi'brate (vī'brāt), to swing; to move to and fro.

vi-cis'si-tude (vĭ-sĭs'ĭ'tūd), change.

vic'tor (vĭk'tẽr), the winner in a contest; a conqueror.

vict'uals (vĭt''ls), food for human beings.

vig'or-ous (vĭg'ŏr-ŭs), strong; robust.

vin'tage (vĭn'tȧj), act or time of gathering grapes or making wine.

vi'o-lence (vī'ȯ-lĕns), highly excited force; fierceness.

vi'per (vī'per), a venomous snake.

Vir'gil (vûr'jĭl), a Roman poet.

vir'gin (vûr'jĭn), an unmarried woman.

vir'tue (vûr'tū), power to produce an effect; goodness.

vis'age (vĭz'ȧj), the human face.

vis'ion (vĭzh'ŭn), act of seeing; a dream.

viv'id (vĭv'ĭd), clear; fresh; brilliant.

vol'ley (vŏl'ĭ), the discharge of many bullets or arrows at the same time.

vo-lu'mi-nous (vȯ-lū'mĭ-nŭs), of great bulk; large; consisting of many volumes.

vo-lup'tu-a-ry (vȯ-lŭp'tu-ȧ-rĭ), a person who cares too much for luxury.

vul'gar (vŭl-gȧr), common; coarse; lacking refinement.

wail (wāl), to lament; to grieve over.

wan (wŏn), pale; pallid.

ward'en (wôr d'n), a guard; a keeper.

warn'ing (wôrn), previous notice; caution.

wa'ter-ing place (wô'tẽr), a place by the sea.

weak'ling (wēk), a feeble creature.

ween (wēn), to think; to believe.

wee'vil (wē'v'l), a beetle which destroys nuts, fruits and grain.

wel'fare' (wĕl'fâr'), well-being; happiness.

whirl'pool (hwûrl'pōōl), water moving rapidly in a circle.

wick'er (wĭk'ẽr), made of twigs.

wile (wīl), a trick; a stratagem.

wind'row' (wĭnd'rō'; wĭn'rō'), a row of hay raked up to dry.

win'ning (wĭn'ĭng), charming; attractive.

wis (wĭs), to think; to suppose.

wis'dom (wĭz'dŭm), knowledge.

witch (wĭch), a woman supposed to have magic power.

wit'ness (wĭt'nĕs), to see; to observe.

wit'ness (wĭt'nĕs), to bear testimony; to give evidence.

withe (wĭth; wīth), a slender twig.

wit'ty (wĭt'ĭ), quick to see humor or fun.

wo'fu (wō'fōōl), full of sorrow; sad.

wont (wŭnt; wŏnt), custom; habit.

wood'chuck' (chŭck), an animal having coars reddish brown fur and living in burrows.

wran'gle (răn'g'l), to argue; to quarrel.

wren (rĕn), a very small singing bird.

wroth (rôth; rŏth), angry; full of wrath.

wrought (rôt), worked.

yearn (yûrn), to long for; to desire greatly.

yeo'man-ry, (yō'măn-rĭ), brave, free men.

yore (yōr), in time long past.

Ze'nith (zē'nĭth), that point of the heavens directly above one.